# THE Unexplained

## STAFF CREDITS

| | |
|---|---|
| CONSULTANTS TO THE UNEXPLAINED | Professor A. J. Ellison<br>Dr J. Allen Hynek<br>Brian Inglis<br>Colin Wilson |
| EDITORIAL DIRECTOR | Brian Innes |
| EDITOR | Peter Brookesmith |
| DEPUTY EDITORS | Lynn Picknett<br>Jean Elgie |
| EXECUTIVE EDITOR | Lesley Riley |
| CHIEF SUB EDITOR | Nigel Flynn |
| SUB EDITORS | Chris Cooper<br>Hildi Hawkins<br>Jenny Dawson |
| PICTURE RESEARCHERS | Anne Horton<br>Paul Snelgrove<br>Frances Vargo |
| EDITORIAL MANAGER | Clare Byatt |
| ART EDITOR | Stephen Westcott |
| DESIGNER | Richard Burgess |
| ART BUYER | Jean Hardy |
| PRODUCTION CO-ORDINATOR | Nicky Bowden |

## REFERENCE EDITION

| | |
|---|---|
| MARKETING MANAGER | Robert Paulley |
| PRODUCTION DIRECTOR | Barry Roberts |
| EDITOR | Mary Lambert |
| INDEX | Moira McIlroy |

**Cataloging in Publication Data**

**The Unexplained, the mysteries of mind, space and time.**
**1. Curiosities and wonders**
**1. Brookesmith, Peter**
**001.9'4. AG243**

**ISBN 0-86307-098-1 (set)**
**ISBN 0-86307-105-8 (vol. 8)**

**Reference Edition Published 1983**





Published by Marshall Cavendish Corporation,
147 West Merrick Road,
Freeport, Long Island
N.Y. 11520





Printed and bound in Great Britain

ISBN 0-86307-098-1 (set)



## PICTURE ACKNOWLEDGEMENTS

**981**: UPI, New York; **982**: Arnold Desser (t and c); artwork by Studio Briggs (b); **983**: Arnold Desser (t); Peter Newark's Western Americana (b); Ann Ronan Picture Library (br); **984**: Arnold Desser (t); **985**: British Museum (t); Ann Ronan Picture Library (b); **986**: Jean-Loup Charmet (t); Werner Forman Archive (c); British Museum (b); **987**: The British Library (t); **988**: Sven Gahlin (tr); **989**: Janet & Colin Bord: *Psychic News* (inset); **990–991**: artwork by Keith Harmer; **991**: Aerofilms (b); **992**: Janet & Colin Bord (b); **993**: Janet & Colin Bord (t); **994**: Atlantic Mutual Insurance Company; **995**: Mary Evans Picture Library (b); **996**: Boston University Library (t); Dennis Gifford (b); **997**: Meteorological Office/© J. H. Golden; **998–1000**: illustrations by Iain McCaig; **1001**: Michael Holford (t); Jean-Loup Charmet (b); **1002**: Topham; **1002–1003**: Jean-Loup Charmet; **1003**: Mary Evans Picture Library; **1004**: Werner Forman Archive/Berlin Museum of Ethnology (tl); Jean-Loup Charmet (tr); Robert Estall (b); **1004–1005**: Kobal Collection; **1005**: Popperfoto (c); D. Farson (b); **1006**: Popperfoto (t); B. R. Grad (b); **1007**: Jean-Guy Thibodeau (t); B. R. Grad (b); **1008**: B. R. Grad; **1009**: artwork by Studio Briggs; **1010**: Bruce Coleman/Hans Reinhard (t); Science Photo Library (b); **1011**: Bruce Coleman/Dr F. Sauer (l); Oxford Scientific Films (r); **1012**: Michael Holford (t); Dr Robin Baker (c and b); **1013**: Bruce Coleman/Prato (l); Oxford Scientific Films (r); **1014**: Jean-Loup Charmet (t); Robert Hunt Library (bl); Süddeutscher Verlag (bc and br); **1015**: UKEAE (c); artwork by Studio Briggs (b); **1016**: Boyer-Viollet (l); **1016–1017**: The British Library; **1017**: Jean-Loup Charmet (b); **1018**: Contemporary Films (t); Bildarchiv Preussischer Kulturbesitz (b); **1019**: Contemporary Films; **1020**: Bildarchiv Preussischer Kulturbesitz (t); Süddeutscher Verlag (c); **1021**: John Cutten (t); Robert Estall (c and b); **1022**: Mary Evans Picture Library; **1023**: John Cutten; **1024**: artwork by Richard Burgess (l); John Cutten (r); **1025**: SORRAT; **1026**: C.E.G.B./Science Photo Library (t); Brown Bros (b); **1027**: artwork by Ed Stuart (t); **1028**: Ann Ronan Picture Library (t and c); Arnold Desser (b); **1029**: Arnold Desser; **1030–1031**: ZEFA; **1030**: Sovfoto (c and b); **1031**: map by Colin Edwards & Partners (c); **1032**: Popperfoto (t); map by Colin Edwards & Partners (b); **1033**: map by Colin Edwards & Partners (t); Sovfoto (c and b); **1034**: Kobal Collection (t); Mary Evans Picture Library (b); **1035**: Mary Evans Picture Library (t); Jean-Loup Charmet (c); D. Farson (b); **1036**: Jean-Loup Charmet (t); **1037**: Jean-Loup Charmet (t and cl); Kobal Collection (cr); **1038**: Pitkin Pictorial/Photo Peter Baker; **1040**: Mansell Collection (b); **1041**: Ground Saucer Watch; Photri (inset); **1042–1044**: Ground Saucer Watch; **1045**: EFE; **1046**: Janet and Colin Bord (top); City of Manchester Art Galleries (bottom); **1047**: Janet & Colin Bord; **1048**: Robert Estall (l); BBC Hulton Picture Library (c); Mary Evans Picture Library (r); **1049**: Spectrum; **1050–1051**: Cooper-Bridgeman Library; **1051**: Mary Evans Picture Library (c); Cooper-Bridgeman Library (b); **1052**: Giraudon; **1053**: Werner Forman Archive (t); British Museum Department of Prints & Drawings (b); **1054**: Tom McAssey (t); Mary Evans Picture Library (b); **1055**: Tom McAssey; **1056**: Mansell Collection (t); **1056–1057**: Tom McAssey (b); **1057**: Mary Evans Picture Library (t); **1058**: UPI, New York (t); John Massey Stewart (b); **1059**: Novosti; **1060**: artwork by Studio Briggs (t); NASA/Science Photo Library (c); Sovfoto (b); **1061**: Werner Forman Archive; **1062**: map by Colin Edards & Partners (tl); Alan Hutchinson Library (tr); artwork by Ed Stuart (b); **1063**: Michael Holford (c and bc); Werner Forman Archive (br); **1064**: Alan Hutchinson Library (t); map by Colin Edwards & Partners (b); **1064–1065**: Alan Hutchinson Library; **1065**: artwork by Ed Stuart; **1066**: illustration by Murrey Aikman; **1067**: *Flying Saucer Review*; **1068**: illustration by Murrey Aikman (t and r); **1069**: *Flying Saucer Review*; **1070**: Photo Meyer (c); Museum of Fine Arts, Antwerp (tr); **1070–1071**: Robert Hunt Library; **1071**: Mary Evans Picture Library; **1072**: Sheridan Photo-Library (ct); Mansell Collection (tr); Press Association (b); **1073**: IWM; **1074**: Photolabs, Edinburgh/Science Photo Library (t); UPI, New York (c); **1075**: Popperfoto (t); UPI, New York (b); **1076**: UPI, New York (t); Popperfoto (c and b); **1077**: artwork by Studio Briggs; **1078**: Greg Edwards Archive; **1079**: Jean-Loup Charmet (b); **1080**: S. C. Bisserôt; **1081**: EPL/Toyne Newton; **1082**: map by Colin Edwards & Partners (t); EPL/Toyne Newton (b); **1083**: illustration by Richard Burgess (t); EPL/Toyne Newton (b); **1084**: illustration by Richard Burgess (t); EPL/Toyne Newton (b); **1085**: EPL/Dave Stringer (ct); EPL/Paul Glover (tr); illustration by Richard Burgess (b); **1086**: Goodyear UK; **1087**: Philip Daly (t and c); Photri (bl and bc); **1088**: Mary Evans Picture Library (t); August C. Roberts (c); **1089**: Topham (t); Rex (c); **1090**: Fortean Picture Library (t); © Udresfeavifen (c); **1090–1091**: illustration by Phil Weare/Linden Artists; **1091**: Fortean Picture Library (t); Werner Forman Archive/Centennial Museum Victoria, Canada (c); **1092**: Bruce Coleman/Jeff Foott (t); Bruce Coleman/Paul Barruel (c); Mansell Collection (bl); Jean-Loup Charmet (br); **1093**: UPI, New York (t); illustration by Phil Weare/Linden Artists (b); **1094**: Michael Holford (t); **1095**: Werner Forman Archive/Collection Philip Goldman (t); Werner Forman Archive/University Museum of Anthropology, Jallapa (b); **1096**: Robert Estall; **1097**: Axel Poignant (t); Michael Holford (c); Werner Forman Archive (b); **1098–1100**: George Champan.

# THE Unexplained

## MYSTERIES OF MIND, SPACE AND TIME



## Volume 8

Marshall Cavendish · New York & London

# Contents

## VOLUME EIGHT

# A to Z Quick Reference

# Flash of inspiration

**Nikola Tesla, neglected pioneer of electrical energy, tapped the elemental forces of the planet in his search for ways to transmit power without wires. NEIL POWELL relates the history of a prolific inventor whose work may yet revolutionise the modern world**

DURING THE NIGHT of 7 January 1943, an 86-year-old man died alone in his room in the New Yorker Hotel in Manhattan. Before his body was removed to Campbell's Funeral Parlor at 81st Street and Madison Avenue, agents from the Federal Bureau of Investigation entered his room, opened the small safe that he kept there, and took all the papers that it contained, on the grounds that they might contain details of an important secret weapon.

The man was Nikola Tesla, an electrical engineer whose genius rivalled that of Edison. He has been strangely forgotten, except in the country of his birth, although his name lives on in the Tesla coil, an invention that exploits some of the more bizarre properties of electrical current discovered by Tesla. But this scarcely represents the scope of his wide-ranging scientific achievements.

Nikola Tesla, a brilliant inventor and a profound scientist, and one of the few people who have refused the offer of a Nobel prize. Among many other remarkable devices he invented the alternating current generator

He was born at midnight on 9 July 1856, in Smiljan, at that time part of the Austro-Hungarian empire, but now in Yugoslavia. It is said that he was accused of cheating at school because he would give the answer to a mathematical question incredibly quickly. Indeed, from his earliest years until the end of his life, Tesla claimed that all his understanding of the complex engineering problems to which he devoted his attention came to him in flashes of intuition.

An interview published in the American magazine *The World* on 22 August 1894 gives us a striking picture of Nikola Tesla at the height of his powers:

> He has eyes set very far back in his head. They are rather light. I asked him how he could have such light eyes and be a Slav. He told me that his eyes were once much darker, but that using his mind a great deal had made them many shades lighter. I have often heard it said that using the brain makes the eyes lighter in color. Tesla's confirmation of the theory through his personal experience is important.
>
> He is very thin, is more than six feet [1.8 metres] tall, and weighs less than 140 pounds [64 kilograms]. He has very big hands. His thumbs are remarkably big, even for such big hands. They are extraordinarily big. The thumb is the intellectual part of the hand. The apes have very small thumbs. Study them and you will notice this.
>
> Nikola Tesla has a head that spreads out at the top like a fan. His head is shaped like a wedge. His chin is pointed

as an ice-pick. His mouth is too small. His chin, though not weak, is not strong enough. His face cannot be studied and judged like the faces of other men, for he is not a worker in practical fields. He lives his life up in the top of his head, where ideas are born, and up there he has plenty of room. His hair is jet black and curly. He stoops – most men do when they have no peacock blood in them. He lives inside of himself. He takes a profound interest in his own work. He has that supply of self-love and self-confidence which usually goes with success. And he differs from most of the men who are written and talked about in the fact that he has something to tell.

## Migration to America

And Tesla certainly had something to tell. He had arrived in New York in 1884, his capital four cents, and his baggage comprising some technical articles that he had written in Belgrade and Paris, a book of poems that he had composed, and some calculations that he had made for the design of a flying machine. But in his head he had all the details of the polyphase alternating current generator, which was to become the basis of the Niagara Falls hydroelectric power installation in 1895 and has since become the standard for industrial machinery. As Lord Kelvin, the distinguished British scientist, put it: 'Tesla has contributed more to electrical science than any man up to his time.'

Soon after his arrival in New York, Tesla was employed by Edison, for whom he designed 24 types of dynamo. But the two men did not hit it off, and in April 1887 Tesla was set up in his own laboratory. Here he rapidly showed that his AC system was much superior to Edison's DC system, and in little over a year he had been granted no less than 30 important patents.

In the next 20 years, Tesla made an astounding number of discoveries in the field of electrical and radio engineering. Unhappily, due to a succession of accidents in which many of his writings were destroyed, and to the neglect that his name has suffered, it is not always possible to determine the date at which many of his discoveries were made, and so he is seldom credited as a pioneer. There is no doubt, nevertheless, that he, not Marconi, was the discoverer of the tuned circuit upon which radio is based, a fact

Left: Nikola Tesla in 1879, at the age of 23. Still a student, he had produced many speculative proposals for daring inventions, but had as yet no practical achievements to show

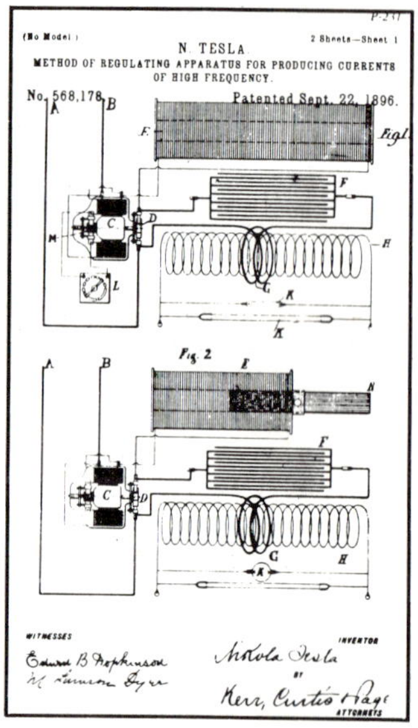


Above: part of Tesla's application for a US patent on the device now known as a 'Tesla coil'. It converts low-voltage direct current into alternating current of very high voltage, which, as Tesla stated in the application, could be used to power fluorescent lamps or produce 'Roentgen shadows' (X-ray images)

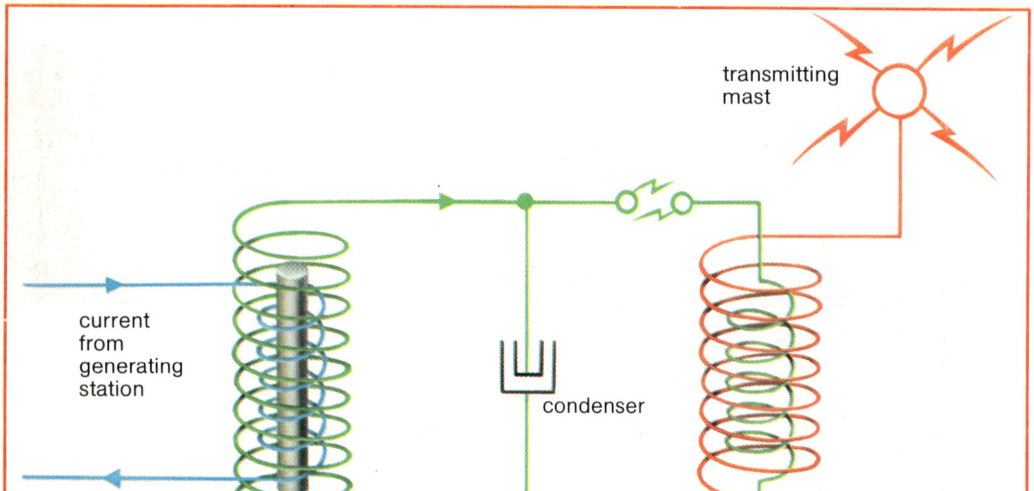


Left: the circuits used at Colorado Springs. A low-voltage AC current (blue) was amplified by a giant modified Tesla coil (green). The voltage was still further boosted in the final circuit, through which current was drawn from the ground and discharged from the transmitting mast

determined by the US Supreme Court only in the year of his death. It is probable, also, that he was the first to observe cathode rays and X-rays, ultraviolet radiation, and the therapeutic effects upon the human body of high-frequency currents. He was the first to design the fore-runner of the fluorescent lighting tube, and he may well have developed a laser-like device.

In 1912 Tesla refused the nomination for the Nobel prize in physics; it was said that he felt that he should have received it in 1909 in place of Marconi. Certainly, as early as 1898, he had demonstrated a radio-controlled boat in Madison Square Garden, New York, and in 1899 he built a powerful transmitting station at Colorado Springs, situated on a plateau in the foothills of the Rockies.

Above: a discharge of millions of volts at Colorado Springs. It was not Tesla's practice to use these artificial lightning strokes as reading lamps, as this picture suggests: he was photographed with flash powder and then moved to a safe distance while the current flowed and the film was re-exposed

Below: Madison Square Garden, New York, where Tesla's demonstration of a radio-controlled boat enthralled spectators in 1898

Unlike Marconi, however, Tesla was concerned with the transmission not only of minute quantities of energy in the form of radio signals but also of huge amounts of electrical energy for domestic and industrial use. In 1899 he succeeded in pumping power into the atmosphere equivalent to many millions of watts with an immense coil generating some 10 million volts.

The experimental installation that Tesla constructed at Colorado Springs was a barn-shaped building nearly 100 feet (30 metres) square. From the centre of the roof a skeletal tower supported a mast nearly 200 feet (60 metres) high on top of which was mounted a copper ball some 3 feet (90 centimetres) in diameter. Inside the building was a circular enclosure like a fence, some 75 feet (23 metres) in diameter, on which was wound the primary coil of his transmitter; the secondary coil was about 10 feet (3 metres) in diameter, and was connected to the mast.

### Circuits in tune

The principle behind the tuned resonant circuit is very like that of the child's swing. A small push starts the swing, and the same small push, applied at the right moment, soon has the swing moving high and wide. In the same way, a succession of electrical pulses, applied with the correct frequency to the primary coil, will produce highly magnified pulses in the secondary coil.

These pulses in the mast connected to Tesla's secondary coil would generate high-frequency radio waves that would travel to the far side of the globe and then return. If they were precisely tuned to the natural frequency of oscillation of electrical currents in the Earth, they would, on their return, exactly reinforce the voltage pulses in the mast, and boost the current that was drawn from the Earth. An ever-increasing current

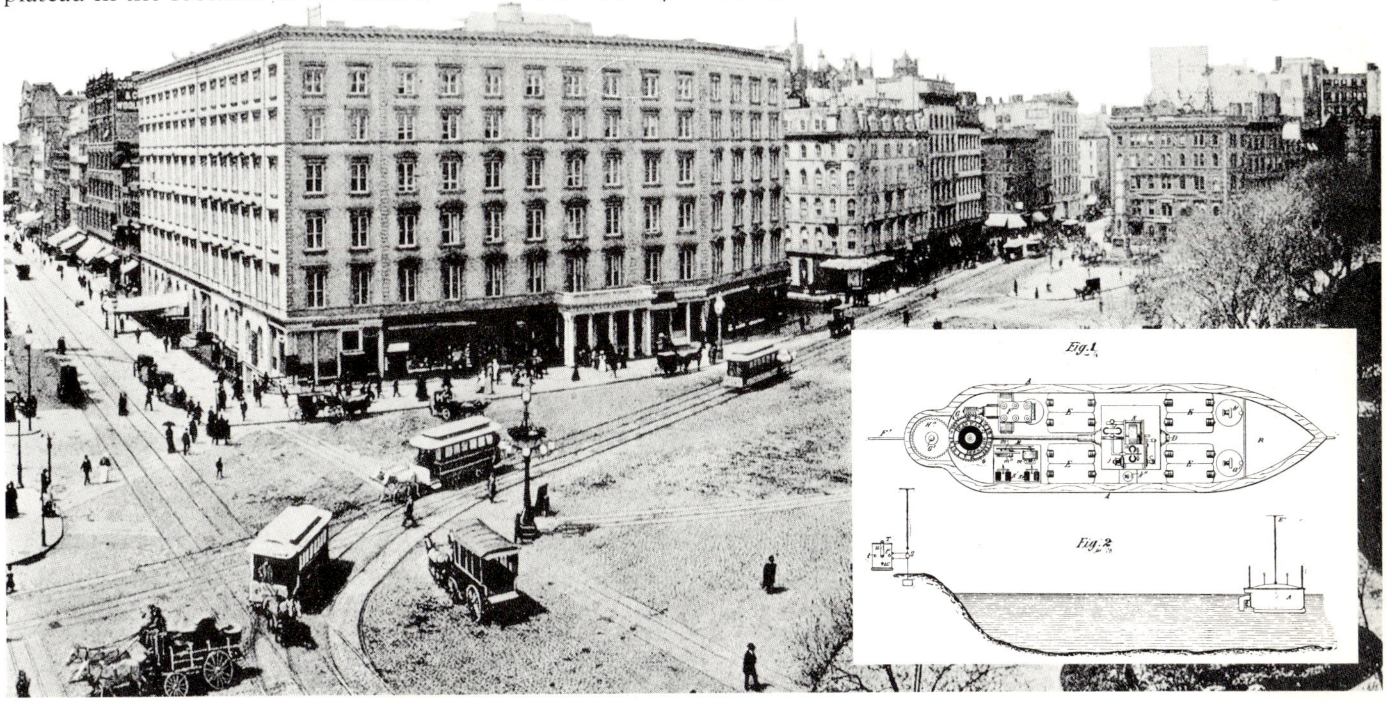

would surge through the apparatus. The entire planet would be used as a further 'secondary circuit' to amplify the current.

The story of how Tesla, 'properly attired in cutaway coat and black derby hat for the auspicious occasion', put his apparatus into operation is dramatically told in John J. O'Neill's *Prodigal genius.* While Tesla watched the top of the mast from outside the building, his assistant Czito stood apprehensively by the controls within. When he closed the switch the secondary coil was surrounded by a halo of electrical fire, sparks crackled through every part of the building, and there came a sharp snap from high overhead.

> Now it was followed by a tremendous upsurge of sound. The crackling from the coil swelled into a crescendo . . . the original staccato snap was followed by a sharper one. . . . They came closer together like the rattle of a machine gun. The bang high in the air became tremendously louder; it was now the roar of a cannon, with the discharges rapidly following each other as if a gigantic artillery battle was taking place over the building. . . . There was a strange ghostly blue light in the great barnlike structure. The coils were flaming with masses of fiery hair. Everything in the building was spouting needles of flame. . . .

Outside, Tesla stood entranced. From the copper ball on top of the mast, bolts of lightning were shooting out: fingers of fire nearly 135 feet (40 metres) in length.

## Testing to destruction

Suddenly the man-made lightning ceased. Tesla hurried back into his laboratory, protesting to Czito that he had given no orders to stop the experiment. But Czito pointed silently to his control dials, which showed that the power supply had failed. The experiment had completely burnt out the generating system of the Colorado Springs Electric Company.

Fortunately, the company's generator was one of Tesla's own design, and within a week he had it operating again. Some of the implications of the results he obtained from his experiments were indicated in a paper he wrote the following year.

> That communication without wires to any point of the globe is practical with such apparatus would need no demonstration, but through a discovery I made I obtained absolute certitude. Popularly explained it is exactly this: When we raise the voice and hear an echo in reply, we know that the sound of the voice must have reached a distant wall, or boundary, and must have been reflected from the same. Exactly as the sound, so an electrical wave is reflected, and the same evidence which is afforded by an echo is offered by an electrical phenomenon known as a 'stationary' wave – that is, a wave with fixed nodal and ventral regions. Instead of sending sound vibrations toward a distant wall, I have sent electrical vibrations toward the remote boundaries of the earth, and instead of the wall the earth has replied. In place of an echo I have obtained a stationary electrical wave . . . reflected from afar.

A standard demonstration of the effects of the Tesla coil is to cause an electric light bulb to burn brightly without any connection to an electrical supply. With his giant Colorado Springs installation, Tesla was able to light 200 of Edison's incandescent lamps at a distance of 25 miles (40 kilometres).

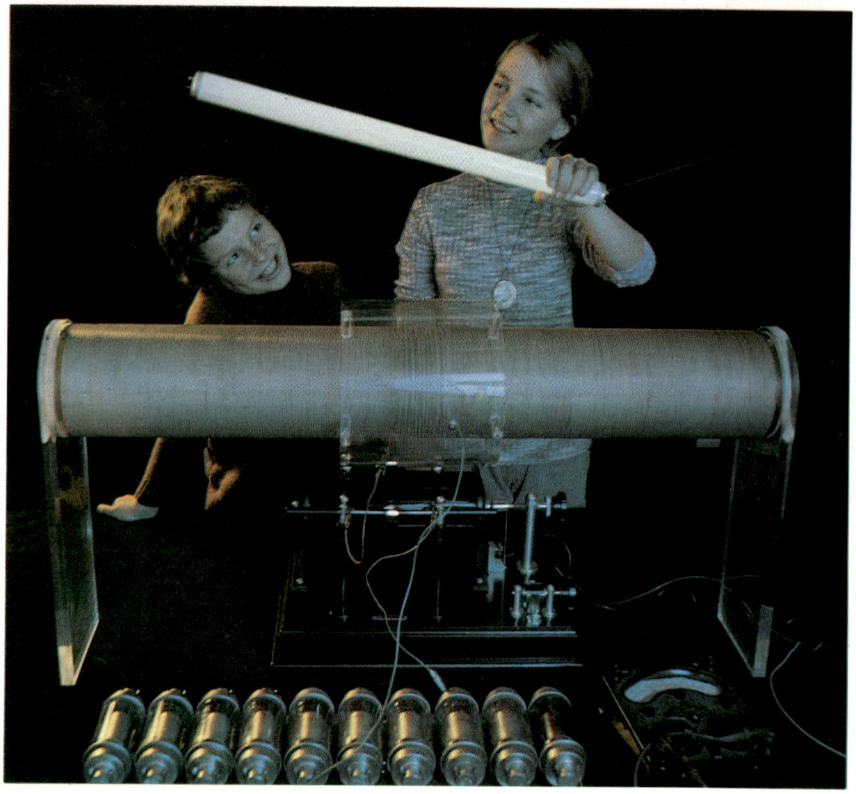

Top: Tesla photographed by the light of a fluorescent lamp of his own invention. High-frequency power is fed to the lamp through wires hidden on Tesla's body. Invisible ultraviolet radiation is produced by low-pressure gas in the lamp and causes a coating on the inside surface to glow. This principle is used in modern fluorescent lighting, with smaller voltages and frequencies

Above: a modern demonstration of Tesla's ideas. The fluorescent tube is being energised by radio-frequency waves from the large Tesla coil, without connecting wires

Seventy-eight years later, the London *Evening Standard* reported that some remarkable electrical storms had been taking place over Canada, and that Tesla's last surviving assistant, Arthur Matthews, had been intensively interrogated by an unnamed Russian electrical engineer. Shortly afterward, the same newspaper reported that Major-General George Keegan, former head of US Air Force Intelligence, had publicly voiced his apprehension that the Russians possessed a 'particle gun' capable of detonating ballistic missiles in flight.

These events were linked to the work of Tesla. For it seemed that the principles that had enabled him to transmit energy to distant places and to tap the energies of the Earth were now being harnessed for war.

*Tesla's claim to have discovered the ultimate secret weapon is examined on page 1026*

**Alchemy in both East and West was concerned with the purification of the soul as much as with the transmutation of metals. BRIAN INNES relates the two traditions to each other and to primitive magic**

# Alchemy: sex and symbolism

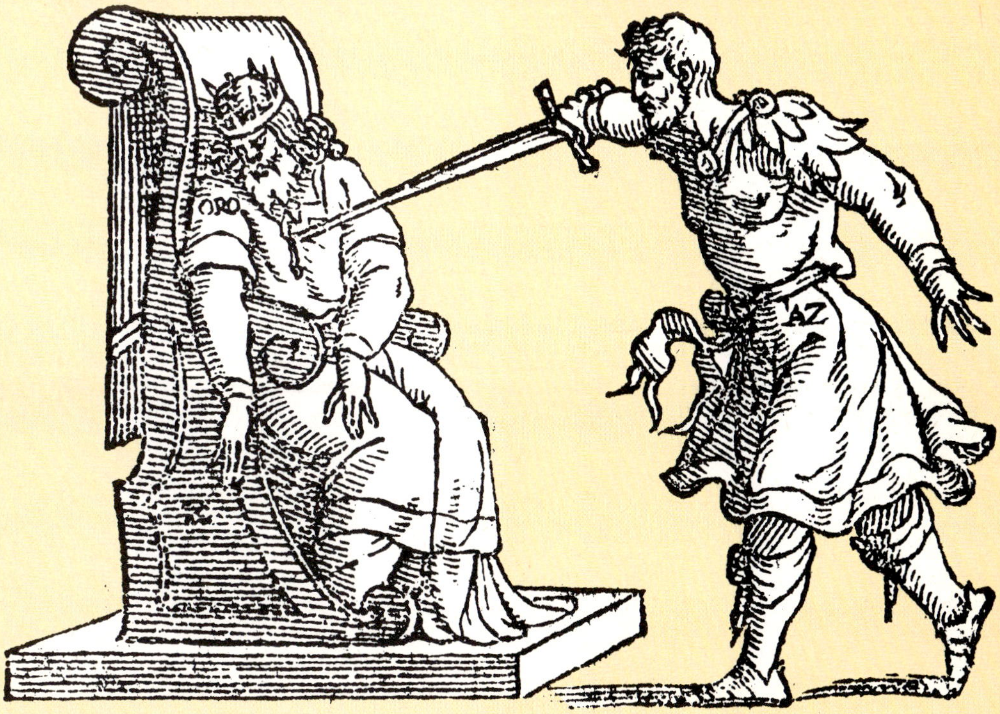


Above: when lead is kept molten in a basin over a furnace, it will form an encrustation of bright yellow crystals of lead oxide, or litharge. Here the aged Saturn symbolises lead, while the gold-crested white dove is the 'sublime' spirit of the lead, its quintessence. That, at least, is one interpretation of this illustration from the 16th-century manuscript *Splendor solis*, but several other equally plausible explanations have been proposed

Right: in this woodcut from *The new pearl of great price* (1546), the crowned king is gold, killed by his son Mercury. After many vicissitudes he rises again

ALCHEMY GATHERED into its literature a whole bestiary of symbols: the black crow; the white pelican, its breast spotted red with its own blood, on which, by popular belief, its young fed; the phoenix; the dove; the peacock, with its tail of wonderful colours; red and green lions; dragons of all hues. There were human symbols as well: the red man and the white woman, sometimes twined together in sexual union; the king murdered by his own son; and above all the androgyne, or hermaphrodite, which represented the combination of opposites that produced the Philosopher's Stone.

The symbols are so striking and so numerous that they caught the attention of the psychologist Carl Jung, who devoted a whole book to them. Throughout his life, Jung had studied the way in which the same kind of symbols appear to have the same kind of meaning in communities and cultures widely separated in time or place. It was, Jung thought, as if these symbols were a part of mankind's fundamental make-up.

One of Jung's predecessors was Herbert Silberer. In his book *Problems of mysticism and its symbolism* he attaches great importance to the work of one of the first alchemists to set his thoughts down in writing, Zosimos of Panopolis, in Egypt. Zosimos, who lived about AD 300, wrote down some of the secrets of alchemy in terms of a strange vision:

> I asked him who he was and in a feeble voice he answered me: I am he-who-is, the priest of the sanctuary, and I am overwhelmed by another's strength. For at break of day came a deputy who

> swiftly seized me, cleaving me with a sword and dividing me in pieces; and after flaying all the skin from my head he mixed my bones with my flesh and burned them in the fire. . . .

When we look at the illustrations from alchemical works written some 1200 years later, or read the descriptions of the Great Work, it is not really surprising to find the same kind of imagery employed, for in this instance it is easy to trace a direct line of descent. But what is remarkable is to compare the vision of Zosimos with the visions of the shamans, the priests of the nomadic tribes of Siberia and North America.

As adolescents, future shamans were suddenly seized by a 'sickness', a kind of divine madness that was the first sign of their priestly vocation. During this phase they saw extraordinary visions. One future shaman, for instance, described how he saw himself enter a mountain, where a naked man was working a bellows to keep a cauldron heating on a fire. The man seized the shaman with a great pair of tongs, cut off his head and sliced up his body, and threw everything into the cauldron, where it cooked for three years. There were three anvils in the cave, and on one of them the man forged the shaman's head; then he rescued the bones, joined them together, and covered them with flesh.

### The mystique of the metalworker

Many of the initiation visions seen by the shamans took similar forms to this, and the famous anthropologist Mercia Eliade has shown that they are closely related to the high priestly standing enjoyed by metalworkers among primitive peoples.

In some very early mythologies, the Sun was seen as plunging every evening into the womb of Earth, sowing the 'seed' of the metals. It was supposed that the metals gradually developed, passing through various stages, until the final result was gold. (We have seen how even the scientist Aristotle believed that the Earth somehow 'bred' metals – see page 954.)

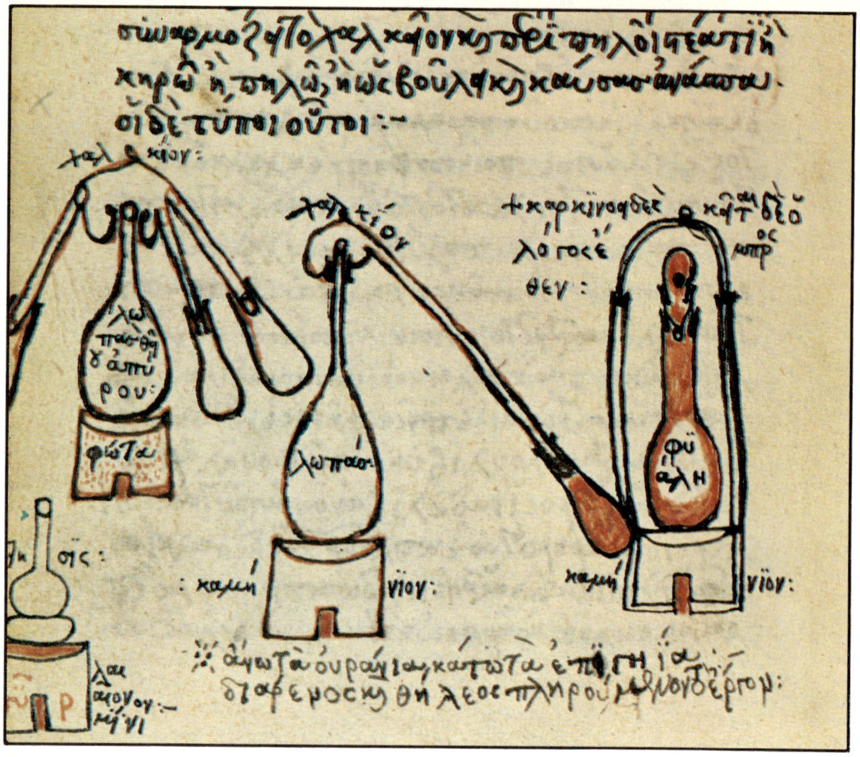

Top: a 15th-century copy of an alchemical treatise by Zosimos of Panopolis

Above: a travelling Tuareg silversmith from Niger. These artisans are often outcasts, regarded with fear and awe

Left: another tantalising illustration from *Splendor solis*. A fair white woman offers a scarlet cloak to a man emerging from primeval blackness into a ruddy form that is reminiscent in some ways of a new-born child

Metalworkers, who knew how to take mineral ores and, by smelting them in a womb-shaped furnace, to produce metals, and who further understood how to shape the metal produced, were thus performing much the same kind of marvel as the Sun-god himself. They were venerated as priests who stood closer than ordinary men to the god.

It was natural to suppose that, if a man could make himself truly god-like, he would gain the power to transform baser metals into gold, by exactly the same processes that they underwent in the Earth. This belief was expressed on the Emerald Tablet, a record said to have been inscribed by the god Thoth, who was supposed to have taught the ancient Egyptians the sciences and the art of writing. (The Greeks identified Thoth with one form of their god Hermes – Hermes Trismegistos, the 'thrice-great'. Hence the term 'hermetic art' for alchemy.)

The principle of the Emerald Tablet can be expressed in a phrase widely used by alchemists: 'as above, so below'. The tablet appears to have carried a set of mystical instructions for the manufacture of gold by transmutation – the 'operation of Sol'. The seventh of these precepts reads: 'Separate the earth from the fire, the subtle from the gross, acting prudently and with judgement.' The eighth reads: 'Ascend with the greatest sagacity from the Earth to heaven, and then again descend to the Earth, and unite together the powers of things superior and things inferior. . . .' These can be read as straightforward metaphors for separating and recombining elements. The 'ascent' and 'descent' could refer to the circulatory action of a kerotakis, a type of still.

But on another level these same precepts

could be, and were, taken as referring to a spiritual work of self-purification – a long and arduous liberation of the divine part of the alchemist's nature from the grossness of his body and senses.

All these various strands came together: the primitive belief that the search for a way to transmute base metals into gold involved a succession of god-like actions developed into the belief that an important part of alchemy was the attempt to become like God – 'as above, so below'. From this, no doubt, stems the conviction that the final result of the alchemical quest was to achieve eternal life.

It is striking that, although there is no evidence of any connection between the alchemy of the Arabs (as it was later transmitted to medieval Europe) and that of the Far East, the Chinese alchemists were also concerned with the attainment of immortality. They were undoubtedly very interested in the production of gold, but principally for its value as an elixir. The substance with which they attempted to prolong life was cinnabar, a bright-red compound of two of the vital substances of western alchemy: mercury and sulphur.

Above: the Emerald Tablet, as it was imagined by Heinrich Khunrath in his *Amphitheatrum sapientiae aeternae* (*Amphitheatre of eternal wisdom*), which was first published in 1609. Below the Latin text, Khunrath provides a translation into German

The ancient philosophy of Tao is concerned with the delicate blending of two fundamental energies: *yin*, the feminine principle, and *yang*, the masculine. The careful commingling of *yin* and *yang* was believed to be a means of prolonging life.

At the lower levels of Taoist practice, the mixing of *yin* and *yang* could be achieved by controlled sexual intercourse; the more advanced mystics practised various meditative procedures, designed to bring about a kind of 'distillation' of *yang* within the body. These practices were commonly known as 'sexual alchemy'.

The body was seen as a tier of three crucibles (*tan-t'ien*) on a central column. The lowest, the cauldron or three-footed furnace, was in the belly below the solar plexus; the second was behind the solar plexus; the third between the eyes.

The 'prime substance' of this inner alchemy was the primitive sexual energy, *ching*, residing in the lowest crucible. It was one of three forces, the others being *ch'i*, the moving vitality, in the middle crucible and *shen*, the luminous personal spirit, in the upper crucible. Meditation began with rhythmical deep breathing: the 'heavenly fire of the heart' began to circulate and was impelled – as if by a bellows – down to the furnace in the belly. Gradually, as energy rose up the 'distillation column' of the spine, the content of *yang* increased; then, as it

## An experiment with immortality

The Tao master Wei Po-Yang went into the mountains one day, accompanied by three disciples and his white dog. The master had concocted a certain 'gold medicine', reputed to be the Elixir of Immortality. He fed a little of the medicine to his dog, which promptly died. Wei Po-Yang said to his disciples: 'To live without taking the medicine would be just the same as to die of the medicine. I must take it.' He did so and, like the dog, expired.

Two of the grief-stricken disciples immediately set off to find implements with which to bury their late master. But the third, Yü by name, was more thoughtful; it seemed to him that Wei Po-Yang must have known what he was doing. Yü therefore took some of the medicine himself, and also died.

A short while later, Wei Po-Yang revived, for his medicine had contained only enough impurity to cause temporary death. He put a little more of the medicine into the mouths of the dog and of Yü, both of whom also recovered after a few moments. Together, the three strolled off into immortality.

Wei Po-Yang lived in the second century AD, and he is credited with the authorship of the treatise *Ts'an-t'ung-ch'i* (*The three ways unified and harmonised*), a work that made Taoism into a coherent system. Among other things it deals with the 'pills of immortality', which, says Wei, are 'extremely efficacious, although their individual size is so small that they occupy only the point of a knife or the edge of a spatula.'

condensed at the top of the head and descended again, *yin* replaced *yang*. Eventually, the heat of the furnace was sufficient to drive the *ching*, transformed, up to the second crucible, where it combined with the *ch'i*. As in the alchemist's vessel known as a pelican, the two were continuously recycled, rising up the central column and then dropping back into the furnace for further purification. As the furnace was fanned to greater heat, the combined *ching* and *ch'i* eventually reached the *shen* in the upper crucible; and suddenly the 'inner copulation of the dragon and the tiger' took place. Su Tung P'o put it this way in AD 1110:

> The dragon is mercury. It is the semen and the blood. He issues from the kidneys and is stored in the liver. The tiger is lead. He is breath and bodily strength. He issues from the mind and the lungs bear him. When the mind is moved, breath and strength act with it. When the kidneys are flushed, then semen and blood flow. . . .

When the *ching-ch'i-shen* was rising and descending like liquid in a briskly bubbling still, it progressively purified until it was one with the energies of the cosmos. Then a special ambrosial fluid flowed like saliva in the mouth. Two lights, gold and silver, slowly descended into the furnace; the body's breathing ceased, to be replaced by the breathing of a foetus formed from the impregnation of the ambrosia by the gold and silver lights. Slowly, the foetus grew into a homunculus, a 'crystal child'; it rose slowly to the crown of the head, and was there born as an immortal.

### The alchemy of Tantra

Taoist inner alchemy possesses a striking resemblance to the basic beliefs of Tantra, which is claimed to be the oldest religion of India. The Tantric meditator begins by visualising the inner central column of his spine, the *sushumna*, as the axis of the cosmos. Up the *sushumna* are strung a series of 'wheels', or *chakras*; there are usually six, with a seventh in the top of the skull. The lowest *chakra* is at the base of the pelvis, and here sleeps the serpent Kundalini, coiled around an inner phallus (*lingam*), with its tip in her mouth. By means of various yoga exercises Kundalini is awakened, straightens herself, and enters the bottom of the *sushumna*. The ultimate intention is that Kundalini shall ascend permanently to the top of the skull, where a transcendental sexual union takes place.

The postures that awaken Kundalini are frequently sexual, and even the Tantric ascetic will imagine an ideal girl as Kundalini ascends. The Tantric obtains his energy through sexual intercourse, and the woman is regarded as the possessor of particularly important power.

The Tantric yogi is credited with many abilities, of which one is the transmutation of base metals into gold; even his urine and faeces may bring about transmutation. He recognises the importance of mercury and sulphur. As an ancient treatise puts it:

> When quicksilver is killed with an equal weight of sulphur it cures leprosy; when killed with thrice its weight of sulphur it cures mental languor; when it is killed with four times its weight of sulphur it removes grey hair and wrinkles; when it is killed by five times its weight of sulphur it cures consumption; when it is killed with six times its weight of sulphur it becomes a panacea for all the ills. . . .

The close similarity of the imagery – and the substances used – in alchemy in all these very different cultures is striking. A major difference is equally striking: that medieval European alchemy does not seem to have had any explicit sexual basis. It was not until ancient Taoist and Tantric manuscripts became available in translation toward the end of the 19th century that sex entered western alchemy. The magical society called the Golden Dawn taught some kind of esoteric link between the two; Karl Kellner, who founded the Ordo Templis Orientis (OTO) in 1906 was more explicit. And Aleister Crowley, who was a member of both secret societies, seized upon the connection with enthusiasm, and developed his own brand of sexual magic. And then the psychologists who found the symbolism of alchemy so fascinating were to teach that sex is at the heart of all human action.

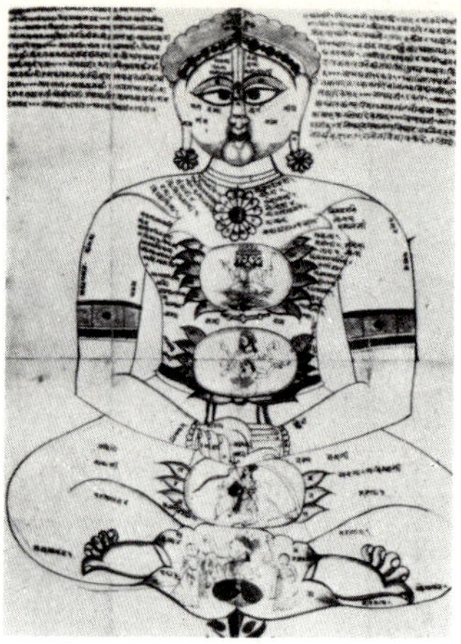

Above: in this Indian drawing from the 18th century, the 'subtle body' is represented as a plant growing from the ground. The *chakras*, or centres of energy positioned along the spinal *sushumna*, are shown symbolically by human and animal figures

Above and top right: the close symbolic relationship between Western alchemy and Tantric 'sexual alchemy' is clearly shown in these two pictures, one an Indian popular print of the early 19th century, the other a 16th-century European woodcut. In the upper illustration, the goddess Kali has beheaded herself, and her blood sprays onto the tongues of her attendants, while a couple make love in a lotus flower at her feet. The lower illustration shows the hermetic androgyne, a being formed when the son of Hermes and Aphrodite became united with the nymph Salmacis – a symbol of the union of opposites in chemical reactions

*Alchemists continue their work today, encouraged by the findings of the atomic scientists. See page 1014*

# Spirit guides at Glastonbury

**Many of the more impressive fragments of the Glastonbury ruins were uncovered in excavations that began in 1909. COLIN WILSON tells the extraordinary story of the 'psychic archaeology' that unearthed them**

GLASTONBURY IS UNDOUBTEDLY one of the most ancient sacred sites in Britain. Standing high above the surrounding countryside, it is an obvious landmark, and archaeological evidence suggests that it has been a place of religious significance since the time of the Druids. But there are other kinds of evidence that suggest the Tor was a holy place long before the Celts came to Britain in the seventh or sixth century BC. A modern investigator, Stephen Jenkins, who studied Buddhism in Tibet, one day asked his guru about Shambala, the legendary sacred place of the ancient Hindus. He was astonished to be told that it was located in Britain at the place now called Glastonbury.

Nestled in the valley beneath the Tor is Glastonbury Abbey, which was founded in the fifth century by St Patrick before he went on to convert Ireland. According to Giraldus Cambrensis, it was the burial place of King Arthur – and the discovery in 1191 of a coffin containing the skeletons of a man and woman, bearing the inscription 'Here lies Arthur, the Once and Future King', seemed to confirm it. Because of its association with Arthur, the abbey became one of the richest and most powerful in England. In 1539, Henry VIII's commissioners executed its last abbot, Richard Whyting, on top of the Tor. The abbey was destroyed. And for almost four centuries it remained a neglected ruin.

In 1907 the abbey ruins were bought by the Church of England for £36,000. Yet,

When Glastonbury Abbey was bought by the Church of England in 1907, it had been in ruins for more than four centuries (below). Many of the ancient buildings had completely disappeared; it was no longer certain even where the abbey monks had lived. The man appointed to excavate the site was an eminent architect, Frederick Bligh Bond (above) – who, through automatic writing, received detailed archaeological information from a group of long-dead monks styling themselves 'the Company of Avalon'

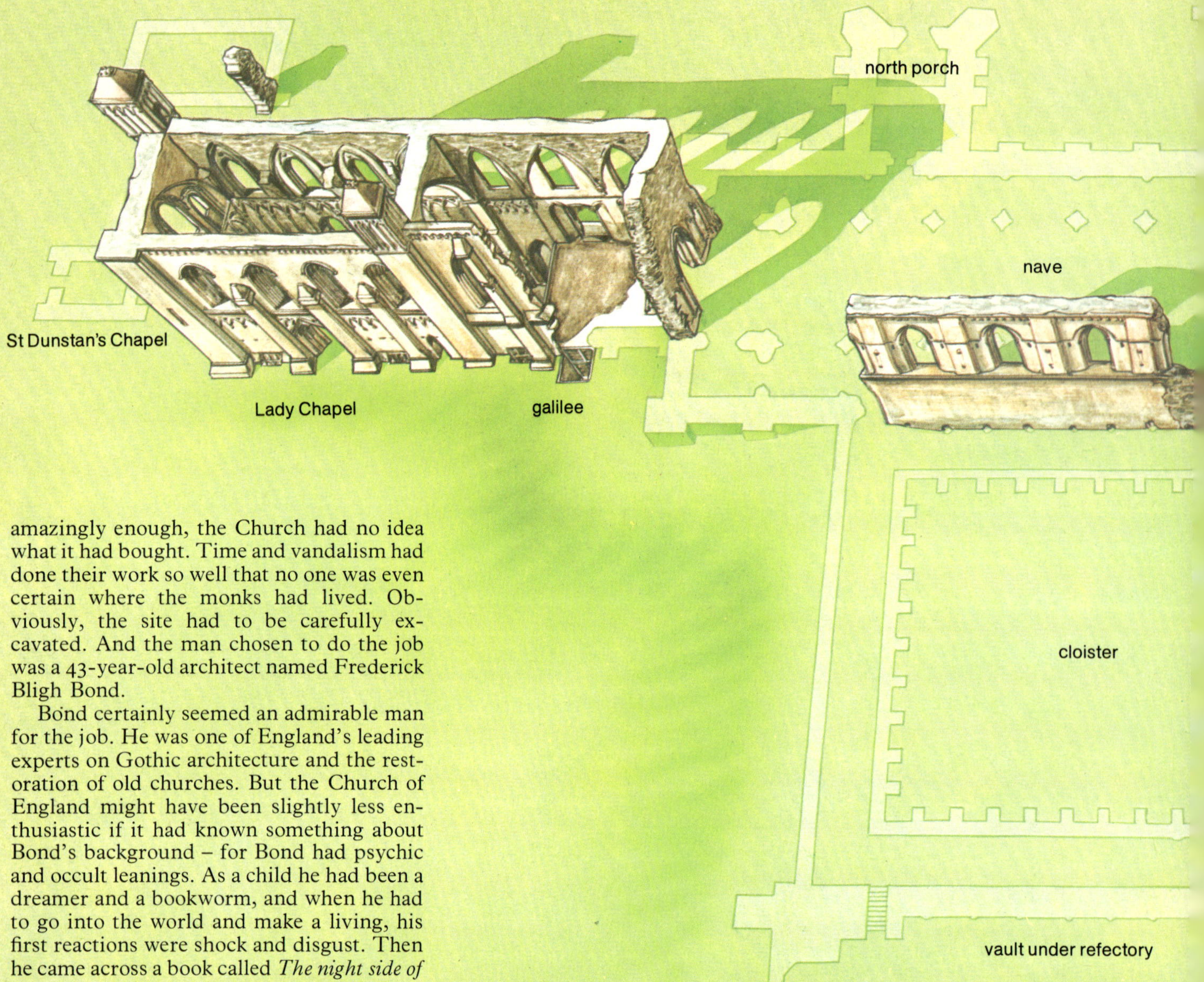


amazingly enough, the Church had no idea what it had bought. Time and vandalism had done their work so well that no one was even certain where the monks had lived. Obviously, the site had to be carefully excavated. And the man chosen to do the job was a 43-year-old architect named Frederick Bligh Bond.

Bond certainly seemed an admirable man for the job. He was one of England's leading experts on Gothic architecture and the restoration of old churches. But the Church of England might have been slightly less enthusiastic if it had known something about Bond's background – for Bond had psychic and occult leanings. As a child he had been a dreamer and a bookworm, and when he had to go into the world and make a living, his first reactions were shock and disgust. Then he came across a book called *The night side of nature* by Katherine Crowe – one of the great Victorian bestsellers, full of discussions of psychic powers and occult mysteries. Bond became a lifelong devotee of psychic studies. When he became apprenticed to the architect Charles Hansen – who specialised in Gothic architecture – he had a chance to turn his romantic love of the medieval period to practical account. By 1907 he was one of England's most successful and respectable architects. But his association with Glastonbury Abbey was to put an end to all that.

In the late 15th century the last Abbot of Glastonbury but one, Richard Bere, had started a cult of Joseph of Arimathea – Christ's uncle – who, according to legend, had visited Glastonbury with the child Jesus, and returned there later with the cup used at the Last Supper – the Holy Grail. Abbot Bere was said to have built two chapels, called the Loretto Chapel and the Edgar Chapel. But these were apparently destroyed by Henry VIII's vandals, and by the 19th century no one even knew where they were situated. Finding them was one of the tasks assigned to Bond.

There was one minor problem – there was no money to organise a full-scale dig. Bond therefore had to rely on luck and 'educated guesses'. Worse still, he had a rival architect called Caroe, who had been appointed to 'preserve' the ruins, and who obviously hoped to stumble upon the right answers before Bond did and take the credit for the discovery. Bond needed results quickly. And he decided upon a bold solution. He would ask the 'spirits'.

This was not, of course, quite the way that he expressed it. He said merely that he was going to undertake a 'psychological experiment'. At this time, everyone who was interested in psychical research was aware of the extraordinary case that has become known as the 'cross-correspondences' (see page 478),

The plan (above) indicates the extant ruins of Glastonbury Abbey, together with the positions of foundations that have been excavated or have been known to exist in the past. Frederick Bligh Bond's great find was the Edgar Chapel, which was known from records to have existed but was completely lost. For some years, it was believed that he had also succeeded in locating the Loretto Chapel. Although there is undoubtedly a building on the site, this is not believed to have been a sacristy. The aerial view (right) shows the extent to which the abbey ruins have been excavated

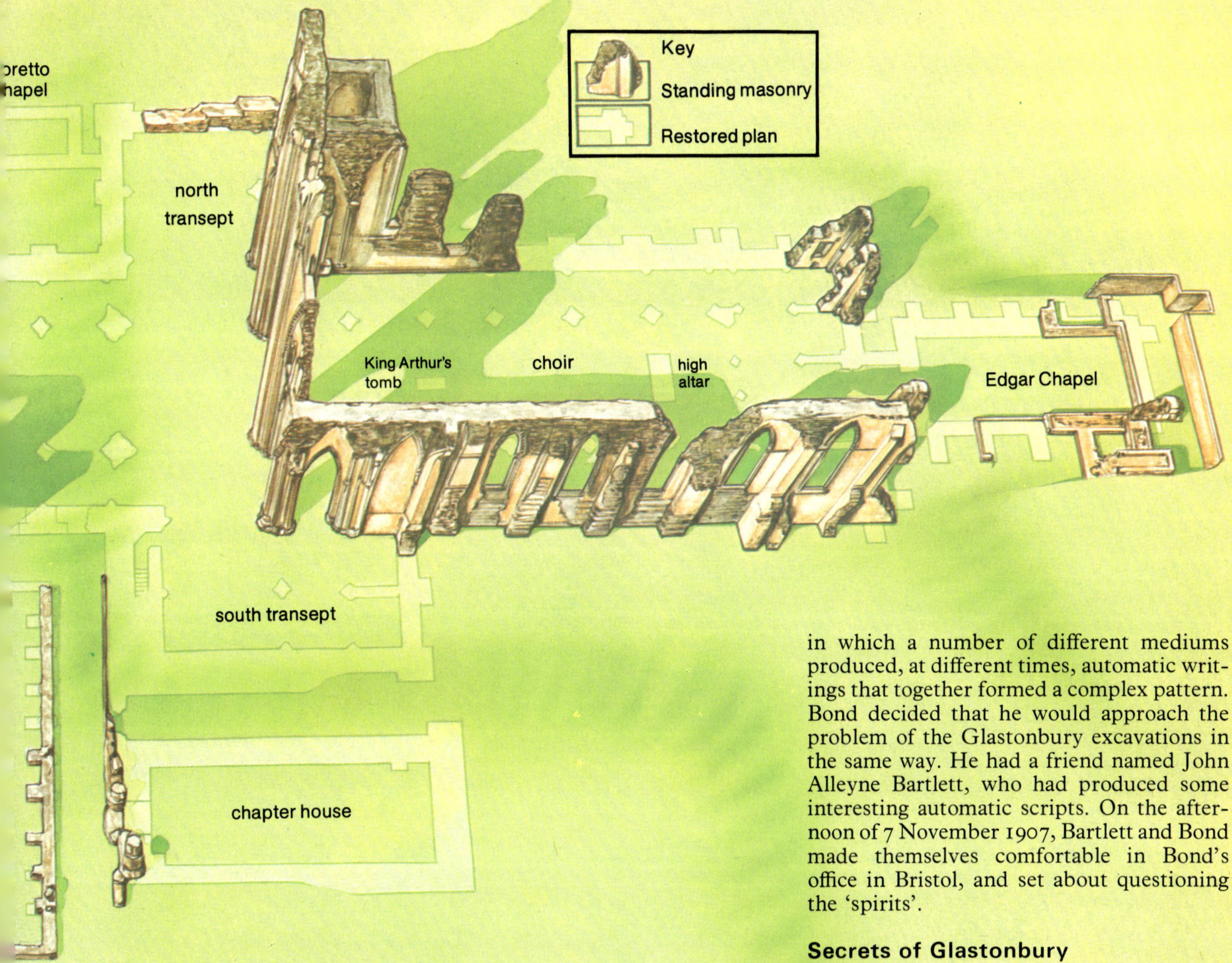

in which a number of different mediums produced, at different times, automatic writings that together formed a complex pattern. Bond decided that he would approach the problem of the Glastonbury excavations in the same way. He had a friend named John Alleyne Bartlett, who had produced some interesting automatic scripts. On the afternoon of 7 November 1907, Bartlett and Bond made themselves comfortable in Bond's office in Bristol, and set about questioning the 'spirits'.

### Secrets of Glastonbury

Their method was simple. Bond sat down opposite Bartlett at a plain wooden table, resting his fingers lightly on Bartlett's hand; Bartlett held a pencil above a sheet of paper. Then Bond cleared his throat and asked: 'Can you tell us anything about Glastonbury?' Bartlett's hand began to write. When the men deciphered the small, irregular writing, they saw that it said: 'All knowledge is eternal and is available to mental sympathy. I was not in sympathy with the monks – I cannot find a monk yet.'

This looked promising. Bond suggested that he knew a few living monks who might form a sympathetic link. At this, the pencil began to move again, tracing an outline that they soon recognised as the abbey, but with a long rectangle stuck on its eastern end. It was signed 'Gulielmus Monachus' – William the Monk. The rectangle looked too large to be a chapel, so Bond asked for a more careful drawing. The pencil obliged, with another precise drawing of a chapel, and also showed two smaller chapels to the north. Bond asked who had built it, and received the answer – in Latin – 'Abbot Bere', and the statement that this was the Edgar Chapel. It was added to, said the writer, by Abbot Whyting, in whose

handwritings. But was it all pure fantasy?

Finally, in 1908, the money for excavation became available. Digging started in 1909. And, to Bond's amazement and delight, it was soon abundantly clear that the monks had been telling him the truth.

Understandably, the first thing he wanted to know was whether there really was a large chapel at the east end of the abbey church. Johannes Bryant had also told him that he would find the remains of two towers at the west end. In May 1909, the workmen began to dig trenches at the east end of the ruined church. When Bond's rival Caroe came and looked at the work, he must have been mystified by the apparently random arrangement of the trenches. Any scepticism he felt must have changed to astonishment as the workmen quickly came upon an immense and unsuspected wall running north and south for 31 feet (10 metres). Moreover, excavation at the other end of the ruined church quickly revealed the outline of two unsuspected towers. To Bond's superiors, it must have seemed like a run of incredible luck, combined with intelligent deduction. As to Bond, he must have wondered many times whether he should reveal the secret of his ghostly 'communicators'. Yet common sense told him that he should be cautious. His employer was the Church of England – and the Church has never been very sympathetic to Spiritualism. Of course, it believes in life after death, since this is part of Christian dogma; but from the beginning, the Church has shown itself hostile and sceptical about the notion of communication with the dead. So how could Bond explain

reign it was destroyed. When they asked the name of the writer, it wrote: 'Ego Johannes Bryant, monk and lapidator.' (Lapidator means 'stonemason'.)

The two men were excited, yet at the same time disappointed. Someone who seemed to know what he was talking about was answering the questions, but the answers looked too good to be true. Did these 'facts' about the Edgar Chapel come from their own minds?

Four days later, they tried again. Their 'communicator' began by saying that he was becoming tired towards the end of the last session, but that the monks were now very eager to communicate. 'They say the times are now ripe and the curse is departing.' Then another hand wrote: 'Benedicite. Go unto Glaston soon. . . .' And later, the hand added: 'Ye names of builded things are very hard in Latin tongue. . . . My son, thou canst not understand. Wee wold speak in the Englyshe tongue. . . .' To the question, 'Tell us more about yourself,' it replied: 'I died in 1533.' He was, he said, curator of the chapel in the time of Henry VII.

From then on, Bond and Bartlett held regular sessions, and the monks of Glastonbury poured out information. There were several different monks, and several different

Above: the foundations of the Edgar Chapel, in a photograph taken shortly after they were restored by Bond. The site of the chapel was identified by one of Bond's ghostly informants, a monk named Johannes Bryant. In one respect, however, it seems that Johannes was mistaken. The angled walls at the far end of the chapel are no longer to be seen: Johannes claimed that they were built as an apse by Abbot Bere, but experts now believe that they are actually a water channel and part of an ancient abbey wall, and they have been removed

Right: the tomb of Arthur, 'the once and future king', seen through the peaceful ruins of the abbey nave

that his communicators called themselves the Company of Avalon – the old name for Glastonbury – and, worse still, described themselves as 'watchers from the other side'? Wisely, he decided to keep his amazing secret. At least, for the time being.

Meanwhile, discovery followed discovery, and Bond's reputation was greatly enhanced. His monkish correspondents proved to be phenomenally accurate. They told him there was a door in the east wall, leading into the street. This seemed unlikely, since eastern doorways in churches are unusual; yet digging revealed the doorway in the middle of the east wall. They told him the chapel would be 90 feet (28 metres) long, which seemed enormous; excavation showed it to be 87 feet (27 metres), and the wall and plinth added another 3 feet (1 metre). They even told him he would find the remains of azure-coloured windows – which again seemed unlikely, since most stained glass of that period used white and gold. But they duly found their fragments of blue stained glass in the Edgar Chapel. A communicator who seemed to be Abbot Bere said the roof was painted in gold and crimson; digging revealed arch mouldings with gold and crimson paint still on them.

In 1918, 10 years after the start of the triumphant excavations, Bond decided to publish the full story behind the discovery. No doubt he assumed that his success would justify his method. But this assumption proved to be a tragic mistake.

*What revelations from the Company of Avalon forced Bond to reveal his secret? See page 1038*

Above: the Lady Chapel, one of the best-preserved parts of the abbey, was consecrated in 1189. It is also known as St Joseph's Chapel, after St Joseph of Arimathea, Christ's uncle, who, according to legend, brought the child Jesus to Glastonbury

Right: Bond and Bartlett were told by one of their ghostly communicators of the location of the unfinished Loretto Chapel. When the site was excavated in 1920, the foundations of a building were found, but it is now believed that they are not, in fact, remains of the Loretto Chapel. The foundations in the photograph have since been covered over with turf

# Voyage into the unknown

**Still-warm tea on the galley table, lifeboats all secure – and the crew of the *Mary Celeste* has vanished. This is the stuff of legend and, as PAUL BEGG reveals, it is complete fiction. So what really happened?**

IT DID NOT TAKE LONG for the myth surrounding the disappearance of the *Mary Celeste*'s crew to be born. Indeed, it could be argued that it began in Gibraltar in 1872 when Solly Flood tried in vain to attach guilt to Captain Morehouse and the crew of the *Dei Gratia*. But the story was seized upon by writers and journalists and soon caught the public imagination.

The first major piece of fiction about the ship was published in January 1884 by the prestigious *Cornhill Magazine*, 11 months before Gilman C. Parker deliberately burnt the ship to a cinder (see box). It was a sensational short story called *J. Habakuk Jephson's statement* and it bore little resemblance to the actual facts. It was picked up by American newspapers however and published as fact, much to the outrage of Solly Flood and Horatio Sprague, the US Consul in Gibraltar, both of whom wrote letters condemning the tale.

Apart from its literary worth, *J. Habakuk Jephson's statement* is interesting for two reasons: it was one of the first literary efforts of a young English doctor named Arthur Conan Doyle, and in it *Mary Celeste* is called *Marie Celeste*, the name by which the ship is now most commonly known. However, Conan Doyle was not the first to make the error – this version of the name first appears in *Lloyd's List* of 25 March 1873.

Above: crewmen of the *Dei Gratia* sight the mystery ship *Mary Celeste*, in a painting by Gordon A. Johnson. This was commissioned in 1965 by the Atlantic Mutual Insurance Company – the original insurers of the *Mary Celeste*

Conan Doyle's story was the first of many fictional accounts that have appeared over the years; for example, a novel based on the mystery was published as recently as 1980. Some of these tales have been presented as straight fiction, others as fictionalised fact (but nevertheless proposing a serious explanation), and quite a few have been intended to be taken as fact.

In the late 1920s *Chamber's Journal* published an article by Lee Kaye purporting to be a true account of what happened aboard *Mary Celeste* as supposedly told by a survivor named John Pemberton (one of the many 'survivors' who have popped up over the years but whose names are mysteriously absent from the crew list).

Pemberton's story was expanded to book length by Laurençe J. Keating in 1929 and called *The great Mary Celeste hoax*. It was a bestseller on both sides of the Atlantic; John Pemberton rapidly became the man of the moment. Many journalists sought interviews with him, but Pemberton remained elusive until a 'special correspondent' of the London *Evening Standard* tracked him down – and obtained not only the coveted interview but a photograph as well. Both were published in the *Evening Standard* on 6 May 1929.

However, one of the few true statements

in Keating's book was its title: the story *was* a hoax; Lee Kaye, Laurence Keating, and the *Evening Standard*'s 'special correspondent' were all one and the same person, an Irish-Liverpuddlian named Laurence J. Keating. John Pemberton was a figment of Keating's fertile imagination and the photograph of 'Pemberton' was of Keating's own father.

While the majority of theories to explain the abandonment of *Mary Celeste* are generally a variation on the theme of murder – committed either by *Mary Celeste*'s own crew or by the men of *Dei Gratia* – other solutions are not uncommon and are frequently bizarre. The 1900s favoured 'monster from the depths' stories in which *Mary Celeste* was attacked by a huge hungry octopus that plucked the entire crew from the deck. Although it has its attractions for illustrators, the theory also has a number of flaws. Even if such a huge creature exists (see page 90) it is highly unlikely that everyone aboard *Mary Celeste* would have been on deck at the same time or that they would have obligingly stayed there as the monster plucked them off one by one. We must also assume that for some reason it craved *Mary Celeste*'s yawl, chronometer, sextant, and ship's papers.

The late Morris K. Jessup, who was involved with the alleged Philadelphia experiment (see page 309), suggested that *Mary Celeste*'s crew were abducted by a UFO. And Bermuda Triangle writers list the vessel's crew among the victims of whatever unexplained force they consider to exist in the area, imbuing that force with a singular selectivity, and in the process enlarging the Triangle so that it reaches the Azores. A superficially acceptable theory put forward by a number of rational people was that the food or drinking water was contaminated and caused the crew to hallucinate, driving them mad so that they threw themselves over the side. But Oliver Deveau and other members of the *Dei Gratia*'s crew used the food and water they found aboard *Mary Celeste* and suffered no ill effects.

Above: the alleged suicide of the *Marie Celeste*'s captain – 'Tibbs' – from an illustration of Conan Doyle's story *J. Habakuk Jephson's statement*. A gripping tale, it was taken by many to be true and popularised the misnomer *'Marie' Celeste*

Below: sea monsters have also been blamed for the tragedy

The United States Consul in Gibraltar, Horatio Sprague, wrote in July 1887 that:

> This case of the *Mary Celeste* is startling, since it appears to be one of those mysteries which no human ingenuity can penetrate sufficiently to account for the abandonment of this vessel and the disappearance of her master, family and crew. . . .

No solution so far offered seems to account for all the circumstances, but it is possible to list some salient facts that might provide a few clues: *Mary Celeste* was abandoned by her captain and crew; those who abandoned ship did so in the ship's yawl. This small vessel would have been overloaded and easily capsized, so the crew's fate is not wholly inexplicable. The ship was abandoned in a hurry: extra clothing was not taken nor – as far as is known – was any food or water, but the crew did not abandon ship in a complete panic, since they took the time to collect the sextant, chronometer, and the ship's papers (apart from the temporary log). Since there was no evidence that *Mary Celeste* had suffered any damage, whatever made the crew abandon her was something they feared had happened or was about to happen, but clearly never did.

The part-owner of the ship, James H. Winchester, suggested that *Mary Celeste*'s cargo of denatured alcohol gave off fumes, which collected in the hold and formed an explosive mixture. This, he speculated, was

Above: a reconstruction of one theory about the disappearance of the crew of *Mary Celeste*: they all fell overboard. The influential *Strand Magazine* heard that a reputable schoolmaster had a servant named Abel Fosdyk who claimed to have been the only survivor. Fosdyk said that Captain Briggs went mad. This may or may not be connected with the 'fact' that everyone else on board was precipitated into the sea from a flimsy play area built for the captain's daughter. Fosdyk threw no light on why no one managed to climb back on board

either ignited by a spark, resulting, perhaps, from friction caused by the metal bands around the barrels rubbing together, or a naked light used during cargo inspection. Or perhaps the fumes had been mistaken for smoke and gave rise to the belief that the ship was about to be blown out of the water.

Experts have expressed the opinion that there could have been no *visible* vapour, but that an explosive mixture could have been formed. However, this would not have resulted in a minor explosion, but would have blown *Mary Celeste* into matchwood.

The most likely solution was in part offered by Oliver Deveau at the salvage hearing. He said that he thought the crew had panicked, believing that the ship was sinking. It was not an opinion that has impressed many commentators and most have dismissed it as idiotic (and Deveau himself as an idiot). But in fairness to Deveau, his comment has to be taken in context. At the hearing he was asked a straightforward question, and he answered it without elaboration. Later researchers, however, have tried to interpret his meaning.

Dr James H. Kimble, once the head of the United States Weather Bureau in New York, and author Gershom Bradford have both suggested that *Mary Celeste* was struck by a waterspout, a tornado at sea; a column of whirling wind and water that can appear without warning, last for up to an hour, and then break up as quickly as it appeared.

At first glance this theory does not seem very plausible, particularly as waterspouts are not common outside the tropics, nor is it common for ships to be struck by them. But the fact is that waterspouts are not totally restricted to the tropics: for example, in December 1920 the steamer *British Marquis* reported no less than 20 waterspouts in the English Channel.

Mr Bradford and Dr Kimble believe that a relatively small and harmless spout, narrow and travelling at an angle, could have struck the ship without doing a great deal of damage; indeed, it would have left the vessel no worse than had she encountered a storm. All this is consistent with the state of *Mary Celeste* when first sighted by the *Dei Gratia*. However, within a waterspout the barometric pressure is extremely low and, as the spout passed over the ship, the marked difference in pressure between the inside and outside of the ship could have caused the hatch covers to blow off – in the same way that a building's walls explode outward when struck by a tornado.

In this context, the method by which *Mary Celeste* was sounded may be extremely significant. This was done by dropping a rod down the pump well to measure the water in the hold, in much the same way as a motorist checks his oil with a dipstick. The drop in barometric pressure could have driven the bilge water up the pump-well, where a valve

Right: in the 1936 film version the bosun goes mad and kills the entire crew, including himself

would have prevented it from returning immediately to the hold. Although this would have been merely a temporary malfunction, the crew may not have realised it.

Suppose, then, that after the waterspout had moved on the crew were shaken and confused. Somebody went to sound the ship to see if she had suffered any underwater damage, and to his horror found that *Mary Celeste* had leaked 6 to 8 feet (2 to $2\frac{1}{2}$ metres) of water in less than a minute – or so the seaman would have thought when he removed the sounding rod. Believing *Mary Celeste* to be sinking fast, Captain Briggs, perhaps panicking out of concern for his wife and daughter, gave the order to abandon ship. Perhaps this was what Oliver Deveau had meant by his cryptic statement. We shall never know, but the waterspout theory certainly seems to fit most of the reported circumstances and also explains the most baffling feature of the case: what monstrous happening threatened those aboard *Mary Celeste*, resulting in their hurried evacuation but still allowing them time in which to grab sextant, chronometer and ship's papers?

One commentator has called the case of *Mary Celeste* 'a detective-story writer's nightmare: the perfectly perplexing situation without any logical solution – a plot which can never be convincingly unravelled.'

On 16 May 1873 the *Daily Albion* of Liverpool reported that two rafts had been found by fishermen at Baudus, in Asturias, near Madrid, Spain. One of the rafts had a corpse lashed to it and was flying an American flag. The second raft bore five decomposing bodies. Curiously, the matter was not investigated, so no one will ever know who they were or what ship they belonged to. But could they have been from *Mary Celeste*?

Above: a waterspout at sea. A fast, angled one could have hit the *Mary Celeste*, causing only superficial damage and temporarily falsifying the crew's soundings. Believing that they were sinking, the crew could have panicked and abandoned ship. Although this is one of the more reasonable theories, it is unlikely that anyone will ever discover the truth

## A terrible risk

In late 1884 an ageing and rather unkempt *Mary Celeste* was bought by Gilman C. Parker and loaded with freight, which he insured for $30,000. The vessel then sailed for Port-au-Prince, Haiti. But she never arrived. On 3 January 1885 *Mary Celeste* ran aground on the razor-sharp coral reef of Rochaelais Bank in the Gulf of Gonave, off the coast of Haiti.

Parker put in an insurance claim, but for some reason the insurance companies regarded it with deep suspicion and sent enquiry agents to investigate. They found that Parker had loaded the ship with rubbish – not the valuable cargo he had insured – had deliberately run *Mary Celeste* aground, unloaded the part of the cargo that he could sell, and then set *Mary Celeste* alight.

Parker was charged with barratry – fraud and/or criminal negligence by a ship's officer or crew against the owners or insurers. In those days this was a crime punishable by death. The case was heard in a federal court in Boston, but it was dropped because of a legal technicality. Gilman C. Parker, a grizzled old sea-dog who was – judging by the evidence – undoubtedly guilty of every maritime crime short of piracy, and his associates walked from the court free men. Free, that is, from the penalties of a court of law, but not from the jinx of *Mary Celeste*. In a short time Parker went bankrupt, and he died in poverty and disrepute. One of his fellow conspirators went insane and was placed in a mental institution where he ended his days. Another killed himself. In the end the jinx of *Mary Celeste* had won, having horribly ruined many lives.

**Further reading**
Paul Begg, *Into thin air*, Sphere 1981
Gershom Bradford, *The Secret of the Mary Celeste*, W. Foulsham & Co. 1966
Macdonald Hastings, *Mary Celeste*, Michael Joseph 1972

# A logic of their own

ONE OF THE MOST curious categories in the UFO files consists of isolated reports of UFOs landing on rivers or lakes and siphoning up considerable quantities of water. We report on two cases, widely separated in both space and time: the first is from Japan in 1973, the second from northern Italy in 1952. In both instances, the amount of water taken on board by the UFOs suggests that it is not intended merely for scientific analysis – yet what else can it be used for? Are we to believe that UFOs are powered or cooled by water, or that their occupants need water for drinking or cooking?

Our third case is one of the weirdest ever to have been reported in Japan. Although it must be classified as a close encounter of the third kind, no UFO was observed during the incident. If some alien entities can survive without spacecraft, why are others so apparently vulnerable that they require regular supplies of water? The reports simply do not add up to a coherent picture of the perplexing UFO phenomenon.

**Two terrifying incidents from Japan and one from Italy give some clues about UFO power. CHARLES BOWEN examines the evidence**

## 'Infinite menace'

**Close encounter of the third kind: Tomakomai, Hokkaido, Japan, July 1973**

In 1975 *Flying Saucer Review* received an exciting account of one of the occasional sightings of UFOs taking on water. It came from a Japanese UFO investigator, Jun-Ichi Takanashi of Osaka; shadowy humanoid beings were also said to have been observed. The event took place at Tomakomai, a small industrial town on the southern coast of Hokkaido, the northernmost island of Japan, in July 1973. The eyewitness was Masaaki Kudou, a university student, then aged 20. He was home on vacation, and had taken a temporary job as a night security guard at a timber yard.

After patrolling the premises in his car, Mr Kudou returned to the prescribed place from which he could observe the premises – and the waters of the bay beyond – and settled back to listen to his radio, light a cigarette, and relax. It was a still night, with the stars clearly visible. Suddenly he saw a streak of light flash across the sky, a spectacular 'shooting star' that suddenly stopped in its tracks, vanished, and reappeared. Remaining stationary, the light now expanded and contracted alternately at high speed, growing until it reached the apparent size of a baseball held at arm's length. It darted about in all directions within a few degrees of arc, and Mr Kudou found himself dizzily trying to follow its gyrations. As it began to descend spirally towards the sea the young student felt a surge of alarm, especially when the light halted near a distant cement works, and began to direct a beam of intermittent pulses of green light towards the north. Next, the object continued its descent towards the sea, this time sweeping in an arc until it was in a position much closer to the student observer. It halted its descent at about 70 feet (20 metres) from the sea, and the student saw a transparent tube emerge and lower itself towards the water. A soft *min-min-min-min* noise could be heard as this was happening, and the pitch of the noise lowered as the tube descended. When the tube touched the water its lower edge glowed, and it seemed that water was being sucked up into the object above.

Masaaki Kudou wondered if he were dreaming or, failing that, if his imagination were playing tricks with him. He lowered his gaze for a minute or so; when he looked again the water-suction operation was over, and the tube had been withdrawn from the water. No sooner had he registered this fact than the hovering UFO began to move towards him with what seemed to be infinite menace; he feared he was about to be attacked, and probably killed.

The object moved into a position some 160 feet (50 metres) above Kudou's car, and he, by leaning forwards and looking up, could keep it in view. He says its surface was as smooth as a table-tennis ball and, emitting its own glow, appeared to be white. Around his car everything was lit up as though by daylight, and he says he saw what appeared to be windows around the diameter of the spherical object. In the middle of one of these there was a shadowy human-shaped figure, while to the right there were two smaller shapes in another of the windows, but Kudou could not see whether or not these were similar to the first. All this, plus a sudden feeling that he was bound hand and foot, was too much for the witness, who rocked his head in his hands, with his chin on the steering wheel, moaning to himself.

Nevertheless, he still felt an urge to look upwards and, straining to do this, Kudou saw in the sky above the car three or four newly arrived glowing objects, similar in all respects to the first one. There was also a large, dark brown object, in silhouette, which looked like 'three gasoline drums connected together lengthwise' and which hovered noiselessly.

Suddenly the whole phenomenal spectacle came to an end. The glowing spheres swiftly manoeuvred into position whence they disappeared into one end of the large 'gasoline can' objects, and this in turn shot off to the north rather like a shooting star. The witness sat motionless, numb all over. He slowly became aware that his car radio was giving forth meaningless sounds, and that he himself was suffering from a severe headache. He was later able to estimate that the terrifying incident had lasted for about 12 minutes in all.

## 'They want to do me harm'

**Close encounter of the third kind: Lucca, Italy, 25 July 1952**

At 3 a.m. on 25 July 1952, a keen fisherman named Carlo Rossi was walking alongside the River Serchio, opposite San Pietro a Vico in Lucca, northern Italy, when he was puzzled by the appearance of an unusual light from an unseen position on the river below. Climbing the high embankment, he looked down to see a huge circular craft bearing a transparent cupola on top, and a shallow turret underneath from which three legs protruded, supporting the body of the craft above the water. There was also a ladder, and a long tube by which, apparently, the craft was taking in water. Suddenly a port opened in the upper part of the turret, and Carlo saw a 'human' figure look out. This figure pointed at the fisherman, who scrambled down the embankment. A green ray passed over his head, and he threw himself down. Looking up, seconds later, he saw the craft rise above the embankment and move off at high speed towards Viareggio.

Rossi was badly shaken by the incident – but something that happened a few weeks later worried him much more. To the outsider, the incident seems trivial – although it is a classic example of an MIB encounter: a strange man approached Rossi and offered him, Rossi said, a 'bad' cigarette. Rossi was terrified; he used later to say, 'I wonder if they want to do me harm, maybe, because of the thing I saw in the river?'

The circumstances of Rossi's subsequent death seem to lend substance to his suspicion. He was riding home on his bicycle one day when he was knocked down by a car. The driver was never identified.

## 'Alarm turned to terror'

**Close encounter of the third kind: Sayama City, Saitama Prefecture, Japan, 3 October 1978**

Mr Hideichi Amano, who owns and runs a snack bar in Sayama City, Saitama Prefecture, Japan, is also a keen radio 'ham'. Jun-Ichi Takanashi investigated Mr Amano's alarming experience after seeing him on the television programme *11 P.M.*

The encounter occurred on the evening of 3 October 1978, when Amano, using his mobile unit radio car, drove up a mountain outside Sayama City at about 8.30 p.m. with his two-year-old daughter Juri. He made the trip so that he could get unrestricted radio transmission and reception for a conversation with his brother, who lives in a distant part of the country. When their hook-up was finished, and a few other local calls had been made, Hideichi Amano was about to drive back down the mountain when the interior of the car became very bright, a light ten times brighter than was normal was coming from the fluorescent tube he had fitted inside the car. He observed that this light was confined to the car's interior; none, he said, was passing through the windows! Moments earlier Juri had been standing on the passenger seat beside him, but now her father was aghast to see the child lying on the seat, and foaming at the mouth. At the same instant he became aware of a round patch of orange light that was beamed through the windscreen and onto his stomach, and he saw that this was coming from a point in the sky. And then alarm turned to terror when he sensed something metallic being pressed against his right temple.

Hideichi Amano glanced sideways and saw an unearthly humanoid creature standing there with a pipe-like device in its mouth, and it was this that was being pressed against his head. From the tube came an incessant babble, as from a tape being played too fast.

The witness said the creature had a round face, but no neck, two sharply pointed ears, two small, motionless eyes that glowed bluish-white, and a triangular depression on its forehead. The mouth was clamped round the pipe, and no nose could be seen. While the babble continued Mr Amano says he found it difficult to move, and his mind became 'vague'. The terrified radio ham tried to start the car to flee the place, but there was no response from the engine, and the lights would not work, either. Then, after four or five minutes, the creature began to dim out and slowly vanished. The orange light disappeared, the interior lighting returned to normal, and other equipment that had been switched on now began to function. When the headlights returned Mr Amano switched the starter and got an instant response. Still in a confused state he roared away down the hill, and it was only when he reached the lower slopes that he remembered little Juri's condition. He stopped and, fortunately, the child stood up and said: 'I want a drink of water, papa.'

The witness decided to report the experience to the police, but they only poked fun at him, so he went home and retired to bed, still suffering a severe headache.

Researchers for the *11 P.M.* programme heard of the affair and eventually arranged for Mr Amano to be questioned under hypnosis in front of the cameras. One piece of information retrieved was that the creature was alleged to have told him to return to the meeting place at a certain time – which, to avoid a stampede by the curious, was not revealed to the viewers. Jun-Ichi Takanashi seemed to have little faith in the regression session because the 'hypnotist's insistence on more information was far too severe'; he suspected that the idea of a second meeting with the humanoid was a creation of the witness's subconscious mind. The fact that no second meeting was ever reported seems to lend weight to this. Yet, despite his reservations, Takanashi considered the encounter, as originally reported, to be 'the strangest ever to have taken place in Japan.'

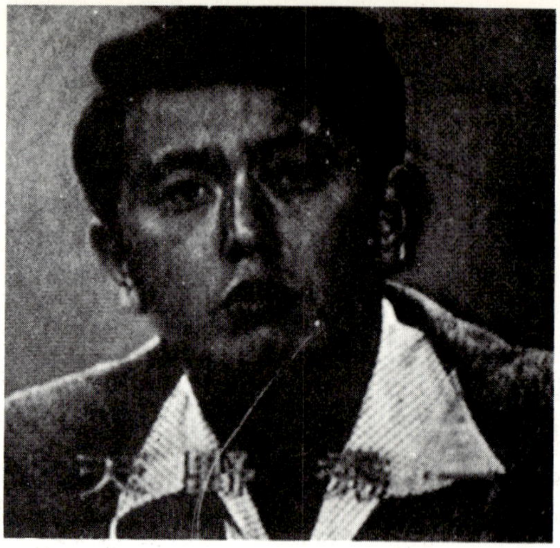

Right: Mr Hideichi Amano, victim of the Sayama encounter, recounts his experience on the television programme *11 P.M.*

# Fear of the undead

**Are all vampire stories the stuff of nightmares or horror films? DANIEL FARSON provides plentiful evidence to prove that the fear of vampires, at least, is as real today as it has ever been**

Left: an ancient Tibetan mask in the shape of a devil's face. The mouth is a receptacle for human blood

BELIEF IN VAMPIRES seems, at first, to be the most far-fetched of superstitions. Ghosts and even werewolves seem relatively rational compared to the idea that corpses creep from their coffins at night to suck the blood of the living, yet legends of vampirism have persisted since the beginning of time and still hold sway today.

The problem that surrounds the legends and belief in vampires is sorting out the fantasy – and to some people that is all there is – from the truth. A rational person might be forgiven for viewing the search for 'real vampires' with more than a little scepticism – for how can there be such creatures? Are they not just figments of the imagination?

Yet there exist reports from Eastern Europe that, in the 18th century, vampirism had reached almost epidemic proportions. The documentation is so detailed, and the witnesses included reputable people such as clergymen and doctors, that it seems impossible that every man was mistaken. But again, the sceptic might point out that 18th-century clergymen may have been telling the truth as they saw it, but the truth had become hopelessly confused with fear, superstition and ignorance. And before we dismiss vampirism as a relic of the dark ages, perhaps we should consider the modern controversy over what constitutes the state of death. If, with the most technologically advanced equipment at our disposal, we still cannot agree on the precise moment of death, then perhaps we should not overlook those vampire reports of 200 years ago. There must be some underlying truth in them – but what?

Left: *The vampire's kiss* by Biegas, 1916: the vampire 'red in tooth and claw'

According to the records, Austria, Hungary, Yugoslavia and Romania (which was then divided into the three separate states of Wallachia, Moldavia and Transylvania) were particularly infested with vampirism in the 16th, 17th and 18th centuries. It was a huge problem that involved hundreds of eye-witnesses from all classes of life. One surgeon, called in to investigate a series of cases, wrote:

> Vampirism . . . spread like a pestilence through Slavia and Wallachia, causing numerous deaths and disturbing all the land with fear of the mysterious visitors against which no one felt himself secure.

Most of the cases reported from these areas at that time showed common features: one classic account concerns a deputation that set out from Belgrade in 1732 to investigate the alleged vampire who was said to be systematically attacking a family in a remote village. When the investigating officers arrived – including some men of impeccable standing such as the public prosecutor – they were told that a villager, who had died three years earlier, had come back as a vampire to terrorise his own family. He had already killed three nieces and one nephew by draining them of their life blood, and would have killed his fifth victim – another, beautiful niece – had he not been interrupted and forced to flee into the night.

The deputation of officials and what was left of the terrified family duly gathered round the 'vampire's' grave as darkness fell. When they opened the coffin they found, to all outward appearances, a sleeping (or perhaps unconscious) man. He should have decomposed long ago; instead he looked as healthy as any of those standing around his grave. His hair and nails were long, his eyes half open – and his heart was still beating. Tradition was upheld: the heart of the 'undead' was pierced through with a stout iron stake. A horrible mixture of white fluid and what looked like fresh blood gushed out. But the task had to be finished; they cut off his head with an axe and buried the grisly remains in quicklime.

Another vampire story from that place and time described how a young Hungarian soldier, billeted on a farm, was greatly disturbed by the reaction of the family he was staying with when, during supper one evening, an old man came in from the dark and sat down to the meal with them. When he touched the farmer on the shoulder the family seemed out of their wits with fear. The next day they told the soldier why. During the night the farmer had died, claimed, they said, by the man who had so lightly touched him – his father who had been dead for 10 years. This was no mere ghost, the bereaved family insisted, but a vampire. Impressed by what he had seen and heard, the soldier told it to his regimental officer, who ordered the old man's grave to be opened up. The previous night's unwelcome visitor lay there like a man newly dead but his veins contained blood 'like a living man'. His head was cut off and his body laid to rest, this time for good.

### A deadly cure

Although the cure for vampirism differed slightly from area to area it was always drastic and never to be undertaken by the squeamish. The favourite technique was to plunge a wooden or iron stake through the alleged vampire's heart (a method also used in Britain to stop the ghosts of suicides wandering at night). Not surprisingly, the staked vampire frequently gave off a disgusting stench and one report described a corpse that was 'puffed up and bloated like a great leech ready to burst'. The normal processes of decomposition, with which most modern readers are unfamiliar, would account for both foul odour and grotesque swelling,

Above: a French illustration from the 1830s shows 'vampires' feasting off a corpse. Their hideous cravings are more typical of the *ghoul*; vampires drink blood from the living, and corpses do not bleed

Left: an artist's impression of the attack on a Victorian girl by the 'vampire of Croglin Grange'. Her brothers chased the skeletal fiend but it escaped, to return a year later. This time the brothers managed to shoot it, finally running it to earth in the local graveyard

Right: the burial of a suicide, 1836. They were buried at crossroads and their graves spiked with crosses to prevent them 'walking'

although superstitious peasants, terrified beyond reason, might not stop to consider this fact before dealing summarily with the 'vampire'. Again, another report stated that 'a quantity of fresh scarlet blood issued, and from the nose and mouth as well as from that part of his body which decency forbids me to name.' Yet those who are acquainted with the physical effects of death – nurses, morticians, and executioners among others – know full well that such discharges are not uncommon when the muscles relax after death, either before rigor mortis sets in or when it finally passes off. With very few exceptions (see page 774), corpses rot. But not all rotting corpses are vampires.

There are, however, curious details that seem to mark some so-called vampire stories as abnormal and worth investigating. One of the 'undead' was said to weep and scream with anguish when the stake was hammered into him. This would have been remarkable indeed had the man been dead beyond doubt when staked, but not quite so unusual if he had been prematurely buried – buried alive but apparently dead, perhaps due to catalepsy. And it does look as if some of these stories have exaggerated the length of time the 'vampire' had been dead and buried, as we shall see.

In 1746 the French monk Dom Calmet, one of the earliest authorities on vampirism, struggled to keep an open mind while searching for the truth. And the truth was not always easy to discern under a welter of superstition and confused eyewitness accounts. But he felt forced to admit:

> We are told that dead men return from their tombs, are heard to speak, walk about, injure both men and animals whose blood they drain, making them sick and finally causing their death. Nor can the men deliver themselves unless they dig the corpses up and drive a sharp stake through these bodies, cut off their heads, tear out their hearts, or else burn the bodies to ashes. It seems impossible not to subscribe to the prevailing belief that these apparitions do actually come forth from their graves.

It is not, however, a statement that would stand up to cross-examination. And it is interesting to note the telling phrases 'we are told' and 'it seems impossible not to subscribe to the prevailing belief'. Dom Calmet's was not an eyewitness account, and his susceptibility to the 'prevailing belief' of the day could have made him a witch-hunter, flat-earther or Nazi with no intellectual struggle at all.

However, the great French philosopher Jean-Jacques Rousseau went much further, stating baldly: 'If ever there was in the world a warranted and proven history, it is that of vampires. Nothing is lacking: official reports, testimonials of persons of standing, of surgeons, of clergymen, of judges; the judicial evidence is all-embracing.'

With all due respect to a great man, Rousseau displays greater faith in 'persons of standing' than he does in vampires. And it is not quite true – in his statement at least – that 'nothing is lacking'. Documents apparently abound, but Rousseau could not lay his hands quite so easily on actual vampires.

### The prevailing superstition

Montague Summers, a clergyman and writer on the occult – on this matter at least – erred on the side of scepticism, claiming that 'in Romania we find gathered together round the vampire almost all the beliefs and superstitions that prevail throughout the whole of Eastern Europe.'

But even in the late 20th century there are people who believe in vampires as real, supernatural beings. The Reverend Neil Smith, a well-known exorcist of Hampstead in London, believes that vampires exist even in the populous capital. They are, he says, half animal and half human – and totally evil. He dismisses the idea that vampire attacks are 'all in the mind' of the alleged victim by citing what constitutes, to him, incontrovertible evidence of their existence. He claims to have dealt personally with several cases of vampirism. One victim showed him 'the marks on her wrists which appeared at night where blood was taken, marks almost like those done by an animal scratching.' He denied vehemently that these marks could have been self-inflicted. He gave a further example of a man from South America who 'had a similar phenomenon, as if an animal had sucked away his blood and attacked him.'

And, of course, not only vampires attack human beings. Judging from the increasing evidence, so do poltergeists, humanoids and other allied phenomena. Perhaps vampires

Left: detail of a Toltec carving showing a priest holding a human head; the serpents symbolise blood

Above: Dom Calmet, 18th-century vampire expert

Below: the grave of a gypsy suicide – at a crossroads in Suffolk, England

are 'real' in the sense that they are from another time and place, another dimension; part flesh, part materialisation. We know so little about the paranormal that literally anything might be possible. Yet a few salient facts about the vampire's *bloodlust* may make matters clearer.

From time immemorial the ritual drinking of blood has been the vital element in sacrifice, gaining power and propitiating the gods. For life, one must have blood, and the primitive mind equated more blood with more vitality. Aztecs poured human blood into the mouths of their idols to appease them, while Indian rajahs drank blood from severed heads in order to gain greater strength. The ancient Chinese ate the brains of the revered dead in order to gain wisdom, at the same time guarding the corpse before burial to prevent a dog or cat jumping over it, which would, they believed, turn the dead person into a vampire.

The Romans, brutalised though most of them were, were horrified by tales of what Christians did as part of their worship – they ate flesh and drank blood. Indeed it seems likely that a tiny minority of the early Christians, misunderstanding the symbolic nature of the communion bread and wine, may have resorted to cannibalism. But blood drinking, disgusting though it may seem to us, is very different from supernatural vampirism, and this all seems light years away from the 'enlightened' modern world. Yet as recently as 1973, in as unlikely a setting as anyone could imagine, the fundamental fear of the vampire actually killed a man.

It happened in Stoke-on-Trent in the heart of Britain's Potteries, a town once bustling with the thriving businesses and

scandals of the nouveaux riches, but now distinguished only by a faded grandeur and sense of waste. Consequently the row of gloomy, Gothic-style houses known as 'The Villas' does not seem out of place in this defeated landscape. But what happened at No 3 does not seem to have been a very natural occurrence at all.

Demetrious Myicura died there in bizarre and grisly circumstances. Nothing much was known about the dead man except that he was a Polish immigrant who had come to work in the Potteries 25 years earlier.

When he did not turn up for work and no one saw him for a few days the neighbours called the police. John Pye, a young and keen policeman, investigated. It seemed that Myicura had been frightened of electricity, for all the light bulbs had been removed from his room. Using his flashlight, John Pye examined the room. There were newspapers scattered all over the floor and a used frying pan under the bed, on which the dead man lay half covered by a pile of old clothes and tattered blankets. Fully dressed, with one hand behind his head and the other lying across his waist, he might have been sleeping, except for the fact that his mouth was wide open as if in stark terror.

### Suspicious circumstances

The pathologist's report said the man had choked to death on a pickled onion. Besides, single, slightly eccentric people are commonly found dead by neighbours and police in scenes of squalor. The incident might have passed into obscurity had not John Pye been puzzling over one or two details of that chaotic room – details not worth mentioning at the time because they seemed to have no bearing on the unfortunate man's death.

For a start the room had been scattered liberally with salt. A bag of it had been placed between Myicura's legs and there was another resting behind his head. There was also salt mixed with urine in various containers placed around the room, and an upturned bowl on the window ledge concealed a mixture of excreta – and garlic.

These curious and unpleasant details seemed to remind PC Pye of something he had heard or read somewhere, and then he remembered what it might all mean. He went to the library and consulted Anthony Master's *The natural history of the vampire* (1972). His suspicions were confirmed; the salt, the urine, the garlic were all features of an age-old ritual to protect oneself against vampires.

The coroner was persuaded to re-examine the 'pickled onion' – it was, as John Pye had gathered, a clove of garlic. What agony and terror Myicura must have suffered in that room on his own, so afraid of vampires that he actually tried to sleep with a clove of garlic in his mouth, and it was on this 'protective device' that he choked to death.

Obsessions, especially among the lonely, take many forms, and this man was obviously obsessed with vampires. He came from Eastern Europe where fear of the 'undead' is still quite common; he lived on his own; perhaps he was simply unhinged.

But although no one will ever know whether the loathsome creatures were hallucinations, projections from his mind, or a sick fancy, his *fear* of them was real. So it could be said that the vampires did get him in the end.

*What part did Count Dracula play in creating the cult of the vampire? See page 1034*

Top: a scene from the Hammer Films' production of *Dracula* (1958), which starred Christopher Lee as the aristocratic vampire. Here a once-beautiful young woman, infected with vampirism, is staked in time-honoured fashion. Already she is visibly ageing and will soon crumble into dust, at last truly dead and able to rest in peace

Above: Montague Summers, a Roman Catholic priest who was famous for his expert knowledge of werewolves, black magic and vampires. He died aged 68 in 1948, a believer in supernatural evil as embodied in the vampire

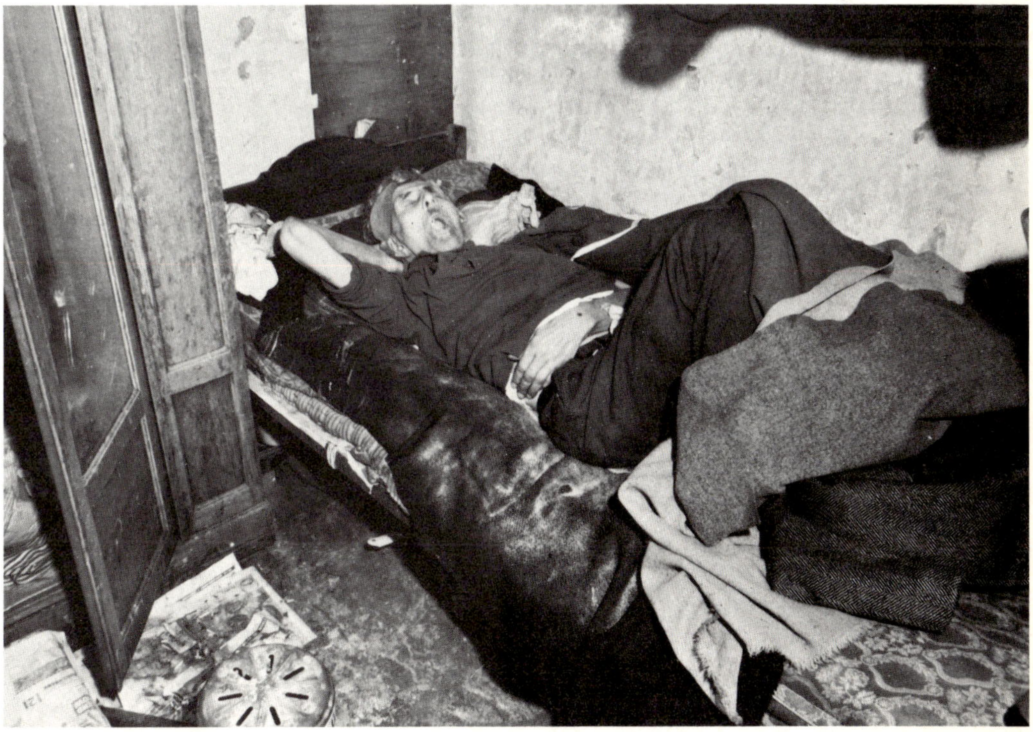

Right: Demetrious Myicura's death in 1973; it appears he died warding off 'vampires'

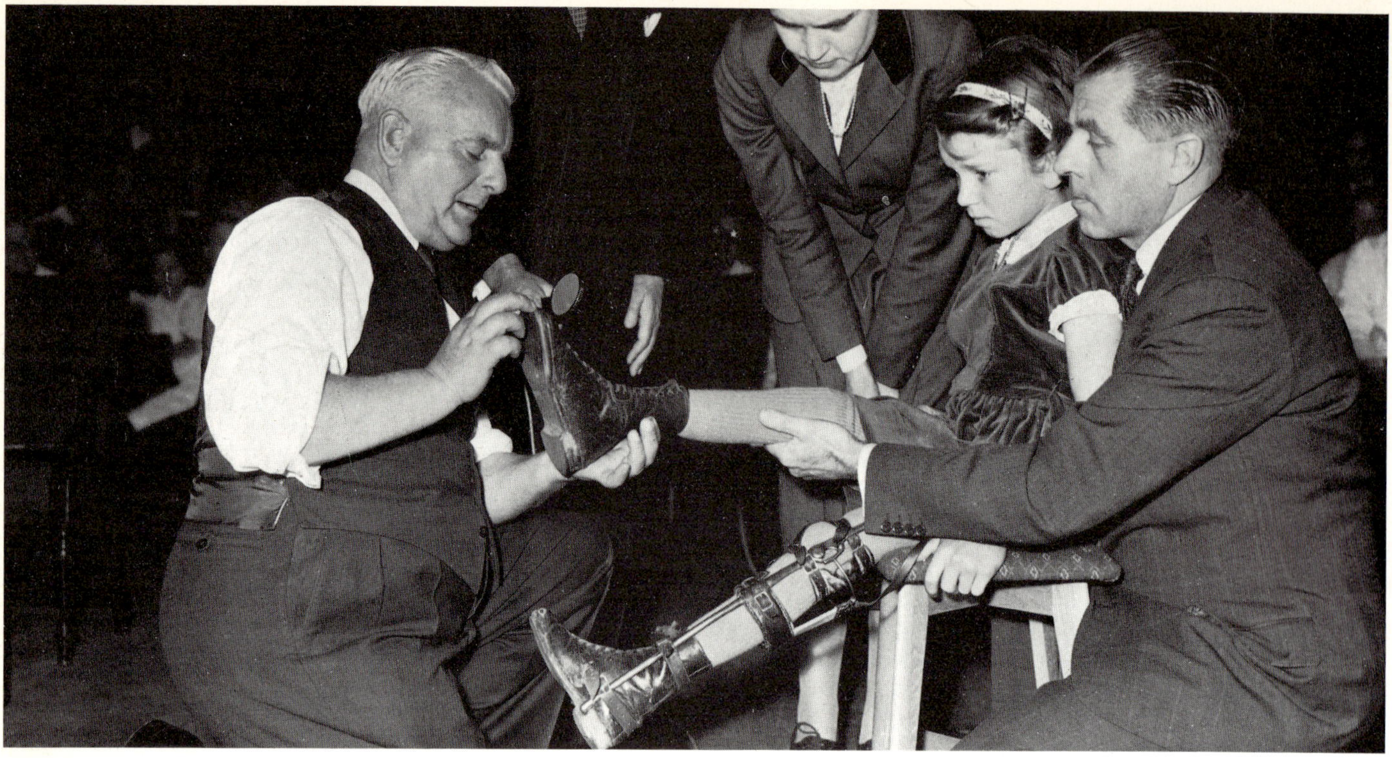

Above: the late Harry Edwards, Britain's foremost spiritual healer of the day, treats a crippled child, watched by a crowd of 6000 people at London's Royal Albert Hall in September 1954. It could be said that by removing the outward symbol of the child's illness – the ugly and constraining leg irons – he is in some way 'shocking' the child into health, in the same way as Christ's 'take up thy bed and walk' healed a paralytic. But are healers more than just clever psychotherapists: do they emit some as yet unnamed force that acts on the body as well as the mind?

# Testing the healer's gift

**Is healing simply a matter of faith, or does the healer really possess a power that can cure diseased tissue? DAVID HARVEY looks at the startling results of some major experiments into this paranormal ability**

IF THE LAYING ON of hands and related 'healing' techniques help people to recover from illness, as so many claim, then the process involved should be of major significance. True, the medical profession would have to rethink its attitude towards healing completely, but if we could discover something about the nature of 'faith healing', then the potential benefits would far outweigh the hostility it is likely to incur from the medical establishment. Even if research into the subject revealed only that the healing process were achieved in some relatively mundane way then it would still be of enormous use; for example, in helping established therapists to improve their techniques and encouraging others to learn how to heal.

Unfortunately those involved in the mainstream of science – and medicine in particular – still regard even the most attested healers with suspicion and open hostility. So, as with most parapsychological research, it is only the rare, brave individual bold enough to step outside the confines of orthodox science who dare investigate the subject.

One of the pioneers in this field was a young biochemist, Dr Bernard Grad of McGill University, Montreal, Canada, who, in the late 1950s, decided that the claims made for the efficacy of the laying on of hands were too important to be ignored. He believed that it was a phenomenon that demanded to be investigated.

To Grad, the fact that no one had run experiments on it before was almost as great a mystery as the healing process itself. As he observed, there was no difficulty in applying suitable biomedical procedures to the process of healing. The explanation for the widespread apathy had to lie elsewhere. Perhaps the very simplicity and apparently unsophisticated nature of the healing process represented an affront to a scientific age dedicated to ingenious, technical solutions to medical problems.

However, Grad was not deterred from delving deeper into the subject. Nor was he alarmed, as many suggested he might be, by the problem of sorting out the genuine from

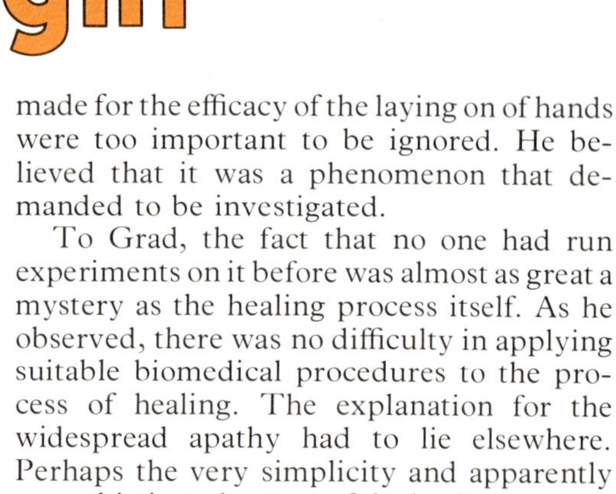

the bogus healers. He argued that if the alleged healer can really heal, this should be obvious from the results obtained under carefully controlled conditions.

Aware of the exciting possibilities ahead, he stated: 'From such studies, it might be possible to develop tests which would distinguish persons with the gift from those without it; and more importantly, it might provide information basic to some aspects of the healing art, namely psychotherapy and the so-called placebo effect.'

Indeed, the discovery of the placebo effect in drug trials had already raised some extremely difficult questions for medical scientists: human beings were not the predictable biochemical machines they had assumed.

Right: Dr Bernard Grad, whose pioneering experiments into the nature of spiritual healing have also provided insights into other aspects of Man's potential. For example, having 'green fingers' may not be a matter of luck, but part of a barely understood gift of regeneration

### Great expectations

When tests are conducted to evaluate the effect of new drugs, a control group is always included. The surprise result on a number of occasions has been that some members of the control group, dosed with plain sugar pills (placebos), have mimicked the physiological response of those who took the actual drugs, a phenomenon known as the placebo effect. Expectation, instilled by taking part in the trials, seems to have been the crucial factor since none of the 'guinea pigs' (and none of the staff who handed out the drugs) knew whether they were receiving sugar pills or the real thing. This type of experiment is known as 'double blind'. So under controlled conditions it has been shown that the mind, primed by suggestion, can influence the body's behaviour to a remarkable degree.

In the early years of the 20th century, the notion that such an interaction could occur was regarded as mere speculation, although many had maintained that the mind-over-body effect was real enough. But interesting though placebo-effect experiments are, Grad considered they did not go far enough. Would his research show that healing depends for its effectiveness on the mysterious power of suggestion? Or would it reveal yet a further layer of complexity in this subtle and imperfectly understood process?

Impressed with the anecdotal evidence for the effectiveness of the laying on of hands, Grad decided to see whether he could devise experiments that would show that this form of treatment involved another force or some, as yet undetected, interaction between the healer and patient. The problem was to find a way of successfully isolating one factor from the others. Just as the placebo effect had upset the results of drug trials, so suggestion might interfere with an attempt to find out what is happening when a healer is at work.

Grad quickly concluded that the use of human beings in any experiment would make the task next to impossible: there would always be doubt as to which factors – suggestion or 'faith' – were responsible for any change or improvement. So he chose to use animals and plants for his project. As far as anyone is aware, neither are susceptible to the power of suggestion nor do they have expectations about the purpose of any experiment. From this point of view, Grad felt he would be on safe ground.

The healer he chose to act as the agent for the research was Colonel Oskar Estebany. A retired Hungarian army colonel, he had discovered his healing ability when working with cavalry horses, and then developed his talents with human patients. In later years, healing became his main activity. He asked nothing for his services and made no extravagant claims about what he could achieve. In 1957 he left Hungary and went to live in Canada, and by 1960 he had a paid job in Grad's laboratory.

In the first experiment, 48 mice had a small piece of skin of similar size removed from their backs under anaesthesia. They were then weighed and the dimensions of the wounds measured and recorded. (For two weeks prior to the experiment the mice had been 'gentled' by handling since it had been found that nervous animals made unreliable

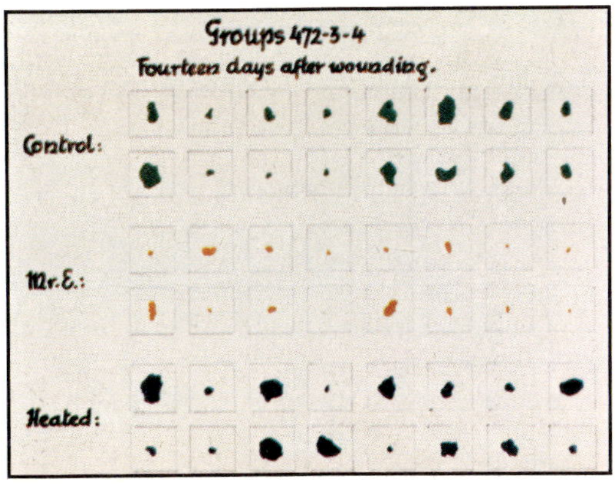


Below, far left: day one of an experiment to test Oskar Estebany's healing through the 'laying on of hands'. Forty-eight mice were 'wounded' by having a piece of skin removed. Here the wounds can be seen to be fairly uniform in size and degree. Some of the mice were then handled by Estebany twice a day for 20 days. The rest were either left untreated – but put in containers heated to simulate the warmth of human hands – or they were handled by other members of the staff in a manner similar to that of Estebany

Left: day 14 and the wounds of the mice treated by Estebany have healed significantly faster than any of the others

subjects for research work.) At this stage in the proceedings no one knew which mice were to serve as controls and which were to receive treatment.

After the operation, the mice were divided into three groups, which were placed in separate wire cages. Estebany treated the first group by standing the cage on his left hand and resting his right hand on the top. There was no physical contact with the mice.

The second group was cared for in an identical way in terms of feeding and other routines, but left alone – this was the control group. The third group also received identical care but, instead of being treated by Estebany, the mice were warmed to a temperature comparable to that generated by the healer's hands, to see whether heat alone would accelerate wound healing.

The skin wounds were measured regularly over a period of 20 days so that their recovery rate could be analysed and compared. The mice that had been warmed showed no significant difference in their speed of healing from the control group. The mice treated by Estebany recovered at a much faster rate than chance expectancy.

The scars of the mice treated by the healer had shrunk almost uniformly to pencil-point size. Those of the mice in the other groups showed varying stages of healing; some scars were as small as those in Estebany's group but about half were markedly larger.

But however promising the results from this one experiment might look, they cannot be regarded as a breakthrough. As in any scientific experiment, replication of results by other laboratories is an important check on the soundness of the procedures and therefore on the validity of the results.

A similar experiment to Grad's was staged at the University of Manitoba, also in Canada. This time it involved a total of 300 mice. Double-blind conditions were incorporated into the project to avoid any possibility of unconscious manipulation by the experimenters. As a further check, one group of mice was 'treated' – copying Estebany's procedure – by people who made no claim to

Could Oskar Estebany's healing power make plants grow faster? Dr Grad set up a simple experiment to test this possibility: barley seeds were planted in two groups of pots, labelled X and Y. Both groups were watered with a weak saline solution, but group X was watered with a solution that Estebany had held, in a flask, for 30 minutes. Group Y was watered normally by a member of staff. By day 10 (below left) group X was already significantly taller and stronger than the control group, and by day 14 (below right) the difference was even more marked

a special healing ability. Once more, those treated by Estebany showed the most rapid rate of recovery.

From these results, Grad felt that he was on the verge of a significant discovery – but where was it leading? To clarify this, his next goal was to learn more about the underlying mechanism involved. If there were some healing force at work, as the animal experiments seemed to prove, there was no reason to suppose that it should be effective only on the animal kingdom. To discover whether any measurable effects could be registered using plants as the healing target, Grad devised an experiment to see if Estebany could influence the germination and rate of growth of barley seeds. And, if successful, the experiment would presumably throw further light on the mechanism involved.

To begin with, Grad watered the seeds with a weak saline solution. The pots, already numbered, containing the seeds were dried out, stood in rows and watered.

The only variable factor in the treatment of the seeds was that some pots were watered with a saline solution that had been held by Estebany. That was the only part he played in the experiment. There was no direct contact between the healer and the seeds or pots. More of those that had been watered with the 'treated' saline solution germinated faster, grew quicker and healthier than the control group.

Grad wondered if the results could be attributable to bacterial growth present in the water and encouraged by the warmth of the healer's hands, but this seemed impossible because only sterile, saline solutions had been used. Grad concluded that there probably was an independent, beneficial force involved, something that could penetrate a barrier of glass and affect the properties of the solution inside.

There were other variables to consider. He had isolated a specific effect for which the healer appeared to be responsible, although Grad was unable to demonstrate exactly what was happening. Even so, there was another aspect of the process that seemed to be worth exploring: the psychological condition of the healer under which this 'force' or 'energy' could be best transmitted.

Taking note that Estebany and other healers maintained that a calm, tranquil frame of mind was a prerequisite for healing to take place, Grad selected three people with obviously different psychological states to treat the saline solution before running the barley seed test. He hypothesised that if the healer had a positive effect on the solution, and thence the seeds, there should be a different result according to the state of mind of the individual.

Of the three people he chose, J. B. was psychiatrically normal, with a reputation for being a 'green-fingered' gardener. The other two, R. H. and H. R., were both disturbed and under psychiatric care. What Grad was looking for was evidence of a differential germination and growth rate: a higher yield from the positive and confident individual compared with the other two participants in the experiment. Each held a sealed flask of sterile saline solution for half an hour and then the experiment proceeded as before; the control set of flasks was not touched by any one. The man with green fingers achieved a significantly higher germination and growth rate than the others.

### A disturbing effect

Pondering on the results of the seed experiment, Grad returned to his earlier supposition that people who were disturbed would have a negative effect on the seeds. He believed that there were still further lessons to be teased from the exercise. Was there any explanation why R. H.'s seeds grew relatively more vigorously than those in the untreated control group, and those of H. R. less so?

On questioning them on their attitude and state of mind at the time when they were treating the water, Grad learned that R. H., a woman, had suddenly perked up and shown an active interest when informed of the purpose of the experiment, and had cradled the flask in her lap. In contrast, H. R.'s mood remained agitated and depressed. This, for Grad, proved the point that it was not the individual's usual, everyday disposition, but that which prevails at the *time* of the experiment that seemed to be the factor.

While Grad had not finally resolved the question of what was responsible for changes that resulted from the laying on of hands, he believed he could advance some conclusions: first, from the mice and barley experiments, he felt that there was evidence that the laying on of hands could induce cell growth and that the way in which this occurred suggested the action of some kind of energy that was not merely heat. Second, he concluded from the differing results achieved by the psychiatrically normal and the disturbed subjects that there was a damming or releasing control associated with the individual's state of mind at the time of the experiment.

Grad speculated further. He wondered whether these experiments underlined the importance of rapport between therapist and patient which, when strong and positive, involved the transfer or generation of some energy that aided the healing process.

Like so much pioneering research, Grad's work raised many questions, all of central importance to medicine and Man. His experiments also inspired other scientists to pick up the trail themselves. Several have reported findings that corroborate those claims made by Grad for some independent healing energy, and the search goes on. Whether or not that energy will be tracked down, we shall have to wait and see.

The significant difference in the growth rate of seedlings treated by Oskar Estebany and those treated similarly by ordinary laboratory staff over a number of days can be seen in the chart (below). But can mentally disturbed people have a dramatically different effect on growing plants? Dr Grad set up a test involving one clinically neurotic patient, one psychotic patient and, as a control, a normal person. Each had to hold, water and care for the same number of pots containing seedlings. The results of these tests (right) seem conclusive. In some way (as yet unknown) the positive mood of a normal person can encourage the growth of organic matter and, more significantly, certain people – 'healers' – can somehow accelerate its healthy growth

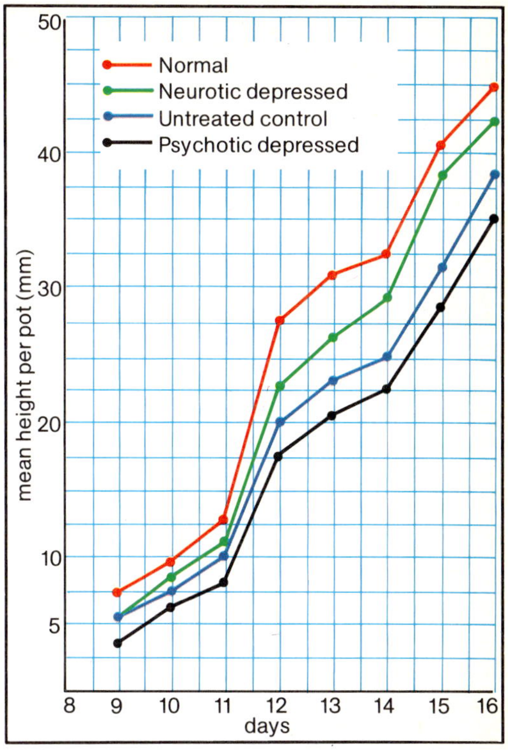


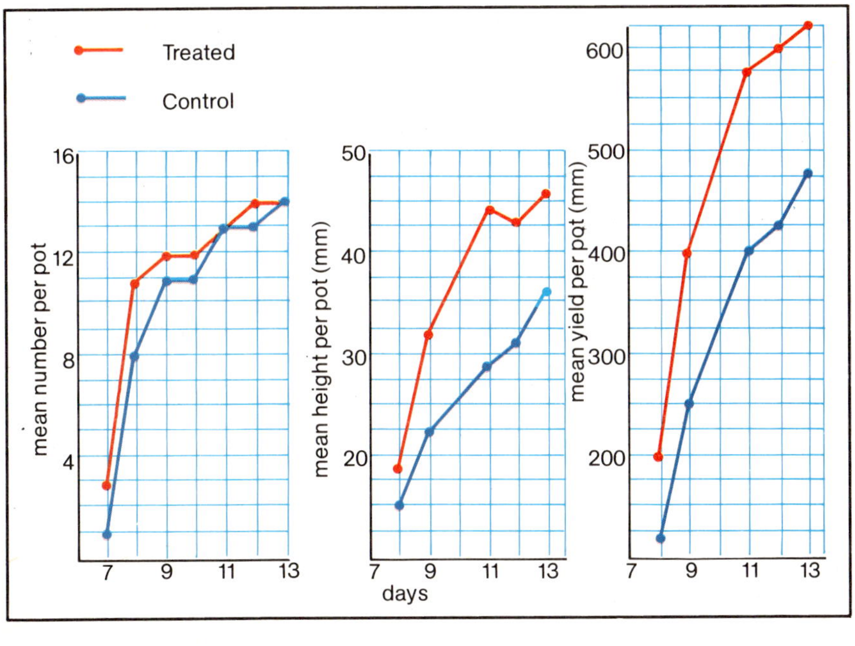

# The sense to survive

**Mankind recognises only five senses – but animals have many more: bats 'see' by sound, rattlesnakes by heat, sting-rays by electricity.** GILL NEVILL **explores the strange world such creatures inhabit**

Left: a pipistrelle bat. Bats hunt by night and have developed a remarkable method of finding their way and locating prey in the dark: instead of using their eyes, they emit high-pitched shrieks that bounce back off nearby objects and enable them to build up a sound-picture of their immediate surroundings

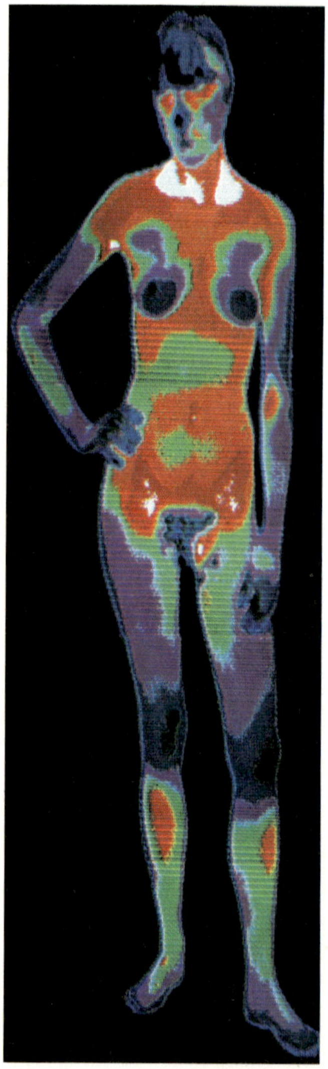

SUPPOSE YOU WERE ASKED to describe somebody to a third person who did not know him. The likelihood is that you would describe in detail what he looked like: brown hair, blue eyes, pink cheeks, a determined walk and so on. You might also speak of his voice and the sort of thing he might say, but you probably would not mention his smell.

Neither would you talk about the pattern of heat waves he exuded, nor the way that sound bounced off him. Nor would you say anything, except in the most metaphorical sense, about his electricity or his magnetism. We simply don't take account of these things. But for a mouse, a bat, a rattlesnake or a sting-ray, such details might contain the information they need to recognise that person.

All this underlines how limited our human senses are: we see, we hear, and we sometimes use our sense of smell. And that is about all. What is more, we subconsciously assume that animals perceive the world in a similar way. But in fact, research shows that the senses of animals are much more varied than our own. In effect, they live in worlds quite different from ours, and as a result much of their behaviour is a mystery to us.

We are astonished that sea salmon can find their way unerringly back to the streams in which they hatched, that pigeons can home on cloudy days, that bats can fly in the dark, and even that police dogs can follow a criminal across country.

It is, of course, very difficult for us to understand senses we do not have. And, not surprisingly, some of our most important discoveries about the mysterious senses animals possess have happened by chance. In 1956, for instance, an American professor of physics, Kenneth Roeder, was giving a party on his terrace. As the evening wore on, moths began to congregate round the Chinese lanterns with which the terrace was lit. There they fluttered until one of the guests absent-mindedly ran a damp cork over his glass. It made a shrill squeak, and immediately all the moths fell to the ground.

At first, everyone assumed that the noise was the moth equivalent of sonic boom, and that the moths had died of shock. But the moths soon began to move, and before long were flying around as though nothing had happened. But when glass and cork were rubbed together a second time, the moths again dived for cover. Professor Roeder was intrigued. Why should moths react so dramatically to that shrill squeak?

His question led him back to a discovery

made nearly 20 years earlier. In 1940 the American scientist Donald Griffin first demonstrated what is now well-known: that bats emit powerful ultrasonic cries as they fly and, by listening to the echoes of these sounds, are able to 'see' in the dark. Commonplace as this knowledge now seems, it was initially met with incredulity: when Donald Griffin first described the phenomenon, which he called 'echo-location', sonar and radar were well-guarded military secrets, and the whole concept seemed so revolutionary as to be almost incredible.

The echo-location system is so sensitive that bats fly quite easily in the dark in a space criss-crossed by wires less than a hundredth of an inch (0.2 millimetres) in diameter. And they have no trouble in detecting something the size of a moth. Squeaking furiously so as to update the information as fast as possible, they close in on their prey. And the end of a successful chase is marked by the bat either catching the moth directly in its mouth, or scooping it out of the air using its wings as a sort of butterfly net.

Many moths, however, have learned to treat the bat's hunting squeaks as a warning siren and to take effective evasive action. They have special sound-sensitive cells tuned to the bat's frequency, and as soon as they hear a bat they either dive for the ground or fall through the air in a tumbling spiral that bats find very difficult to follow. So here was the explanation for the behaviour of the moths at Professor Roeder's party: they had mistaken the sound made by cork on glass for an approaching bat.

Mysterious as the capacity for producing and detecting ultra-sound may seem to us, it is quite widespread among animals – particularly among rodents. Baby mice falling out of the nest utter what to us are inaudible shrieks. But other mice hear the SOS loud and clear. Not just the mother, but any other adult mouse in the vicinity, will rush to rescue the baby and carry it back to the nest in much the same way as a retriever carries a puppy.

This capacity to use ultra-sound has evolved more than once. The oilbird, *Steatornis caripensis*, which lives in caves in the West Indies, has it. So do many species of dolphin and whale. The only thing that these creatures have in common is that they live mostly in the dark, and darkness seems to be a wonderful spur to sensory ingenuity.

It is not just ultra-sound to which animals turn in the absence of light. Sting-rays, for instance, have on their snouts the most sensitive detectors of electricity in the animal kingdom. They detect creatures hidden in the sand merely by the distortion their bodies produce in the electric field.

Rattlesnakes, on the other hand, have pits near their nostrils containing rank upon rank of cells rather similar to our own heat detectors. But where Man has only 19 to the square inch (three to the square centimetre), the rattlesnake has 150,000. Massed like this, the detectors give the snake a complete heat picture of its environment. So even in darkness it is entirely able to pick out the best camouflaged mouse or rat from its colder background.

It is well-established that birds migrating by night can use the stars and the Moon to help them find their way, just as those migrating by day use the Sun. But far more debatable is what happens when the sky is covered by cloud. Some birds certainly fly in such conditions, and the suggestion has been made that they orientate by magnetism. In the 1970s only the lunatic fringe held this view; today the situation is rather different.

The suggestion began with the knowledge that the Earth itself is a magnet: not a very strong one, nor a very stable one, but a magnet, nevertheless. What is more, the two magnetic poles at either end of the globe are linked by a magnetic field whose strength varies systematically between them. So in theory at least, animals could use it to find their way.

But do they do so in practice? We humans, after all, need a compass to make use of the Earth's magnetic field. But that is not an option open to animals. At first it seemed inconceivable that animals should be biologically sensitive to the Earth's very weak magnetic field. But slowly the evidence began to accumulate.

If robins are put in a cage just before they

The Italian wall lizard, *Podarcis sicula*, has a 'third eye' – a spot on the top of its head that is extremely sensitive to heat (above: the 'third eye' is the small green spot). Using this, it can build up detailed heat pictures of its surroundings even in complete darkness – rather like those provided by a thermograph (left), in which the hottest areas are white, the coldest blue-black

Above right: the oilbird, *Steatornis caripensis*, lives in dark caves in the West Indies – and, like the bat, it has developed the capacity to use ultra-sound for echo-location

## The third eye

The pineal gland is an organ about the size of a pea situated near the lower part of the brain. Although it is considered by modern doctors to be vital to the healthy functioning of the body, it is still not fully understood.

For thousands of years, Hindus and Buddhists have believed that the pineal gland is, in fact, a 'third eye'. Many statues and paintings, such as this one (right) of the Hindu goddess Kali, show the third eye firmly planted between the normal two eyes. The Tibetan Buddhists believed that the third eye, when opened, enables one to see a person's aura, the reflection of the life force burning within.

In his book *The third eye*, Tuesday Lobsang Rampa writes of an operation he believes he had in a previous incarnation to 'open up the eye'. He describes how Tibetan monks drilled through his forehead; a sliver of wood was then inserted and pushed until Rampa felt a blinding flash. It then remained in his forehead for three weeks, during which time, Rampa says, he was kept in a darkened room with only the minimum food and drink. When the wood was removed, Rampa could see coloured auras around people; in time, he learned to tell whether someone was ill by the colour of his aura. He could also tell whether someone was lying.

When it was discovered that Rampa was actually an Englishman, the authenticity of his claims was challenged. But the real Rampa – one Henry Hoskin – could only repeat that he was a reincarnation of the Tibetan lama Tuesday Lobsang Rampa, and many people are convinced of the truth of his story.

would normally migrate, they perch in a direction facing their intended destination. Normally, of course, they take their directional cues from the sky, but scientists have found that, even in a completely featureless environment, the robins were able to maintain a correct bearing. If, however, the magnetic field around them was distorted, they immediately became disorientated.

But the matter was clinched, at least as far as birds are concerned, by a discovery in 1976 about the anatomy of the common or garden pigeon. A whole sport has grown up around the fact that pigeons can not only find their way home but can do so very fast. Six hundred miles (1000 kilometres) in a single day is a good average, and experienced birds not only home on cloudy days, but even when temporarily blinded by frosted glass contact lenses. So the question is, do these pigeons use magnetic clues – and if so, how?

The answer seems to lie in a small piece of tissue between the homing pigeon's eyes. Analysis shows that it contains exactly the same mineral as mariners once used for a crude compass: a permanently magnetised mineral of iron – lodestone or, more technically, magnetite. More than a million tiny bar-shaped lumps of this material are clustered together in a tiny patch of tissue – more than enough, the scientists say, to enable the bird to detect the variation in the Earth's magnetic field.

That the magnetite is actually used by pigeons as a compass is more difficult to prove. No nervous pathways have yet been traced, and we do not know how these detectors – if that is what they are – work. One thing, however, is certain. With powerful bar magnets strapped on their backs, pigeons fail to find their way home, whereas with non-magnetic brass bars they return just as well as with no interferences. But the precise nature of the connection with magnetite remains a mystery.

Zoologist Dr Robin Baker tests the theory that human beings use the magnetic field of the Earth in navigation. He blindfolds subjects and takes them to a secret location (left). There, he asks them to point in the direction of their home (below left). Then he repeats the experiment, strapping either a brass bar or a magnet to the subjects' heads. Only those with the brass bars point correctly

Bees, too, contain magnetite, but its primary purpose does not seem to be to help them orientate. Rather, it is thought, that in the darkness of the hive bees lack visual cues to set their biological clocks, and so they tune in to the daily variation in the magnetic field and use it to keep their own clocks running accurately. A great variety of animals are able to tell the time, so could it be that magnetism is a much more widespread sense than, until 1976, everyone assumed?

Even human beings may not be as insensitive to magnetic fields as we imagine. As part of his studies Dr Robin Baker, a zoologist of Manchester University, has been taking people blindfolded from their homes and driving them along a twisting route to a secret destination. There he asks them to point in the direction of home – which they do with surprising accuracy. He then straps either a magnet or a brass bar onto the heads of his victims and repeats the experiment with a different destination. Only those with the brass bars are able to point correctly.

Magnetism is likely to play a more dominant role in the lives of birds, which have a very poor sense of smell, than in mammals, in which the sense of smell is well-developed. Even though this is a sense we share with other mammals, it is surprisingly hard for us to understand. Not only is there no easy way to measure and identify smell, but there is the further problem that we tend to disregard what information *does* come from our noses. It has been estimated that over 90 per cent of our sensory information comes from our eyes – and our other senses suffer accordingly.

In fact, our sense of smell is quite acute. A skilled sniffer like a perfumier can identify up to 10,000 different odours, and on one occasion a Water Board official on BBC television's discussion programme *Panorama*, sipping water from seven glasses drawn from different points on the River Thames, identified unerringly the places from which they had come.

And even if we don't automatically include smell in our descriptions of people, we immediately recognise the smell of those close to us, while other scents can recall vivid memories. The much-quoted episode in Marcel Proust's novel *A la recherche du temps perdu* when the savour of a tea-soaked madeleine cake evokes the memory of a whole episode from his childhood is one example.

The fact remains, however, that our use of our sense of smell pales into insignificance beside that of animals. Dogs, for instance, have 50 times the area that we have given over to olfaction, the sense of smell, and so they are able to detect substances in a concentration a thousand or even a million times less than our own.

Because smell is so difficult to measure, we must often infer the part it plays in the lives of animals by watching their behaviour. Badgers leave smelly faecal messages in open pits round the edge of their territories, which serve as 'no trespassing' notices. Hippos scatter their dung with their short flat tails so that it hangs conveniently at nose height, so that passing animals cannot but smell it. Dogs anoint lamp posts. Otters leave their dung, or spraints, at well-marked vantage points . . . and so it goes on.

Animals of the same species are often quite extraordinarily sensitive to these chemical messages. Salmon coming back from the sea home on the special scent of the particular race living in their birthplace. This smell they somehow pick up even in the estuary and they follow it unerringly up to their spawning ground. If, however, their nostrils are plugged, they lose their way.

But these chemicals are also capable of carrying more intimate messages. Female sexual attractants are common among insects – the female silk moth, for instance, summons her mate by special chemical from a couple of miles down wind.

At the other end of the scale, the rhesus monkey produces a substance called copulin, which attracts the male. Since chimpanzee females and gorilla females possess similar chemicals, the question arises: do we? Certainly we are sensitive to chemical influences of which we are entirely unaware.

In one American study, for instance, it was shown that women college students sharing the same dormitory tend to menstruate at identical times. In another study men, pregnant women and children have been shown to be very insensitive to a chemical relative of civet and musk. Women, on the other hand, smell it easily – and their sensitivity is most acute at the time of ovulation, when they are at their most fertile. A similar chemical is found in men's urine, so the question arises: are men producing a chemical specifically to appeal to fertile women? The whole subject of chemicals and human sexuality is still relatively unexplored, but the little knowledge we have suggests that animals may not have the monopoly of home-produced aphrodisiacs. It has even been suggested that pubic and underarm hair exists precisely in order to provide a large evaporative area for our body odours and their important messages.

The more scientists piece together information about animal senses, the more they realise how much is still a mystery. Ultra-violet-sensitive pigments have been discovered in the chicken's eye – what are they doing there? Amphibians and reptiles have heat-sensitive 'third eyes' – what for? What will be the next sense to be discovered? And could we learn to use our neglected and undiscovered senses?

Below left: mulberry silk moths, *Bombyx mori*, mating. When they are ready to mate, female silk moths produce a chemical to which males are immensely sensitive – and use it to summon their mates, sometimes from as much as a couple of miles away

Below: the Australian stingaree, a member of the sting-ray family, whose snouts bear the most sensitive detectors of electricity known in the animal kingdom

**Further reading**

John Cloudsley-Thompson, *Animal migration*, Orbis 1978
Richard Dawkins, *The selfish gene*, Oxford University Press 1976
Matthieu Ricard, *The mystery of animal migration*, Constable 1969
E.O. Wilson, *Socio-biology: the new synthesis*, Harvard University Press 1975

# Alchemy's hidden truth

**In the 20th century science has achieved the alchemical dream of transmuting the elements. But modern alchemists still use traditional methods in pursuit of their quest. BRIAN INNES brings their story up to date**

THE GROWTH OF experimental science during the 18th and 19th centuries; the work of chemists such as Lavoisier, Priestley and Davy; the establishment of Dalton's atomic theory; and the subsequent discoveries of a host of scientists in all aspects of chemistry and physics – such developments should have sounded the death knell of alchemy. And yet they did not.

During the 19th and early 20th centuries, it is true, alchemists retreated into the mystical, spiritual aspects of their study. They were drawn into the Rosicrucianist occultism of societies such as the Golden Dawn and the Ordo Templi Orientis (OTO), which contrived to combine ill-digested snippets of oriental philosophy with the western European magical tradition.

Then, in 1919, the British physicist Ernest Rutherford announced that he had successfully achieved the transmutation of one element into another.

He had, in fact, changed nitrogen into oxygen. Admittedly, the amount of oxygen produced, some 20 parts per million, was minute, and the technique used, involving high-energy radiation, did not resemble in the slightest the procedures of the alchemists. But the experiment refuted the insistence of most scientists that transmutation was impossible, and all aspiring alchemists took heart.

It was in fact already known that transmutation took place in nature. The radioactive elements gradually 'decay', giving off radiation and producing further radioactive 'daughter' elements, which in turn decay. After a series of decays the end product, lead, is formed.

What Rutherford had done was to reverse the process. He had bombarded nitrogen gas with radiation consisting of fast-moving nuclei from the gas helium and had produced oxygen and hydrogen. The experiment can be expressed very simply in terms of atomic numbers (the chemical properties of each element are determined by its atomic number, which is the number of protons in its nucleus):

$$N(7) + He(2) = O(8) + H(1)$$

What every alchemist now asked himself was whether a similar kind of sum could be used

Opposite, top: the directors of the *Société Alchimique et Astrologique de France* in their laboratory in 1903. Despite the discoveries of 19th-century chemistry and physics, alchemy refused to die. The magazine that featured this picture said: 'To turn astrology into a true science, in which there is no room for fantasy – this is what they preach in their journal, *Rosa Alchemica*'

Opposite, below: the young Adolf Hitler (far left), with his patron, Erich Ludendorff. In association with Franz Tausend (centre), Ludendorff formed Company 164 to 'manufacture' gold. As a result they were able to divert 400,000 marks into Nazi Party funds. Tausend set up his gold-production laboratory at a quarry near Munich (right)

as a guide to the conversion of lead (82) into gold (79). Or perhaps another element might be a better starting point?

One of those who took renewed inspiration from the results of this experiment was a 36-year-old chemical worker in Munich, Franz Tausend. He had a theory about the structure of the elements that was a peculiar blend of the beliefs of Pythagoras, who had regarded the Universe as a combination of musical harmonies, and the discoveries of modern chemistry.

Tausend had published a pamphlet called *180 elements, their atomic weight, and their incorporation in a system of harmonic periods*. He believed that every atom had a frequency of vibration characteristic of that element, related to the weight of the atom's nucleus and to the grouping of electrons in orbital rings around it. Later research showed that this part, at least, of his theory was basically true. Tausend went on, however, to suggest that matter could be 'orchestrated': by adding the right substance to an element, it should be possible to change its vibration frequency into that of another element.

In 1924 Adolf Hitler was sent to prison for attempting to organise an armed uprising; one of his fellow conspirators, General Erich Ludendorff, was acquitted and in the following year stood for election as President of the German Republic. After being resoundingly defeated by the national hero Hindenburg, he turned his attention to raising funds for the infant Nazi Party. There were rumours in government circles that a certain Tausend had succeeded in making gold by transmutation, and Ludendorff got together a group of industrialists and businessmen to investigate the matter.

On Tausend's instructions one of the group, the merchant Stremmel, purchased the necessary materials – mainly iron oxide and quartz. They were melted together in a crucible, which Stremmel then took to his hotel bedroom for the night so that it could not be tampered with. In the morning, Tausend heated the crucible again in his electric furnace, in the presence of his visitors, and then added a small quantity of white powder to the molten mass. When the crucible had cooled it was broken open, and a gold nugget weighing a quarter of an ounce (7 grams) was found inside.

## Financing the Nazis

Ludendorff was overjoyed and immediately set about forming a company, which he called 'Company 164' – a number that, intriguingly, is twice the atomic number of lead. Ludendorff was to receive 75 per cent of the profits and Tausend 5 per cent. Investment money poured in and within a year the General had managed to divert some 400,000 marks into Nazi Party funds. Then, in December 1926, he resigned, leaving Tausend to handle all the debts. Nevertheless, Tausend contrived to continue raising money and on 16 June 1928 allegedly made 25 ounces (723 grams) of gold in a single

## Atomic alchemy

Rutherford's work strengthened the conviction of orthodox scientists that the methods of the alchemists could never lead to the transmutation of elements. It was found that the atom has a central nucleus consisting of particles called protons, with positive electrical charge, and an equal or greater number of neutrons, lacking charge. Relatively light negatively charged electrons orbit the nucleus and fix the atom's chemical properties. The number of electrons is equal to the number of protons in the nucleus, so that the atom's positive and negative electrical charges balance.

So to change one element into another it is necessary to change the number of protons in the nucleus of each atom. The nucleus must be bombarded with fast-moving particles – either to force in additional protons or to disrupt the atom so that it loses protons. Today physicists use particles artificially accelerated by 'atom-smashing' machines. And they insist that chemical processes affect only the outer electrons, not the atom's deep interior.

Above: a modern particle-accelerating device

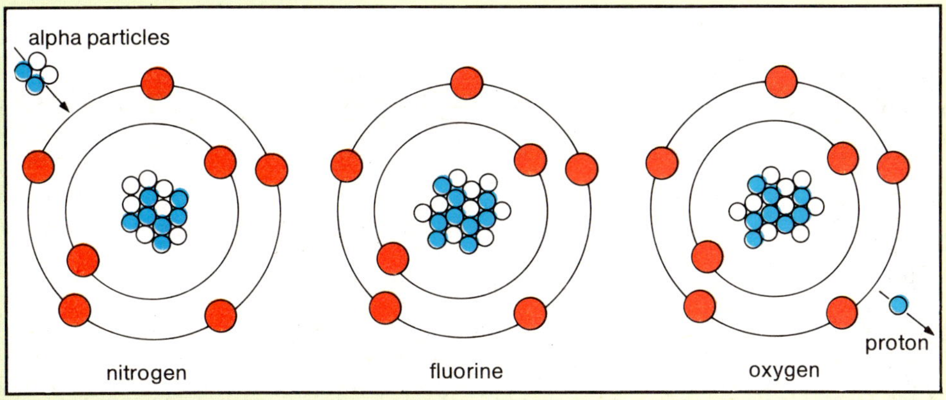


Left: Rutherford bombarded nitrogen atoms (seven protons, seven neutrons) with alpha particles (two protons bound to two neutrons), forming fluorine atoms (nine protons, nine neutrons). These lost a proton, forming a type of oxygen (eight protons, nine neutrons)

operation. On the strength of this he was able to issue a series of share certificates, each to the value of 22 pounds (10 kilograms) of gold.

But when, a year or so later, no more gold had been produced, Tausend was arrested for fraud; and on 5 February 1931, after a sensational trial, he was found guilty and sentenced to four years' imprisonment. While awaiting trial he had succeeded in producing gold under strict supervision in the Munich Mint – but the evidence was contested in court and did not save him.

The same fate was to befall a Polish engineer named Dunikovski who, in the same year that Tausend was convicted, announced in Paris that he had discovered a new kind of radiation – 'z-rays' – which would transmute quartz into gold. The mineral, spread on copper plates, was melted by an electric discharge at 110,000 volts, and was then irradiated with the z-rays.

The world was becoming accustomed to new types of radiation with remarkable properties. X-rays had been discovered a few decades before. Three kinds of radiation – alpha, beta and gamma – had been identified in the emissions from radioactive substances. Intense 'cosmic' radiations had been discovered bombarding the Earth from space.

Rays with miraculous properties were a staple of futuristic fiction. The public was ready to believe that gold-creating rays could exist – even if their nature was rather inadequately explained by Dunikovski. Investors poured some two million francs into his process.

But within a few months, when no gold was forthcoming, he also was tried and found guilty of fraud. After two years in prison his lawyer succeeded in obtaining his release, and Dunikovski went with his family to San Remo in Italy, where he resumed his experiments.

Soon there were rumours that he was supporting himself by the occasional sale of lumps of gold. His lawyer, accompanied by the eminent chemist Albert Bonn, set out for San Remo to see for himself.

It was found that the quartz being used by Dunikovski already contained minute amounts of gold; but whereas the usual methods of extraction produced gold in quantities of only 10 parts per million, Dunikovski's methods yielded almost one hundred times as much. Each experiment, however, involved only minute quantities of quartz, so the quantity of gold produced was very small.

In October 1936 Dunikovski demonstrated his process before an invited group of scientists. He was very secretive about his apparatus, but gave a theoretical explanation that is reminiscent of the primitive origins of alchemy. He proposed that all minerals contained 'embryonic atoms' undergoing a transformation that in nature took many thousands of years to complete. He claimed that his process merely accelerated the natural growth of embryonic gold in quartz.

### Making gold from sand

The demonstration attracted considerable attention and an Anglo-French syndicate was formed, which was to bring sand from Africa and treat it in a big new laboratory on the south coast of England. But the Second World War broke out and little more was heard of Dunikovski. There were rumours that he had established a factory on the Swiss-French border, and there were stories that when the Germans occupied France they manufactured gold to bolster their failing economy – but there is no proof.

There have been, and still are, many more practitioners of alchemy in the 20th century. One was Archibald Cockren, who was killed when a bomb struck his tiny laboratory during the blitz on London. He was a respected osteopath who practised gold therapy. He began his investigations with the metal antimony, then turned his attention to iron, copper, silver, mercury and gold. Then:

> I entered upon a new course of experiment, with a metal . . .with which I had had no previous experience. This metal, after being reduced to its salts

Above: an engraving from the 17th-century alchemical work *Atalanta fugiens*, illustrating the ubiquitous nature of the Philosopher's Stone. It may be of significance that the form of the Stone shown here could represent crystals of salt or sand

Left: the Polish engineer Dunikovski, escorted by police officers, leaves the Paris polytechnic where he had been demonstrating his alchemical process while awaiting trial for fraud

Above right: wringing out canvas sheets that have been spread to collect the morning dew. This illustration is from the alchemical treatise called *Mutus liber*

Right: Armand Barbault followed the directions of *Mutus liber* in his 20th-century alchemical work

> and undergoing special preparation and distillation, delivered up the Mercury of the Philosophers, the Aqua Benedicta, the Aqua Coelestis, the Water of Paradise. The first intimation I had of this triumph was a violent hissing, jets of vapour pouring from the retort and into the receiver, like sharp bursts from a machine gun, and then a violent explosion, whilst a very potent and subtle odour filled the laboratory and its surroundings. . . .

Whatever Cockren's true achievement, nearly all his discoveries were lost in the bomb blast that killed him. A liquid that he called 'oil of gold' was used in later years, however, for medical purposes.

## Postwar alchemy

Since the Second World War, much of the publicly known activity in alchemy has been centred in France. Apart from Eugène Canseliet, who claimed to have been a pupil of Fulcanelli (see page 830), and who has been seen on television at work in his laboratory, there were others such as the writer Roger Caro and the painter Louis Cattiaux.

But undoubtedly the most notorious was Armand Barbault. An essential part of the Barbault process was the gathering of dew in canvas sheets every morning between 21 March and 24 June. This is not a new idea: it is shown in the wordless book of engravings known as the *Mutus liber* ('silent book'), and it is recommended by Salmon in his *Polygraphica*: 'If you are indeed an Artist, you may by this turn all metals into their first matter.' Barbault described his first matter as a 'germ', which grew in black earth.

It is time to ask whether there might be any truth in the tales of the alchemists. Did competent scientists such as van Helmont, Schweitzer and Boyle really witness the transmutation of a base metal into gold? Did Archibald Cockren isolate the ideal 'mercury' and 'sulphur' sought by the alchemists? And did Tausend and Dunikovski really succeed in producing gold from quartz?

Although the ancient alchemists could not possibly have had access to sources of energy sufficient to perform Rutherford's transmutation, perhaps they had some kind of intuitive understanding of what could happen. We wrote Rutherford's experiment as:

$$N(7) + He(2) = O(8) + H(1)$$

Now look at the three alchemical essentials postulated by Paracelsus: sulphur (symbol S, atomic number 16), mercury (symbol Hg, atomic number 80) and salt (sodium chloride, symbol NaCl – the atomic numbers of sodium and chlorine are 11 and 17, respectively). We can write a hypothetical reaction among these three as follows:

$$NaCl(28) + S(16) = NaS(27) + Cl(17)$$
$$NaS(27) + Hg(80) = Au(79) + NaCl(28)$$

Salt and sulphur are added together; chlorine gas is given off (to the alchemists this would simply have been 'air'); when mercury is added, the result is the original salt – and gold (Au).

The atomic numbers balance impressively. However, this is not the sort of reaction that ordinarily takes place in the chemical laboratory, where everything is either solid, liquid or gaseous. But there is a fourth state of matter, called plasma, in which atoms lose or gain electrons and can take part in chemical reactions that are impossible for them in their normal state. One of the easiest ways to produce a stream of plasma is to burn salt in the flame of the mundane Bunsen burner. Could this give a hint as to how the alchemists might have succeeded in bringing about 'impossible' reactions?

In our present state of knowledge, these are mere games with numbers. But they may bear further examination. Cockren began his research with antimony (Sb), but achieved his successes with 'a metal . . . with which I had had no previous experience.' He might have been referring to silicon (Si), which is not, in fact, a metal but a metalloid, belonging in a group of elements comprising carbon, germanium, tin and lead. It is the essential component of quartz, which is an almost pure compound of silicon and oxygen, silicon dioxide. We can easily write another 'Rutherford equation':

$$Si(14) + Si(14) + Sb(51) = Au(79)$$

A chance relationship among these atomic numbers? Or a guide to a possible gold-producing process involving silicon and antimony?

It seems improbable, despite the testimony that has accumulated over the centuries, that physical transmutation of a base metal into gold was ever achieved by any alchemist. But did those alchemists, striving to make themselves one with God, perhaps gain some intuitive understanding of the structure of matter? And when they described the Philosopher's Stone as 'the vilest and meanest of things . . . cast away and rejected by all', were they speaking of silicon dioxide – known to us as ordinary sand?

**Further reading**

Allison Coudert, *Alchemy, the Philosopher's Stone*, Wildwood House 1980
E.J. Holmyard, *Alchemy*, Penguin 1968
Stanislas Klossowski de Rola, *Alchemy*, Thames and Hudson 1973
F. Sherwood Taylor, *The alchemists*, Paladin 1976

# Who was Kaspar Hauser?

Left: Bruno S as Kaspar Hauser in Werner Herzog's film, which was made in 1975. The enigmatic foundling is still a source of fascination, and numerous books have been written about him – yet his true identity has never been established

Below: the first attempt on Kaspar's life, at the home of his guardian Dr Daumer. The masked assailant struck Kaspar then fled, leaving the boy unconscious in the cellar

**As Kaspar Hauser's fame spread, investigators doubled their efforts to piece together his background. But, as GRAHAM FULLER and IAN KNIGHT reveal, just as the puzzle seemed to be solved, Kaspar was brutally murdered. Who killed him – and why?**

KASPAR HAUSER'S AUTOBIOGRAPHY, when it appeared in August 1829, proved something of a disappointment to the people of Nuremberg. It revealed nothing new about his background, but merely gave a more detailed account of his life in confinement, a story already widely known – and in some cases embellished by popular rumour to the extent that the facts seemed decidedly dull in comparison.

If the public felt at all cheated, however, it did not have long to wait for a new sensation. On 7 October 1829 Kaspar was found prostrate in Dr Daumer's cellar with a wound in his forehead. He was carried upstairs and put to bed, but little about the incident emerged beyond the fact that he had been hit by a man with 'a black face', which was taken to mean a man with a mask.

Nuremberg was aghast, taking the assault as proof that Kaspar had enemies in high places who were disturbed by the publication of his life story, and who feared it would let some secret slip. Anxious to avoid another attack on their most famous son, the town council moved Kaspar to an undisclosed address and provided a police guard. For two years the boy was surrounded only by his champions, but the novelty of supporting a celebrity on their taxes began to lose its appeal to the people of Nuremberg and several citizens complained about the cost.

Fortunately a solution was to hand. An English aristocrat, Lord Stanhope, had taken an interest in the case and wanted to adopt the youth. Nuremberg's councillors were prepared to allow Stanhope to assume temporary custody of Kaspar in return for a contribution towards his upkeep. Stanhope, who seems to have regarded the boy as an unusual toy with which to amuse his friends, then took him on a tour of Europe and presented him at the courts of various minor principalities and kingdoms. It does not appear to have been a complete success, novel entertainment though Kaspar undoubtedly was, and certain members of the Bavarian royal house threatened law suits if their name continued to be linked with his. Meanwhile, Kaspar and Stanhope, wilful foundling and eccentric Englishman, began to quarrel. Finally, in 1833, Stanhope applied to the Nuremberg Council for permission to lodge Kaspar permanently in the town of Ansbach some 25 miles (40 kilometres) away, in the care of his friend Dr Meyer. The Nurembergers were reluctant to sever the tie completely, but Stanhope's influence was considerable and eventually they agreed.

Kaspar's tutelage began anew with Meyer. The doctor had him confirmed in the Protestant Church and attempted to school him in Latin and history as well as practical subjects. Kaspar did not thrive; he became introspective and moody, and seems to have resented the way Meyer treated him. No longer the centre of a crowd of admirers, he may well have simply refused to learn. Meyer pronounced in disgust that Kaspar's mental abilities had been grossly exaggerated and that he had the mind of an eight-year-old. Stanhope's interest began to fade.

Kaspar himself longed to return to Nuremberg and to the friends and supporters he had left behind there. He made one brief visit in 1833, which further fuelled this desire – but events overtook him.

On 14 December 1833 Kaspar Hauser staggered into Dr Meyer's house clutching his side. Gasping 'Man stabbed! Knife! Park! Gave wallet! Go quick!', he collapsed to the floor in a pool of blood.

Below: the fatal attack on Kaspar Hauser, as portrayed in Herzog's film. Kaspar managed to stagger home, but died from his wounds three days later, on 17 December 1833

For several days the people of Nuremberg and Ansbach held their breath. Kaspar lay seriously ill, the knife having entered the left side of his chest, damaging his lungs and liver. He did manage to reveal some details of the attack. A stranger – 'tall, with dark whiskers and a black coat' – had approached him and asked, 'Are you Kaspar Hauser?' When told that he was, the man promised to give information about the boy's family and led him to Ansbach's city park where he handed him a wallet. When Kaspar opened it the man stabbed him and ran off.

The police moved rapidly to catch the assailant, but he could not be traced. The wallet was found where Kaspar had dropped it, but all it contained was an enigmatic note. Written back to front, to be read in a mirror, it said:

> Hauser will be able to tell you how I look, whence I came from and who I am. To spare him the task, I will tell you myself. I am from . . . on the Bavarian border . . . on the river. . . . My name is MLO.

### Death of an enigma

The nonsensical nature of this message led some to believe that Kaspar had fabricated the attack. Captain Hickel of the Ansbach police questioned the boy as he lay wounded, but all he would say was, 'I didn't do it myself.' These were to be his last words. The wound set up complications, and on 17 December 1833 Kaspar Hauser died.

The public, throughout Bavaria, was outraged, and large rewards were offered for any information concerning the identity of the assassin. None was forthcoming. When huge crowds followed Kaspar's body as it was taken to its last resting place, they saw it buried beneath a headstone that ably summed up his life: 'Here lies Kaspar Hauser, the riddle of his time. His birth was unknown, his death mysterious.'

The strange circumstances of his murder strike right at the heart of the mystery that surrounds Kaspar Hauser. His last guardian, Dr Meyer, was convinced that the boy had inflicted the wound on himself to attract attention, possibly with an eye to getting himself returned to Nuremberg, but that the dagger had done rather more damage than Kaspar had expected. Certainly there were no witnesses to either of the attacks upon Kaspar, and both wounds could have been self-inflicted. It was reported that police investigating the scene of the fatal assault scoured the Ansbach gardens but found no footprints other than Kaspar's. And the timing, too, may have been significant. The first attack took place following the disappointment of Kaspar's autobiography, which it soon overshadowed, and the second attack

occurred when his fame was beginning to wane – instantly, and ironically, bringing his name into the limelight once more.

But perhaps Kaspar's enemies wanted him dead. Many of his friends argued that he was the victim of a conspiracy. Someone with something to hide, they said, had ordered the first attack to cast doubts on his credibility, or more likely to warn him to keep his mouth shut; with the second they silenced him forever. If the attacks were linked, they suggest a motivating party with enough influence – and reason – to have Kaspar followed over a period of four years and then eliminated. The assault in Daumer's house could have been a bungled murder attempt, the would-be assassin panicking and fleeing when Kaspar cried out. Since Kaspar was seldom left alone, his killer would have had to wait perhaps years to find the right moment to strike, which could partly explain the great length of time between the attacks. If the motive of the murder had been to silence Kaspar, then it is also worth considering that several prominent Nurembergers, including Bürgermeister Binder, died in mysterious circumstances in the years following Kaspar's death. What had Kaspar told them?

### 'Citizen of another planet'

Lastly, there is the possibility that Kaspar Hauser was murdered by the man who had raised him, whoever that might have been. Kaspar's descriptions of his assailants were vague, but the masked man who tended to him in childhood might easily have been the same man with 'a black face' who attacked him at Daumer's house, or the man 'with dark whiskers and a black coat' who finished him off. If so, motivation is harder to find: if Kaspar came from a family of no particular note, why should the man have felt the need first to release him and then to kill him? And what was the significance of the bizarre murder note? Did it have a meaning in the eyes of a royally paid assassin, or of an ex-soldier of the 6th Cavalry? Or was it purely intended to throw the police off the track? No rational motive can easily be found, although of course murder is not always a rational business.

All the unknown quantities concerning Kaspar Hauser's brief life, and the five years he spent in the public eye, have continued to fascinate investigators. The original accounts of his appearance and behaviour have been meticulously studied, and inconsistencies exaggerated beyond all importance. A comment by Anselm von Feuerbach, a patron in Ansbach, has even been taken as proof of an extra-terrestrial connection:

> Kaspar Hauser showed such an utter deficiency of words and ideas, such perfect ignorance of the commonest things and appearances of Nature, and such a horror of all customs, conveniences and necessities of civilised life, and, withal, such extraordinary peculiarities in his social, mental and physical disposition, that one might feel one's self driven to the alternative of believing him to be a citizen of another planet, transferred by some miracle to our own.

Kaspar Hauser's life has been the subject of books, novels, plays and a film (Werner Herzog's *The enigma of Kaspar Hauser*, made in 1975), each with its own contribution to make to the nature of the mystery.

But the question remains: who *was* Kaspar Hauser?

Top: the monument marking the spot where Kaspar was stabbed in Ansbach park

Above: the last resting place of Kaspar Hauser, 'the riddle of his time. His birth was unknown, his death mysterious'

**Further reading**

Carlo Pietzner, *Kaspar Hauser, the child of Europe*, Rudolf Steiner Library 1965

Jacob Wasserman, *Caspar Hauser, the enigma of the century*, Rudolf Steiner Publications (New York) 1973

# A romantic fiction

**The raps, table-lifting and messages produced by the spirit of Philip, a 17th-century aristocrat, were undoubtedly real. No less important, says A. J. ELLISON, was another fact: Philip himself was a complete fiction**

The group who invented Philip based his story around a real 'stately home' in England – Diddington Manor in Warwickshire, two views of whose time-honoured walls are shown here (above and right). As befits such a setting, the life that they created for their imaginary ghost was a classic romantic concoction of passion, intrigue, treachery and violent death. To add an extra realism to Philip, one of the experimenters sketched his portrait (top), which was taken into each session of the group to act as a focus for their efforts

ONE OF THE MOST IMPORTANT and successful experiments in the young science of parapsychology began in Toronto in 1972. Drawing on the wide experience of poltergeist phenomena of its founder, Dr George Owen, a group of members of the Toronto Society for Psychical Research decided to try consciously to create a 'ghost'. The experiment threw a flood of light onto matters of enormous scientific importance, relevant to many areas of parapsychology – as well as psychology and physics.

The group decided that one of their members would write a totally fictitious life story of the ghost. The story centred round Diddington Manor in Warwickshire, England. The house was real, but its name was altered slightly. The tale was set in the middle of the 17th century and involved a member of the aristocracy, Philip, and his cold and frigid wife Dorothea. Philip had a very unhappy married life. One day he encountered by chance a kind and beautiful gypsy girl called Margo; they took to meeting secretly and fell in love. Philip installed Margo in a cottage on his estate when the gypsies she was travelling with moved on. But, after a period of blissful happiness, the liaison was discovered by Dorothea, who denounced Margo as a witch. Philip did little to try to save her, and she was burned at the stake. After her death, Philip was filled with remorse and paced the battlements in anguish, eventually casting himself from them to his death.

The Toronto group researched the Philip story thoroughly. They read history books of the period; one member of the group visited England and took photographs of Diddington and of other places involved in the story. Philip and the other characters became very clear in all their minds; one member of the group even made a sketch of Philip. They meditated together on every aspect of the story. In the meetings, meditations and discussions, a complete rapport between the group members developed; they became very relaxed in each other's company. Eventually, they tried to produce Philip as a 'shared hallucination'.

### No sign of a 'ghost'

But Philip did not appear. The members of the group were becoming discouraged when, in 1973, they came across reports of the work of three British psychical researchers, C. Brookes-Smith, D. W. Hunt, and K. J. Batchelor (*Journal* of the Society for Psychical Research, 1966 and 1970). These papers described how, in experiments that started in 1964, seemingly paranormal physical phenomena had been produced – table tilting, rapping and the like – without the intervention of any external psychic agency. And the researchers claimed that these psychokinetic phenomena could be produced by almost anyone in the right frame of mind. They gave a few guidelines: if a paranormal event were to occur, no one must feel personally responsible for it, or the phenomena would be inhibited; no surprise must be felt or expressed; the possibility of a paranormal event happening must be firmly believed in, and the event itself expected. They also advised that a light, jocular atmosphere, with singing and leg-pulling, helped to produce results.

So the group changed its method. Instead of quietly meditating, members produced the jocular, light-hearted and relaxed atmosphere of a Victorian seance. No medium was present to serve as a focus of attention; the phenomena, if any, were to be produced by 'Philip'. They addressed the table around which they sat as Philip. Full light was used from the beginning, so no instrumentation was needed to monitor the results.

After only a few weeks, phenomena began to appear. There was no hallucinatory image of Philip, but movements of the table on which the group members gently rested their hands became evident; at first they were rather like vibrations. It was obvious from

Below: one of the tens of thousands of women who were burnt as witches in Europe during the late medieval period. Very few of them were genuinely witches, but had often been innocent victims of prejudice or dislike – or had offended a social superior. In having Philip's wife denounce his gipsy lover as a witch, the Philip group were being true to historical fact

Two views of Philip's inventors in session. The dedicated but relaxed atmosphere was much more effective in producing psychokinetic effects than the quiet meditation that the group tried at first. In the background (left) can be seen Philip's portrait and the lights that he caused to turn on and off

the movements that no one was pushing the table, either consciously or unconsciously. Speculating on the cause of the movements, one of the group members remarked: 'I wonder if by chance Philip is doing this?' At once there was a loud rap from the table top. Philip had arrived.

A code was established, with one rap for 'yes' and two for 'no'. What would the invented ghost have to say to them? The group decided to pursue the new phenomena, and leave their aim of actually producing an image of Philip for the time being. So began their extraordinary study of psychokinesis.

### A room of his own

The group of eight ordinary people – thoughtful and interested professional men and women and housewives – met regularly in a particular room in Toronto reserved exclusively for the Philip group. In good light, they would sit round a table, place their hands gently on it and say, 'Hello, Philip.' Each sitter who addressed Philip would receive a definite tangible and audible rap under one of his hands. The phenomena quickly built up, so that the table would career round the room and the sitters had great difficulty in keeping their hands on it. Sometimes the raps appeared on the pipes overhead or on the walls. On at least one occasion, the table floated clear of the carpet with all four legs off the floor. A real rapport was built up with the imaginary Philip, and what happened depended entirely on him. Sometimes, if Philip did not want to answer a question, scratching sounds were heard instead of raps. Philip's portrait was kept in the room on top of a lighting panel consisting of coloured bulbs behind frosted glass, switched from a control panel. Occasionally, in response to requests, Philip was able to make these lights flicker – with no one near the plug or control panel. No other lights flickered at that time.

What did Philip have to say for himself? The answers he gave to questions tallied with the facts of the invented story, and occasionally extended it. These extensions were not always historically accurate. Philip's answers tended to depend on who was present – four members of the group were enough to produce phenomena. One of the members was allergic to cigarette smoke. When that member was present, Philip objected to smoking, but not otherwise. When the group sang an uproarious drinking song, the table would keep time by bumping up and down.

After a time, it became perfectly acceptable to Philip for one or two visitors to join the group. The raps continued with up to three visitors, but the table movements were reduced. It is important to stress that the raps came appropriately in answer to questions. They were not random. When the visitors and sitters said good night, answering raps were received under their hands. Careful examination of the table indicated clearly no 'normal' explanation.

On more than one occasion, the table chased someone across the room, leaving the rest of the group helpless with laughter. The victim escaped through the doorway, and the table got itself wedged there. All hands were clear of the table while this occurred. It was also found that when Philip was asked to go to the room upstairs – with the instruction, 'See what George is doing. Give him a knock' – a loud thump came from beneath the feet of the people sitting in the upper room. The thump was not heard by the Philip group below.

### Philip meets the public

Early in 1974, the Toronto group decided to make a documentary film to tell the story of the creation of Philip and, it was hoped, record the table movements and raps. There was no difficulty whatever: a larger room and bright lights and cameras and crew proved no obstacle and the result was the film 'Philip, the imaginary ghost'. Philip also performed before a live audience for a television programme including a discussion. The table was placed on the floor with the group and the audience, while the discussion panel sat on the platform. The table moved rapidly around the studio, eventually, with some gymnastics, climing up three steps to the platform, where Philip clearly felt he should be – with the presenter and the panelists. The whole incident was filmed. The presenter was asked to say 'Hello' to Philip and, to his surprise, received a loud rap under his hand. Further questions from him were answered by raps. This programme was broadcast on Toronto City Television. It is interesting to note that no member of the audience made any suggestion in his questions that implied suspicion of fraud or trickery. Philip's gyrations took place and were accepted. No one, the group included, had any clear understanding of how a 'joint thought' could produce physical effects in a table. This remains a mystery today.

### A signature in sound

In earlier experiments in table rapping in England, Dr Alan Gauld had found that 'paranormal' rappings were quite different in character from those produced on the same table with fingers or a solid object. The Toronto group recorded Philip raps and raps made by rings, pencils, erasers and other objects. The Philip raps, too, were quite different from 'normal' raps, dying away much more quickly.

A great deal has been learned about the psychological background needed to create phenomena of the Philip kind. From the very beginning, the Toronto group had the benefit of advice from two experts, Dr George Owen, a Fellow of Trinity College, Cambridge, who now works at Toronto University and is an expert in poltergeist phenomena, and Dr Joel Whitton, a medical practitioner and clinical psychologist. Dr Whitton is a member of the medical committee of the Toronto Society for Psychical Research, which tries to ensure that no experiment leads to any psychological or physical harm to any member.

Below: Dr George Owen and his wife Iris, who acted as mentors to the Toronto group. Mrs Owen was later to write a full-length account of the experiment

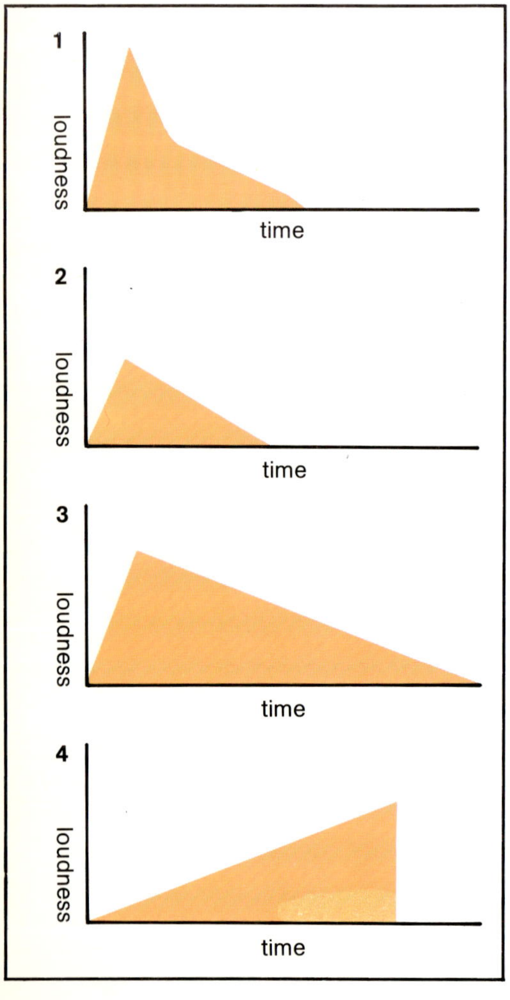


Left: how the sound made by Philip's raps differed markedly from noises made by natural objects – and even other paranormal rappings. Philip's noises (1 and 2) died away more rapidly, though not necessarily as evenly, as natural sounds (3). But they did follow a normal pattern, unlike some paranormal noises (4), which seem to be 'back to front'

The group noticed, as has already been mentioned, that Philip's opinions tended to depend on which members of the group were present. He was clearly a composite of them all – his creators. One day Philip's rappings were much weaker than usual, and one member of the group said that unless he did better than that, they could send him away – 'We only made you up, you know.' The phenomena decayed almost to zero, and the experimenters had to act quickly to build up again their belief in Philip as really existing. Obviously one part of their minds knew all the time that they had created him themselves: some 'mental gymnastics' were necessary, but this was not difficult.

The dangers of self-deception are obvious; thus the independent assessment of scientific visitors and the instrumental recording of the phenomena on tape and film by other independent people is important. The state of mind they showed was necessary for results reminds one of the Biblical injunction to become childlike in order to be fit for the Kingdom of Heaven, and of the saying that faith can move mountains. We are here, clearly, dealing with the 'creative power of thought', and the implications, as suggested at the beginning of this article, are enormous, ranging into other fields including 'faith healing'. A knowledge of the important psychological principles involved will be of great help – even if a physical theory modelling the mechanism by which raps are produced in solid objects, or the forces levitating these objects, is still elusive. A number of scientists are working on such theories. The difficulty, as even orthodox modern physicists now well know, is that the observer affects the results of the experiments. It is well-known to parapsychologists that some investigators have a catalytic effect on their psychic subjects and tend to achieve better results than do other investigators, who have an inhibiting effect. These effects, partly in the unconscious regions of the mind, are not at all understood.

### Psychokinesis as psychotherapy

A major part of the psychological theory for the poltergeist phenomena involves conscious and unconscious psychological stress, which is discharged through physical phenomena. If this is true and is applied to the Philip group, then the group's unconscious stresses will be a necessary part of the explanation. There should therefore be psychotherapeutic effects evident after the display of physical phenomena: the members of the group should become more tranquil, friendly and well-integrated as a result. This does indeed seem to be a result observed by them all, as well as by Dr Whitton: the members seemed to grow in self-confidence. Another part of the psychological theory is that the ego cannot accept that it is filled with emotional conflict, and that it has an extraordinary power to control objects from a distance. Thus subjects explain telekinetic activity on the basis of external agents – guides or spirits or something else. The Philip group were able to attribute everything to Philip, at least while they were in the 'childlike' state needed for success in the seances.

A card table flies into the air, propelled by psychokinetic energy. This picture was taken by the SORRAT group from Rolla, Missouri, USA, who have developed ideas similar to those suggested by the Philip group – with startling success

What can be said in conclusion? First, several other groups using quite different fictitious stories and basing their activity on the results learned by the Philip group have been able to produce similar results in a much shorter time, measured in weeks rather than months. Secondly, a relatively large number of scientists and engineers (applied scientists) have observed the phenomena and are convinced that they occur. Thirdly, the amount of serious research aimed at the construction of better theories should be, and appears to be, growing. Fourthly, the financial support available for this vitally important work is still pitifully small.

One question, of course, remains unanswered by the Philip group's experiments. Are the effects produced in the seance room really evidence of survival after death, or do they result from the unconscious workings of those present – perhaps using the medium as a focus? At least the work with Philip may help in designing experiments intended specifically to investigate this problem.

One observer said of the Philip group that if a Nobel prize were awarded for research in parapsychology, then it should be awarded to them. Many will agree.

**Further reading**

Lawrence LeShan, *The medium, the mystic and the physicist*, Turnstone 1974

A. R. G. Owen, *Can we explain the poltergeist?*, Helix Press (New York) 1964

Iris M. Owen, *Conjuring up Philip*, Paperjacks (Ontario) 1977

# Tesla's brave new world

**Towards the end of his life, Nikola Tesla left hints that he had devised a weapon of unprecedented power and precision. NEIL POWELL asks whether today's superpowers are trying to rediscover Tesla's secret**

RETURNING FROM THE GIANT electrical transmitting station he had built at Colorado Springs in 1900, Nikola Tesla embarked upon an even more ambitious project, his so-called 'World System' – a way of using the Earth's natural 'electrical vibrations' to provide universal and inexpensive electrical power. With the financial support of railroad magnate J.P. Morgan, he began the construction of an enormous broadcasting complex on a 2000-acre (800-hectare) estate known as Wardencliff, on Long Island some 60 miles (100 kilometres) from New York. A skeletal wooden tower some 154 feet (45 metres) high was erected, on which Tesla proposed to mount a giant copper electrode 100 feet (30 metres) in diameter, shaped like a huge doughnut with a tube diameter of 20 feet (6 metres).

But somehow, things began to go wrong. There was never enough money, and although the tower stood for 12 years until it was demolished during the First World War as a defence risk, the whole scheme came to nothing. And of the associated project, the industrial 'city beautiful' that he had envisaged with his architect friend Stanford White, there was no sign.

From that time on, Tesla seems to have been a spent force. He was never destitute, he never starved; but, while other scientists and engineers developed the practical applications of ideas for which he could claim the original idea, he found few opportunities to advance his own theories. Indeed, as he grew older, he seemed to lose touch with the scientific community, and increasingly made dogmatic assertions that conflicted with the

Above: a shower of glowing droplets flies from the point of impact of a ruby laser beam on a metallic surface. Military scientists are working on missile-destroying lasers

Left: Tesla in about 1910, surrounded by a battery of sophisticated equipment

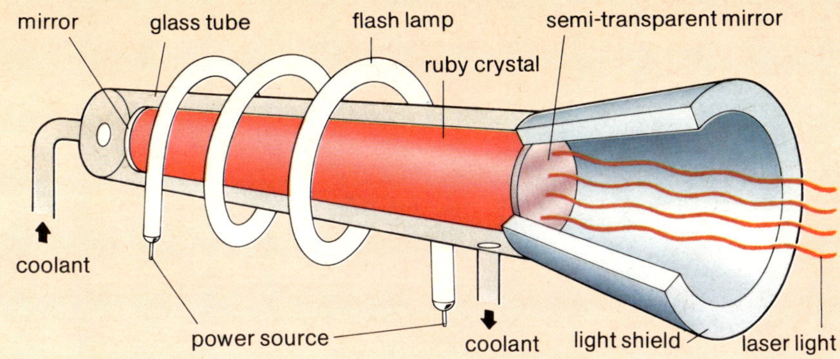


## The light fantastic

The ruby laser (above) consists of a rod of synthetic ruby around which an ordinary flash lamp is coiled. When this lamp is fired, its light energy is stored by chromium atoms present in the ruby as an impurity. They begin to re-emit the energy as pure red light, which is reflected back and forth between the precisely angled mirrors at the ends of the crystal. The light intensity builds up until the chromium atoms have all released their energy. The light gradually 'leaks' out through one of the end mirrors, which is semi-transparent, and emerges as a brief pulse of red light.

White light, such as sunlight (below), is a mixture of light of all wavelengths, each wavelength corresponding to a particular colour. Light of even the purest colour obtained from sources other than lasers has a 'spread' of wavelengths; the waves are also out of phase – they are not 'in step'. Laser light, by contrast, is of a single precise wavelength, its waves are in phase, and it can be extremely intense for short periods.

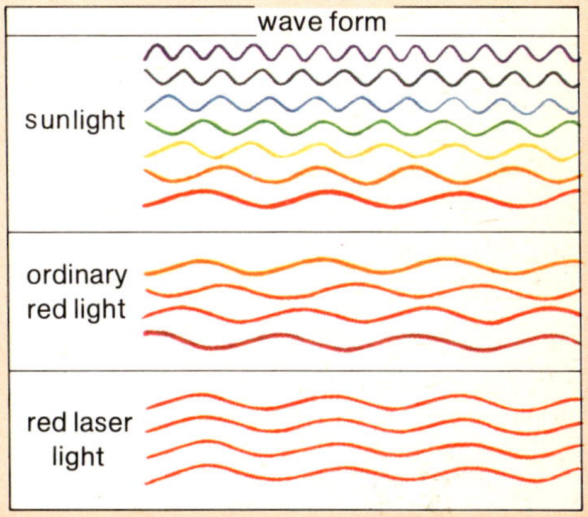


way in which physics was going.

For instance, he could not be persuaded to accept the modern picture of the discrete structure of the atom, and the idea of 'smashing the atom' was to him inconceivable. He accepted the existence of atoms as the indivisible 'billiard balls' of Victorian physics, and he accepted the idea of the independent existence of the electron, but he could not reconcile one concept with the other. As a result of his experiments with extremely long-wave, high-energy electrical oscillations, he was convinced that matter existed in a state of vibration, but he saw this in terms of a simple physical relationship between objects rather than in the sophisticated concepts of quantum mechanics.

### Planet in resonance

In his experiments at Colorado Springs, Tesla had set up a kind of pumping action of electrons in and out of the earth, which he understood as setting up planetary electric currents in resonant motion. It is certainly possible that Tesla's extremely long-wave transmissions could have set up such a resonance. Whether a way can be found to exploit this in the generation of usable energy remains to be seen.

At the other end of the wavelength scale, there is evidence to suggest that Tesla also discovered the principle of the laser. The name 'laser' is an acronym for 'light amplification by stimulated emission of radiation', and the light from a laser is produced by exactly the kind of tuned oscillation that Tesla used to produce his high-voltage discharges, but, of course, at high frequency and short wavelength. It was not until 1960 that the first successful laser was made, when the American physicist T.H. Maiman forced a bar of synthetic ruby to produce red light by 'pumping' light energy into it at exactly the right frequency.

The most important aspect of the light produced by the laser is that it is of a single wavelength. Ordinary light sources produce light of a wide range of wavelengths, which emerges in all directions. Lasers produce light all of one wavelength, the emission moving only in one direction, and with the waves exactly in step (this is called 'coherence'). As a result, a laser beam can be sent over enormous distances without losing its power or being diffused in any way. The first men on the Moon left behind them a reflector designed to send back laser beams transmitted from the Earth. The beams returned without any marked diminution in their power.

Writing in 1934, Tesla described an apparatus that sounds strangely similar to the laser. He claimed it 'projects particles which may be relatively large or of microscopic dimensions, enabling us to convey to a small area at a great distance trillions of times more energy than is possible with rays of any kind. Many thousands of horsepower can thus be transmitted by a stream thinner than a hair, so that nothing can resist.' At his 82nd birthday dinner at the New Yorker hotel in 1938, he was asked 'could he produce an effect on the moon sufficiently large to be seen by an astronomer watching the moon through a high-power telescope?' He replied that he 'would be able to produce in the dark

John Pierpoint Morgan was head of the most powerful finance house in the United States when he became favourably impressed with the achievements and character of Tesla. His support enabled Tesla to begin work on his 'World System' but, surprisingly, Morgan did not demand a share in the future profits of the enterprise

## An electrifying idea

The 'World System' envisioned by Tesla would, according to him, have made possible 'not only the instantaneous and precise wireless transmission of any kind of signals, messages or characters, to all parts of the world, but also the interconnection of the existing telegraph, telephone, and other signal stations without any change in their present equipment.' The radio signals would have been 'non-interfering as well as non-interferable. . . . There is virtually no limit to the number of stations or instruments that can be simultaneously operated without the slightest mutual disturbance.' Tesla described numerous applications. They included the worldwide distribution of news by radio telegraph or radio telephone, and the interconnection of the world's stock market tickertape machines. Clocks of cheap, simple construction would be synchronised anywhere in the world by the system without requiring attention. ('The idea of impressing upon the earth American time is fascinating,' said Tesla, 'and very likely to become popular.') Facsimile transmission of documents would have been possible. A 'universal marine service' would enable ships to steer without compasses. Tesla promised that 'when the first plant is inaugurated . . . humanity will be like an ant heap stirred up with a stick. . . .' The varied means of communication that he foresaw all exist today, and are becoming more widely integrated – but on a principle quite different from Tesla's: by relay from satellites in orbit.

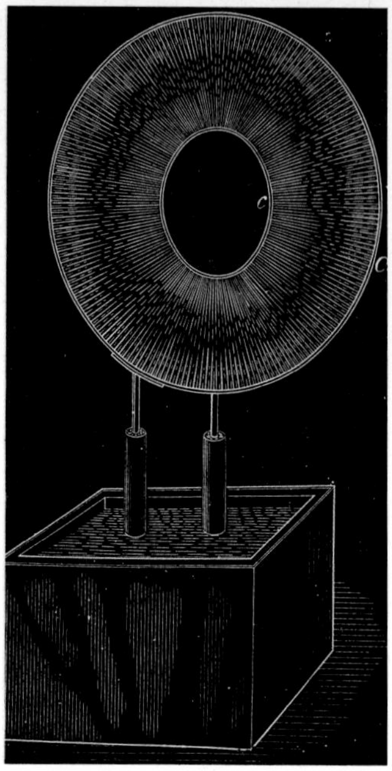

region of the thin crescent new moon an incandescent spot that would glow like a bright star so that it could be seen without the aid of a telescope'.

All this talk on the part of Tesla led to persistent rumours that he had invented a 'death ray', but in an article written in 1935 he stated categorically that 'this invention of mine does not contemplate the use of any so-called "death rays".' He hated war, and he wrote:

> We cannot abolish war by outlawing it. We cannot end it by disarming the strong. War can be stopped, not by making the strong weak but by making every nation, weak or strong, able to defend itself. . . . I was fortunate enough to evolve a new idea and to perfect means which can be used chiefly for defense. If it is adopted, it will revolutionize the relations between nations. It will make any country, large or small, impregnable against armies, airplanes, and other means for attack. My invention requires a large plant, but once established it will be possible to destroy anything, men or machines, approaching within a radius of 200 miles [320 kilometres].

### Soviet death ray?

In the light of this claim, the concern felt by Major-General George Keegan over the freak electrical storms that occurred over Canada in 1977 takes on a new significance. Major-General Keegan believed that the storms were caused by trials of a Soviet 'particle gun' capable of detonating intercontinental ballistic missiles while still in flight in the upper atmosphere.

The first hints that particle gun experiments were taking place came when satellite data indicated the unexpected presence of hydrogen, with traces of tritium ('heavy

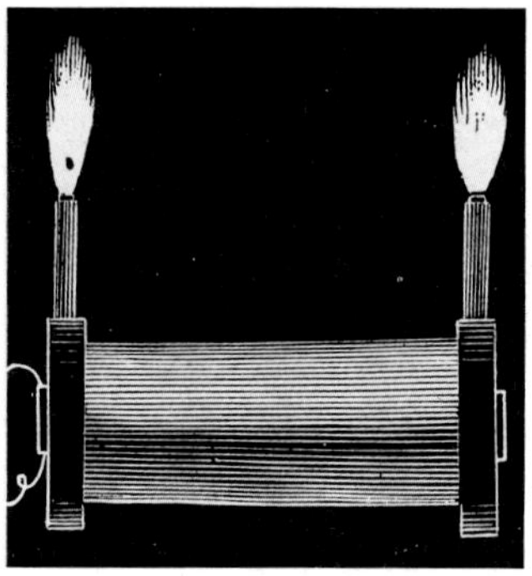

Top: Tesla experimented with various forms of lighting that could be used for advertising. This is a discharge between concentric loops of wire, forming a brilliantly luminous disc that could be used in a display

Above: luminous discharges from the ends of a high-voltage coil. Tesla believed they resembled flames in more than appearance: when fire was fully understood, he thought, it would prove to involve high-frequency electrical fields

Right: the experimental station at Colorado Springs. Bolts of artificial lightning were cast from the mast-top globe

Far right: the all-wooden structure on Long Island that was to be the heart of the World System; it stood until the First World War

hydrogen', the fuel of the hydrogen bomb) in the upper atmosphere. Intelligence assessors linked this observation with the information that the Soviets were carrying out experiments at an establishment in Semipalatinsk, Kazakhstan – experiments apparently devoted to the development of a weapon that would accelerate and focus a beam of subatomic particles on a target, such as a missile.

Subatomic particles that could be used in such a weapon are electrons or protons. In modern physical theory, these can be regarded alternatively as tiny solid bodies that can be accelerated by means of the controlled oscillation of an electromagnetic field, or as 'packets' of wave energy that can be 'pumped' forward in exactly the same way as the power is built up by a Tesla coil, or light waves are generated in an intense beam in a laser (see page 856).

What is particularly significant about a particle gun, or a laser, is that its beam consists of packets of wave energy produced at exactly their own inherent frequency, giving what is called a 'coherent' emission – effectively a standing wave of exactly the same kind as that described by Tesla in his paper of 1900.

**Further reading**

Philip S. Callahan, *Tuning in to nature*, Routledge and Kegan Paul 1977

John J. O'Neill, *Prodigal genius*, Spearman 1968

Nikola Tesla, *Lectures, patents and articles*, Nikola Tesla Museum (Belgrade) 1956

At an installation code-named 'Tora', at Sary-Shagan, about 500 miles (800 kilometres) from Semipalatinsk, the Soviets have been experimenting with a particle beam weapon since November 1979, and it seems probable that at Gomel, near Minsk, they have been carrying out development work over a considerably longer period. Indeed, what the Soviets vaguely described as 'certain experiments in the high frequency band' caused severe radio blackouts during 1976, leading to protests from several governments, including four from Britain.

### Assault on the ionosphere

Of greater importance than such a radio blackout is the possible effect of uncontrolled or – more sinisterly – of controlled firing of a particle beam gun upon the upper atmosphere. At a height of about 65 miles (100 kilometres) above the Earth's surface, the ionosphere begins; this is a series of layers of extremely rarefied air in which atoms are partly broken down into electrically charged ions. The ionosphere is responsible for the reflection of long-wave radio round the globe; it is also the part of the atmosphere in which the remarkable electrical displays of the *aurora borealis* take place, in response to bombardment by cosmic rays from space.

Like a laser, a finely focused particle beam can (almost literally) 'punch' a hole in the ionosphere. The particles – either positively-charged protons or negatively-charged electrons – can seriously affect the distribution of ions around the path of the beam, producing auroral displays and radio blackouts very similar to those recorded over northern Canada in 1977. And who knows what effect these disturbances could have upon currents in the upper atmosphere, and thus upon our weather?

Andrew Michrowski, a scientist working on a power scheme in eastern Canada, had no doubts. 'It is quite clear to me that the Russians are doing experiments based on Tesla's ideas, and in doing so have changed the world's weather,' he said.

Watson W. Scott, director of operations at the Canadian Department of Communications in Ottawa, was even more uncompromising. 'Are these experiments connected with the great [1976] drought in Britain, warm weather in Greenland, snow in Miami? . . . [It] seems to suggest an important new level of competence has been reached in the handling of very powerful physical forces. One person has told me it may be a pin-pointing, at last, of the exact frequencies used by Tesla in his work. Those who talk do not necessarily know. Those who know are the sort of people who are paid very good money to say nothing.'

**In 1908 a vast area of Siberia was devastated by the explosion of a huge fireball. Trees were scorched and felled, and the skins of many animals broke out in scabs. Could this have been a nuclear explosion? IAN RIDPATH analyses the facts**

ON THE MORNING OF 30 JUNE 1908, farmer S. B. Semenov was sitting on his porch in the isolated Siberian trading station of Vanavara, 500 miles (750 kilometres) north-west of Lake Baykal. It was still only 7.15 a.m., but the day was already well under way; the Sun rises early in midsummer this far north. Nearby, Semenov's neighbour P. P. Kosalopov was pulling nails out of a window frame with pincers. Neither man could have had an inkling of the drama they were about to witness.

Suddenly, Semenov was startled to see, towards the north-west, a brilliant fireball that 'covered an enormous part of the sky'. Semenov twisted in pain, for the fireball's heat felt as though it were burning his shirt. Next door, Kosalopov dropped his pincers and clasped his hands to his ears, which felt as though they were burning. He first glanced at his roof, suspecting it to be on fire, then turned to Semenov. 'Did you see anything?' Kosalopov asked. 'How could one help but see it?' replied the frightened Semenov, still stinging from his burns.

A few seconds later, the blinding, bright blue, fireball, trailing a column of dust, exploded 40 miles (65 kilometres) from Vanavara with a force that knocked Semenov off his porch, where he lay unconscious for a few seconds. On coming to, he felt ground tremors that shook the entire house, broke the barn door, and shattered windows. In the house of Kosalopov, earth fell from the ceiling and a door flew off the stove. Sounds like thunder rumbled in the air.

The great Siberian fireball of 1908 was an event so exceptional that it excited a controversy that continues to this day. Explanations for it range into the realm of the bizarre, including the remarkable hypothesis that it was caused by nothing less than the emergency landing of a nuclear spacecraft,

The aftermath of the explosion on 30 June 1908 of a huge fireball that 'covered an enormous part of the sky' over Tunguska, Siberia (map inset, right), must have looked much like a forest fire (top); for up to 20 miles (30 kilometres) around the site of the explosion, trees were blown down, and the intense heat of the blast set the forest alight

Thirteen years after the Tunguska explosion, Soviet mineralogist Leonid Kulik (above) led an expedition to the site, travelling by horse-drawn sled and boat (right). His route is shown in the map (above right). Kulik found dramatic evidence of the blast – whole forests of scorched and uprooted trees (left)

perhaps even of extra-terrestrial origin.

The area on which the object fell, in the valley of the Stony Tunguska river, was sparsely inhabited by the Tungus, a nomadic, Mongol-like people who herded reindeer. Near the centre of the fall, north of Vanavara, several Tungus were thrown into the air by the explosion, and their tents were carried away in a violent wind. Around them, the forest began to blaze.

As the dazed Tungus cautiously inspected the site of the blast, they found scenes of terrifying devastation. Trees were felled like matchsticks for up to 20 miles (30 kilometres) around. The intense heat from the explosion had melted metal objects, destroyed storehouses, and burned reindeer to death. No living animals were left in the area but, miraculously, no humans were killed by the blast. There were also reports that a mysterious 'black rain' had fallen in the area.

The effects of the Tunguska blast were seen and felt for 600 miles (1000 kilometres) around. Reports from the district of Kansk, 400 miles (600 kilometres) from the blast, described boatmen being thrown into the river and horses being knocked over by shock waves, while houses shook and crockery crashed off shelves. The driver of the Trans-Siberian express stopped his train for fear of a derailment when the carriages and rails began to shake.

Other effects were noted around the world, but their cause remained a puzzle for a long time, as news of the fireball and explosion did not become widely known for many years. Seismic waves like those from an earthquake were recorded throughout Europe, as well as disturbances of the Earth's magnetic field. Meteorologists later found from microbarograph records that atmospheric shock waves from the blast had circled the Earth twice.

### Echoes of distant Siberia

A woman in Huntingdon, England, wrote to *The Times* to report that the night skies were so bright that shortly after midnight on 1 July 'it was possible to read large print indoors. . . . At about 1.30 a.m. the room was quite light, as if it had been day. It would be interesting if anyone would explain the cause of so unusual a sight.' But, at that time, no one *could* explain.

Similar eerie night-time effects were noted over much of Europe and western Asia after the fall. Reports from this area record nights up to 100 times brighter than normal and crimson hues in the sky, like the glare from fires towards the north. The strange lights did not flicker or form arches like the *aurora borealis*; they were like effects that followed the outburst of Krakatoa, which injected vast clouds of dust into the atmosphere.

At the time of the Tunguska fall, Russia was entering a period of major political upheaval and the national press did not give any coverage to what it saw as a minor event in a remote part of the empire. Despite the exceptional nature of the Tunguska event, news about it remained buried in local Siberian newspapers until 13 years later, when word of it reached a Soviet mineralogist, Leonid Kulik.

Kulik had a particular interest in fallen meteorites, not least because of the rich source of iron they could provide for industry. He became convinced that the object that had fallen on 30 June 1908 in the valley of the Stony Tunguska river was an iron meteorite even larger than that which formed the vast Barringer crater in Arizona 25,000 years or so ago.

After years of planning, Kulik set out in 1927 on an expedition to reach the site of the

Above: members of the Tungus tribe, who were the most directly affected by the Tunguska explosion. They reported that, after the blast, many of their reindeer broke out in scabs – a fact that has led some scientists, assuming that the scabs were evidence of radiation sickness, to suggest that a nuclear explosion had occurred

Tunguska fall. From the railway town of Taishet, Kulik and his team crossed 400 miles (600 kilometres) of frozen *taiga* by horse-drawn sled until they reached Vanavara. There, they heard the remarkable stories of the inhabitants, convincing Kulik more than ever that he was on the track of a truly enormous meteorite.

A sudden snowfall held up progress for over a week. On 8 April, Kulik, a colleague, and a local guide set out on horseback on the final leg of the journey. They marched northwards through scenes of increasing devastation: birch and pine trees lay on the ground where they had been uprooted by the force of the shock wave 19 years before. Many of the trees had been scorched or even set alight by the same intense heat that farmer Semenov had felt in Vanavara.

Surveying the blast area from a ridge, Kulik wrote:

> From our observation point no sign of forest can be seen, for everything has been devastated and burned, and around the edge of this dead area the young twenty-year-old forest growth has moved forward furiously, seeking sunshine and life. One has an uncanny feeling when one sees 20- to 30-inch [50- to 75-centimetre] thick giant trees snapped across like twigs, and their tops hurled many metres away to the south.

## Visit of the god of fire

Kulik wanted to press on the remaining few miles to the centre of the blast, but the Tungus guides were superstitious, for their legends said the area had been visited by the god of fire, and they would go no further. Kulik had to return to Vanavara to recruit new guides, and another month passed before he arrived again at the devastated area and finally reached the centre of the fall – to discover the great riddle of Tunguska.

Of the giant crater he had expected there was not a sign. Instead, he found a frozen swamp and a curious stand of trees which, despite being at the centre of the explosion, had escaped the effects of the blast that had levelled everything around them. Whatever object caused the explosion, it had never reached the ground. Although he returned to the area with bigger expeditions in subsequent years, Kulik never found any fragments of meteoric iron.

So if the Tunguska blast was not caused by the impact of an iron meteorite, what *was* the cause? In 1930, the English meteorologist Francis J. W. Whipple, assistant director of the Meteorological Office, proposed that the event had been caused by the collision of the Earth with a small comet, a suggestion supported by the Soviet astronomer A. S. Astapovich.

The popular view of a comet is a giant glowing ball of dust and gas trailing streamers for millions of miles, as with the spectacular Halley's Comet in 1910. But such brilliant comets are the exception rather than the rule. A dozen or more comets may be tracked by astronomers each year, but few or none of them ever become visible to the naked eye. Most comets are smaller and fainter than those illustrated in astronomy books; some comets, particularly old ones, may show no tail at all.

According to the most popular theory, a comet resembles a dirty snowball of frozen gas and dust. Old comets run out of gas to become nothing more than loose 'bags' of low-density rocks. Such an object would indeed cause a blazing fireball as it burned up by friction after plunging at high speed into the Earth's atmosphere, eventually shattering explosively as the forces of deceleration overcame its own strength. The mid-air blast of such an object would explain why there was no crater or meteorite fragments at

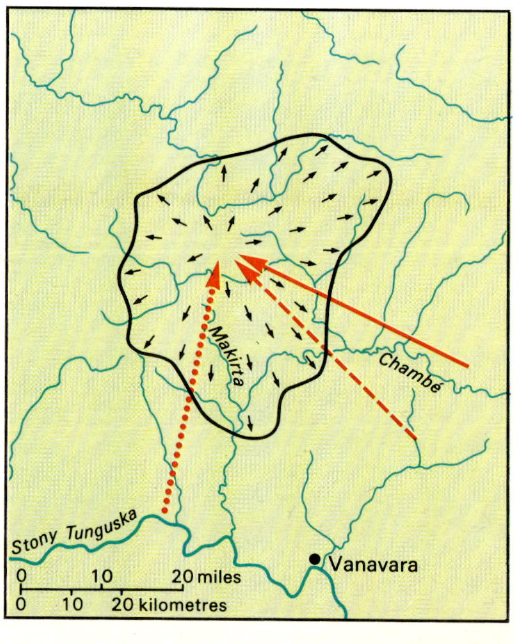


Right: The area of devastation in Tunguska, showing the centre of the explosion and the direction of the fallen trees, together with three different suggestions of the path taken by the fireball. The path indicated by the solid red arrow was proposed by scientists K. P. Florensky and V. G. Konenkin, and is now generally considered to be the correct one

Tunguska. But critics of the comet theory argued that no comet had been seen in the sky before the Tunguska blast.

There has been a host of alternative explanations, including a bizarre suggestion that a mini black hole blasted into Siberia. According to astronomical theory, mini black holes, with the mass of an asteroid packed into the size of an atomic particle, could have been formed in the maelstrom following the Big Bang explosion that is believed to have marked the origin of the Universe. The passage of a mini black hole through the Earth would, according to University of Texas physicists A. A. Jackson and Michael Ryan, have all the observed effects of the Tunguska fireball – except that the mini black hole should have carried right on through the Earth and emerged in the north Atlantic, producing similar spectacular effects as it departed. Unfortunately for the theory, no such effects occurred.

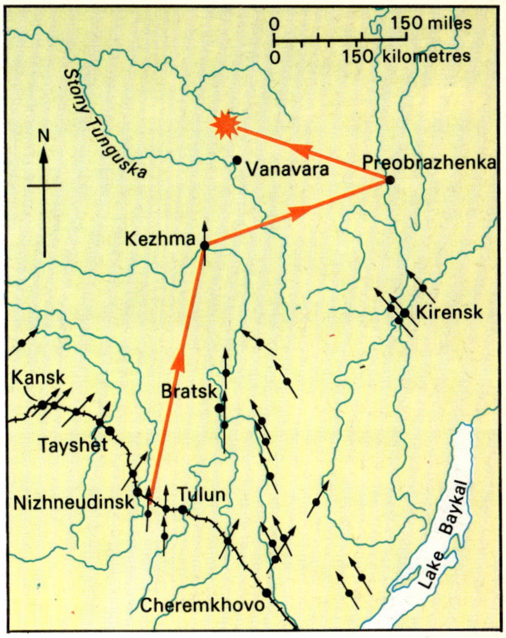


Right: the flight path of the Tunguska fireball in the area immediately surrounding the impact point, as reconstructed by Soviet ufologist Felix Zigel from the study of the damage created by the atmospheric shock wave, and the evidence given in a number of eyewitness accounts. The arrows through towns indicate the direction in which the object appeared to be travelling

## Spacecraft from Mars?

Of all the theories for the Tunguska blast, the most controversial was put forward in 1946 by the Soviet science-fiction writer Alexander Kazantsev. Disguising his theory as a fictional story, Kazantsev proposed that the explosion over Siberia had been caused by the burn-up of a nuclear-powered spacecraft, perhaps from Mars. Kazantsev speculated that the aliens had come to collect water from Lake Baykal, the largest volume of fresh water on Earth. As the craft plummeted into the atmosphere it heated up by friction until the engines erupted in a mid-air blast like the Hiroshima bomb.

Soviet ufologists Felix Zigel and Alexei Zolotov have supported the exploding nuclear spacecraft idea. Zigel even proposed that the craft performed a crazy zig-zag as it desperately attempted to land, although none of the eyewitnesses actually reported seeing the fireball change course.

Below: some of the evidence of large-scale destruction found by Kulik and his team 13 years after the blast: scorched trees, knocked flat by the force of the explosion or, where they were still standing, of stunted and scrubby growth

Another science-fiction writer, John Baxter, in his book *The fire came by*, published in 1976, followed Kazantsev in comparing the effects of the Tunguska explosion with those of the Hiroshima bomb – the strong thermal flash, the updraught of heated air that caused a 'fiery pillar', and the characteristic clump of trees that remained standing at the centre of the Tunguska devastation, as they had under the explosion point of the Hiroshima bomb.

There was even talk of deadly radiation at the site. One of the characters in Alexander Kazantsev's story speaks of a man who, shortly after examining the Tunguska blast area, died in terrible pain as if from an invisible fire. 'It could be nothing other than radioactivity,' explains the fictional character. In fact, there is no record that anyone died from the Tunguska blast – but the Tungus people reported that reindeer in the area broke out in scabs, which modern writers such as Baxter have attributed to radiation burns.

Expeditions to the area noted an accelerated growth of vegetation around the blast site, again attributed by some to genetic damage from radiation. There were reports in popular writings that radioactivity had been detected in the wood from the area, and an analysis of radiocarbon from tree rings in the United States by Nobel prize-winner Willard Libby showed an increase in radiocarbon following 1908. All of which seemed to indicate that the Tunguska explosion could have been nuclear.

This theory raises some alarming questions – for the Tunguska explosion occurred a good 30 years before the first nuclear tests. Who, or what, could have caused a blast of such proportions?

*New investigations shed light on the Tunguska mystery. See page 1058*

# The rise of Count Dracula

**Dracula – the most famous vampire of them all – was created as the anti-hero of a novel written in 1897. Yet, as DANIEL FARSON shows, the truth about the bloodsucking aristocrat is far stranger than the fiction**

THE CULT OF THE VAMPIRE in the 20th century is very largely due to books and films based on one larger-than-life character, Count Dracula. Created in 1897 by the Irish-born theatre manager Bram Stoker, Dracula (from the book of the same name) has become synonymous with vampirism, indeed popularising it. It is ironic that Jack the Ripper, who committed real atrocities about the same time as the publication of *Dracula*, should have become part of our folklore, whereas many people today believe that Dracula was a real person. In one respect, in fact, they are right, but the fictional Dracula was a complex creation.

While the young Bram Stoker was making his way in the world a fellow Dubliner, Sheridan le Fanu, was also making money out of vampirism. His *Carmilla*, published in 1872, was a sensation. The average Victorian reader almost certainly did not perceive what is today the overt lesbianism of the book, but it still made an enormous impression on its readers. Echoes of its dreadful, awe-inspiring climax can be found in *Dracula*, but the end of the undead Carmilla, as told by le Fanu, is strongly reminiscent of the case histories of alleged real vampires recorded in such horrific abundance in Eastern Europe (see page 1001).

The combination of necrophilia, seduction of virgins from beyond the grave, and an atmosphere heavy with sex and violence, made vampirism very popular. After all, the wicked creature was always destroyed in the end so it must be a moral tale.

The scene had been set over 30 years before Victoria came to the throne. Lord Byron, accompanied by his doctor, Polidori, spend the summer of 1816 on the shores of Lake Geneva in Switzerland, conveniently close to their friends the poet Shelley and his mistress Mary Godwin – who later became his wife. The weather was bad so they amused themselves by staying indoors and writing ghost stories. It was to be a remarkably productive way of passing the time. For Mary Godwin – inspired no doubt by the lengthy talk of ghosts and ghouls and by the tempestuous elements – dreamed the entire story that she duly wrote down and called *Frankenstein*. Polidori, at first loath to enter into competition with his literary masters, eventually produced a long story called *The vampyre*, which he proceeded to publish, hinting heavily that it was, in fact, written by Byron. Polidori's tale was a sensation. Professor Leonard Wolf claims in his book *The annotated Dracula* (1975) that 'Polidori gave us the prototype vampire . . . that is to say, as a nobleman, aloof, brilliant, chilling, fascinating to women, and coolly evil.'

Polidori's vampire was the forerunner of the legion of vampires who began to invade English literature, such as *Varney the vampire, or The feast of blood* (1847) by Thomas Prest, who had also written the more famous *Sweeney Todd, the demon barber*. Varney appeared in 220 weekly parts in a pulp magazine and was as popular as the most successful television soap opera today.

Above: Nosferatu (played by Klaus Kinski) sinks his teeth into his entranced victim (Isabelle Adjani) in *Nosferatu – the vampyre*, the 1979 German remake of the 1922 film of the same name

Below: Bram Stoker (1847–1912), famous for his blood-curdling novel *Dracula*

With this sort of background, Stoker began to write what was to become the vampire classic. It was his idea to bring the vampire novel up to date, setting *Dracula* in late-19th-century England, even including references to such innovations as Kodak photographs and a dictaphone. And although the Count originated from Transylvania, his London address was Piccadilly.

Count Dracula is a complex literary creation. His background – the wild, sinister country of what is now Romania – may seem like poetic fiction and indeed should be, for Stoker never visited the country himself. Instead he consulted an old guide book and spent many hours talking with a colourful Hungarian professor, Arminius Vambery. The result was that the country of Dracula's origin was described with uncanny detail; a modern visitor to the Borgo Pass (which is mentioned by name in the novel) needs no stretch of the imagination to fit fiction to fact.

### Vlad the bloodthirsty

But Vambery did more than leave Stoker with a vivid impression of topography; he told him tales of Transylvanian vampires, and the enduring vampire superstition. And he also told him of the 15th-century Transylvanian prince, Vlad, whose extreme sadism and bloodlust had earned him a special place in Transylvanian history. He had another name: Dracula. This has two meanings: his father was called Dracul, so Dracula may well mean simply 'son of Dracul'; the other meaning is 'devil'. It may be, given his perverted exploits, that the two meanings became inextricably linked, for the son of Dracul was indeed a 'devil'. His favourite pastime was impaling prisoners – or indeed anyone – on high, pointed poles. Impaling was to him a fine art and meant a slow death for his victims. He particularly enjoyed having his meal set out on a table under the forest of mass impalings where he would invite others to join him.

But Vlad Dracula was and is known to Romanians as a hero, for he rid them of their enemies, the Turks. It is said that in so doing he impaled 30,000 Turks in one day.

The fictional Dracula says: 'One of my own race . . . who crossed the Danube and beat the Turk on his own ground! This was a Dracula indeed!' This and other features of the story seem to prove the contention that the Count was based almost entirely on the historical warrior. But although undoubtedly *bloodthirsty*, even by the standards of the time, Vlad Dracula was not a vampire. As far as anyone knows, he never actually drank blood and despite some rumours – generated, one suspects, mainly by the tourist industry – he has never risen from his grave. (In fact no one is sure where it is.)

It may be, however, that Professor Vambery also told Stoker of a distant descendant of Vlad Dracula, whose behaviour was decidedly vampiristic. The 15th-century Countess Elisabeth Bathory had a penchant for kidnapping village girls and 'milking' them of their blood, in various slow and agonising ways. The object of this unpleasant exercise was to bathe in it, in order to maintain her – alleged – beauty. She was probably the inspiration for the Countess in le Fanu's *Carmilla* and certainly was for Mark Ronson's *Bloodthirst* (1980).

Other blood-obsessed historical figures have included the notorious Gilles de Rais, one-time patron of Joan of Arc. His particular passion was the torturing of little boys, finally dispatching them by ordering his servants to slit their jugular veins so their blood would spurt over him.

And nearer our own time was the 'acid bath murderer', John George Haigh, who was also known as 'the vampire killer'. Haigh

Right: the frontispiece of *Varney the vampire* by Thomas Prest (who also wrote *Sweeney Todd*). This lurid epic, which was written 50 years before Stoker's *Dracula* appeared, took 220 weekly parts to unfold, then ended abruptly. The vampire, 'tired and disgusted with a life of horror', threw himself into a convenient volcano

Below: the cover of an early French version of *Dracula*, which is unusual for faithfully depicting Dracula as he was actually described in the story

Bottom: Bran Castle, an imposing relic of old Transylvania, now part of Romania. This is believed to have been one of Vlad Dracula's residences and is consequently a great tourist attraction today

is said to have killed a young man named Swann (among others) so he could collect his blood – 'a wineglassful' – and drink it. Basil Copper, in his *The vampire* (1971), claims that Haigh 'was a vampire in the classical tradition, possibly the only true monster in this field in the 20th century. By this, of course, I do not mean that he was a vampire in the supernatural sense, but there is at least a strong suggestion that he needed to drink blood in order to refresh and sustain himself.' Haigh was hanged in 1949.

The reservation about vampires in 'the supernatural sense' is vital. None of these perverts actually rose from the dead; some enjoyed the sight, feel and occasionally the taste of human blood.

### Vampires all around

However, just as the Aztecs and Indian rajahs drank blood believing it would give them strength, so it seems there are quite ordinary people who by design – or by accident – drain people surrounding them of their 'life force' or energy. This phenomenon is extremely common; we all know of someone who seems to 'feed' on the energy of others, leaving them drained and tired. This so-called 'psychic vampirism' is a recurring theme in occult writings but one of its least controversial aspects is the 'preying' of men on women, or vice versa, for sexual reasons in ways often remarkably similar to those lovingly detailed in *Carmilla* and *Dracula*.

The connection between supernatural vampirism and sex is profound. Normal, decent folk who would ordinarily find tales of corpses and running blood offputting, find themselves enjoying vampire stories perhaps against their will, just as the prim and proper Victorians did. Why? What is the extraordinary hold of vampirism on the subconscious minds of most people?

Of all the screen 'Draculas' – since the Count's film début in 1931, when he was played by the Hungarian Bela Lugosi – no one actor has been so closely identified with the great vampire as the British actor Christopher Lee, who explained the appeal of the character by saying:

> He offers the illusion of immortality . . . the subconscious wish we all have of limitless power . . . a man of tremendous brain and physical strength . . . he is either a reincarnation or he has never died. He is a superman image, with erotic appeal for women who find him totally alluring. In many ways he is everything people would like to be – the anti-hero, the heroic villain. . . . For women there is the complete abandonment to the power of a man.

And although American horror-film star Vincent Price has never actually played a vampire except in the spoof *The Monster Club* (1980), almost everyone thinks he has. Price says, 'Often when I'm walking along the street, a middle-aged matron comes up to me and says "please bite me".'

The virgin's ecstatic swoon, half fear, half pleasurable excitement, as the superhuman figure in the swirling black cape materialises in her bedroom; the oppressive, languorous feeling; the total abandonment; the pleasure and the pain of the vampire's teeth sinking into her neck while she cannot move or cry out – all this can be seen clearly as a romanticisation of seduction and defloration, with the added thrill of the supernatural. In Victorian days decent girls were 'ruined' by seduction, but what if their seducer were a demon from beyond the grave? Then the more innocent the victim the greater her excuse – and the greater her attraction for the vampire.

The sexual excitement of vampirism was made explicit in a painting by Philip Burne-Jones called *The vampire*, exhibited in 1897, the same year as the publication of

Top: Čachtice Castle, in Slovakia, once the lair of the infamous Countess Elisabeth Bathory (above), a distant descendant of Vlad Dracula. Obsessed with her own beauty, she sought to preserve it by bathing in the blood of tortured virgins. Luring them to her mountain retreat, she would 'milk' them of their blood by various means, her favourite being hanging them up in spiked cages and then delighting in their screams as their blood dripped over her. Over 600 girls fell victim to her lusts, but in 1611 she was sentenced to be walled up alive for her crimes. The screams of her ghost have been reported many times

Left: the historical Dracula – 'Vlad the impaler' – seen enjoying his favourite kind of picnic, which earned him his nickname

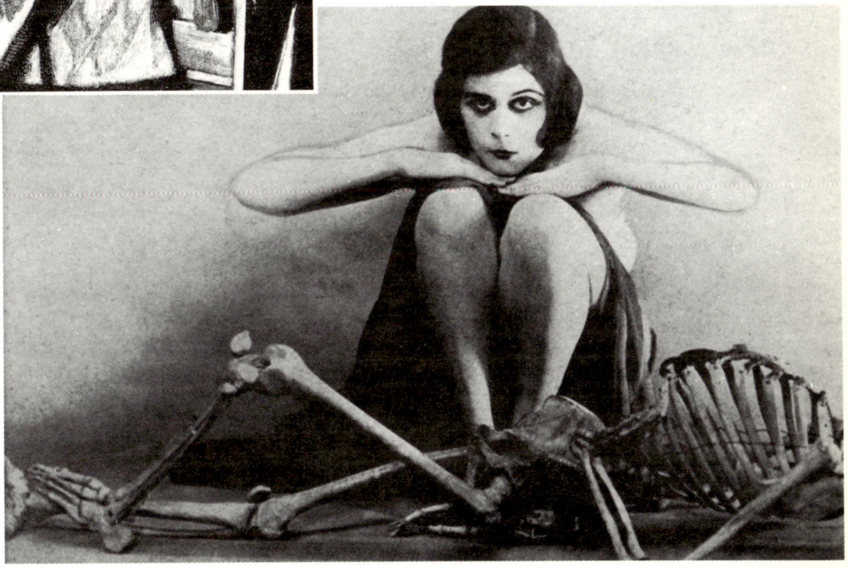

Stoker's *Dracula*. London society flocked to see it. It portrayed a voluptuous woman bending over a man whose chest is bare, and there is blood trickling from the punctures made by her teeth on his skin. The catalogue to the exhibition contained a poem by the young Rudyard Kipling, opening with the line 'A fool there was . . .'. When the painting and catalogue appeared in New York they made such a profound impression that within months a play opened on Broadway, entitled *A fool there was*. This in turn led to a film of the same name, launching one Theodosia Goodman (or, as she is more popularly known, Theda Bara, an anagram of 'Arab death') as one of the first film stars. Despite her real-life ordinariness, the film moguls decided to cast her in the image of a female sexual predator, showing her in one scene crouching triumphantly over a male skeleton and treating all men with superior scorn. She was given the line – or rather the subtitle, for this was in the days of the silent screen – 'Kiss me, my fool', which became all the rage. And perhaps most significantly, her 'type' became known as the female 'vamp', short for vampire.

As the 20th century progresses, perverted sex, violence and all manner of horrors are taken as a matter of course. Yet the odd fact remains that many people are fascinated by the idea of vampirism. In the early 1970s the British Dracula Society was formed, and there are Count Dracula appreciation societies in several parts of the United States and in other countries. The Romanian tourist industry is booming, thanks to the confusion in many people's minds between the real and the fictional Draculas. If anything the fascination seems to be increasing.

Top: a 19th-century German engraving by Max Kahm, entitled *The vampire*, an expression of the predatory nature of the female vampire who drains innocent men of their sexual energy

Above: the early film star Theda Bara, posing for a publicity still as a 'vamp' – or metaphorical vampire – a heartless but totally irresistible female who eventually destroys the male

Above left: Gilles de Rais, patron of Joan of Arc, gloats over the torture and sadistic murder of one of the many boys – over 140 – he had killed for his pleasure. Finally justice caught up with him and he was executed in 1440

Why? Perhaps it is the curious blend of sexuality, explicit and implicit, of surrender, of possession, of the promise of immortality, of being supermen and women in the atmosphere of thrilling evil. As one film producer said to the Dracula Society: 'sex and the supernatural never fails.'

The upright and very Victorian Bram Stoker would have been horrified to discover what the post-Freud world has made of his masterpiece. But it seems hard to ignore the sexual connotations, subliminal though they may be, in his story. Take the passage where Jonathan Harker is surrounded and caressed by vampire women in Castle Dracula:

> The fair girl went on her knees and bent over me, fairly gloating. There was a deliberate voluptuousness which was both thrilling and repulsive, and as she arched her neck she actually licked her lips like an animal, till I could see in the moonlight the moisture shining on the scarlet lips and on the red tongue as it lapped the sharp red teeth. Lower and lower went her head. . . . I closed my eyes in . . . ecstasy and waited.

*We know of vampire bats, but are there really human vampires? See page 1078*

# A career in ruins

**The success of the excavations at Glastonbury convinced the man in charge that he could safely reveal the paranormal source of his information. But, as COLIN WILSON explains, he was tragically wrong**

IT MUST BE FRANKLY CONFESSED that, as a human being, Frederick Bligh Bond, discoverer of phenomenal architectural remains at Glastonbury, left something to be desired. Even his admiring biographer William Kenawell admits that he was paranoid, and tended to suspect plots and conspiracies everywhere. But at Glastonbury his suspicions were not entirely unjustified, for his two chief associates, W. D. Caroe and Dean J. A. Robinson, who found him eccentric and disorganised, would have been glad to see the back of him.

But the extraordinary success of the excavations at Glastonbury Abbey placed him in a very strong position. His 'enemies' had no suspicion that this success was due largely to the advice of dead monks. Moreover, the invisible communicators who called themselves the 'Company of Avalon' were not merely concerned to help him dig up the past; they declared that their aim was to restore Glastonbury as a centre of religious power and significance. A man who carried around a secret like that was bound to behave a little oddly.

And Bond had more than one secret to keep to himself. The long-dead monks who guided John Bartlett's pencil were able to provide him with all kinds of historical titbits. In 1908, he was digging along the south side of the nave, hoping to find evidence for the two towers that the 'communicators' had described, when he came upon a giant skeleton. It was that of an old man, nearly 7 feet (2 metres) tall, and he had been buried without a coffin. Stranger still, there was another skull between his legs. It was the kind of mystery that gives archaeologists sleepless nights. Had the old man been murdered? That seemed unlikely, since a stone pillow had been carefully placed underneath his head.

Bond, of course, had easy access to a solution. He merely had to sit down beside his friend Bartlett, ask the dead monks to explain the matter, and wait for Bartlett's pencil to trace out a reply. In this case, the reply was precise and fascinating. The skeleton, said the monk who called himself Gulielmus (William), was that of Radulphus Cancellarius – Radulphus the treasurer – who had slain someone called Eawulf in fair fight. Eawulf had caused considerable damage to Radulphus with his axe, and had broken several of his bones. However, Radulphus lived on for many years, and died at the age of 103. He asked to be buried right outside the church he loved so much. Oddly enough, his old enemy Eawulf had been buried in the same spot, and when the monks buried Radulphus, they were startled when

The tranquillity of the ruins at Glastonbury conceals the abbey's turbulent and chequered past. Once the richest and most powerful church in all England, it was destroyed by Henry VIII and remained neglected and crumbling for four centuries until its former glory was all but extinguished. In 1907 a new and disturbing phase in its history began when the man appointed to excavate the ruins, Frederick Bligh Bond, enlisted the help of long-dead monks in his search for some of the vanished buildings

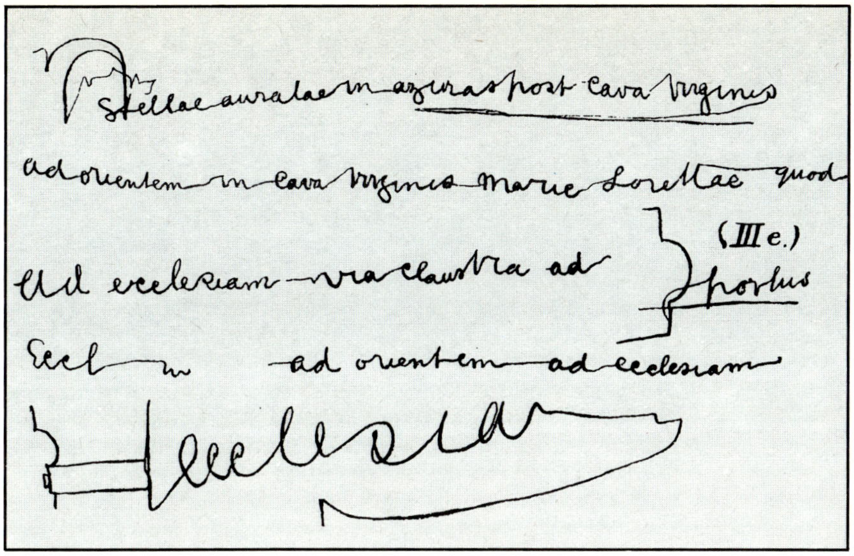


they disturbed the bones of Eawulf. So they put them into the same grave.

And who were these men? It seemed that Radulphus (or Ralph) was a Norman who came to England with William the Conqueror – Gulielmus mentioned the date 1087 – and Eawulf was a Saxon earl. This had been in the time of a Norman abbot, Thurstan.

Now history tells us that, when Norman monks took over Glastonbury Abbey, they treated the Saxon monks (who belonged to an Irish order) with considerable brutality. Abbot Thurstan was their chief persecutor. In fact, Thurstan was so brutal that William the Conqueror dismissed him. But history mentions no one called Eawulf. So who was he? The 'communicator' answered this question promptly. Eawulf, it seemed, was the Earl of Edgarley, of royal blood, 'a doughty Saxon he, and one who said that Glaston was builded by the Saxon, and Saxon it should remain.' What happened, apparently, is that Norman soldiers killed some Saxon monks of Glastonbury Abbey. Earl Eawulf of Edgarley – a village a mile (1.6 kilometres) south-east of Glastonbury – retaliated by attacking the Normans. He was killed in a fight with Thurstan's treasurer Radulphus, and buried (without a coffin) outside the abbey church.

### Testing the ghostly fathers

It was a fascinating story. But was it true? Here was a good opportunity to test the accuracy of the ghostly monks. No one had ever heard of Earl Eawulf of Edgarley, and neither Bartlett nor Bond had any recollection of having heard of him. So if he really existed, this would prove that the message came from real communicators, not from Bond's or Bartlett's unconscious mind.

Gulielmus claimed that Radulphus had had his bones broken by Eawulf's axe. They examined the skeleton, and found that, in fact, the right forearm *had* been fractured, but had healed. A man defending himself from an axe would fling up his right forearm, and it might well get broken.

The monk said that the Saxon monks had their reward, for 'a Saxon again was Abbot for a time.' That proved to be accurate. Thurstan was removed by William the Conqueror, and in his place was appointed Herlewin – a Saxon name.

But did Eawulf exist? Bond, who was nothing if not thorough, searched the records, but without success. History had nothing to say about Earl Eawulf of Edgarley.

Then, in an ancient chronicle by someone called Fabius Ethelwerd, and dated AD 866, there was a sentence that read: 'During this year died Eanulf, nobleman of the province of Somerset.' It went on to say that his body now rested 'in the monastery at Glastingabyrig' – Glastonbury. This showed that a nobleman with a very similar name – only an 'n' instead of a 'w' – was associated with the abbey and Somerset. But *was* 'Eanulf' really another version of 'Eawulf'? Bond continued his search – and found another ancient chronicle, Asser's *Annals of the exploits of Alfred*, dated AD 855, which mentioned 'Eanwulf, Earl of the district of Summurton.' This is definitely the same man who is referred to as 'Eanulf', for both chronicles associate him with a certain Bishop Ealhstan. Somerton is very close to Edgarley.

Of course, *this* Earl Eanwulf is two centuries too early to be the one killed by Radulphus the treasurer. But he was obviously an ancestor; Bond had proved that there *was* an Earl of Edgarley in the Glastonbury area two centuries before the fight between Radulphus and Eawulf. It is one of the most remarkable and convincing proofs of the objective existence of Bond's ghostly communicators.

Perhaps one of the most charming things about this curious tale is the positive character of the 'communicators' that emerges in the writing. For example, Bond thought at first that Radulphus the treasurer was another Radulphus called Fitzstephen, who rebuilt the abbey church after the great fire of 1184. But this, of course, was a century after Radulphus Cancellarius's time. Bond asked

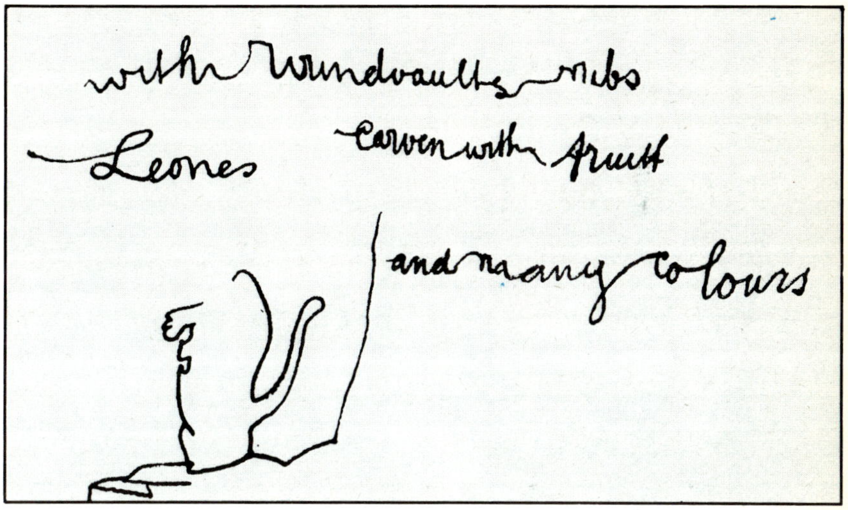


Architectural details of the lost Loretto Chapel, supplied by a monk who signed himself *Camillus Thesiger* – probably Camel, the purse-bearer to the Abbot Bere who built the chapel. Camillus told of a 'covered way, or cloister, leading to the church, to the east' (top), of the undervaults, whose ribs are 'carven with fruit and many colours', and drew an unfinished sketch of one of the statues of sitting lions to be found in the Loretto Chapel (above). Unfortunately, although Bond believed that his informants had given him the location of the Loretto Chapel, experts now believe that this is not, in fact, the true site – which remains unknown

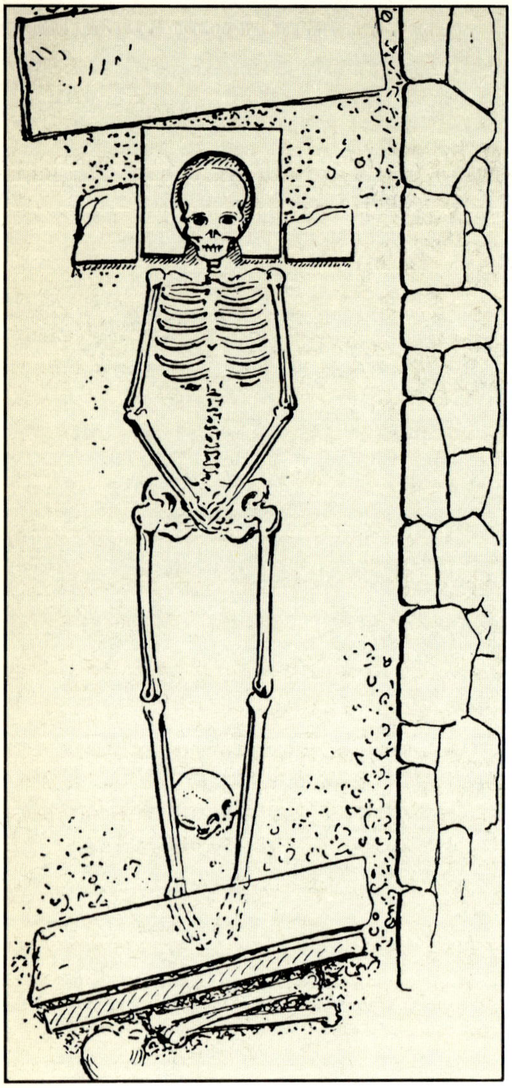

Left: in 1908, while excavating the south wall of the nave, Bond came across this 7-foot (2-metre) skeleton, which had been buried without a coffin, but with a skull between its legs. The reason for this strange method of burial was a complete mystery – until Bond resolved to consult the Company of Avalon

Below: an engraving of the romantic ruins of the abbey church at Glastonbury as they appeared in the early part of the 19th century. When Bond began his excavations, many of the original buildings had completely disappeared; it was all the more extraordinary, then, that he found so many of them through automatic writings

the communicator to clarify this matter, and got the reply: 'Ne [not] Radulphus of Henry the King' – that is Radulphus Fitzstephen. 'Radulphus the Treasurer was a Norman of the time of Thurstan. . . .' Bond was still a little confused by all these Radulphuses, and asked 'Why do you say that Ralph the treasurer was Ralph of King Henry?' In reply he got an irritable blast: 'Rede!' (In other words, 'Read – use your eyes!') 'I said it not. I said not "Ralph of King Henry" but "Ralph ye Norman." ' Then, in an outburst of furious Latin: 'Listen to me, you stupid barbarian! To me, the Emperor, who have been trying to make these things clear to the minds of you Islanders!' It was signed: 'CAESAR'.

It is easy to see that Bond found himself in a very peculiar position. *He* knew the answer to the mystery of the 7-foot (2-metre) skeleton with the second skull between its legs; yet he could not reveal it unless he could also find some documentary evidence to justify it. Understandably, Caroe simply thought Bond was arrogant and dictatorial.

And there was more. Bond had also been told by the 'watchers' that 'Our Abbey was a message in stones. In ye foundations and ye distances be a mystery – the mystery of our Faith, which ye have forgotten.' Now it is believed by some people that many medieval abbeys and cathedrals were built according to some kind of numerical code, enshrining the occult secrets of the ancients. Bond himself became increasingly fascinated by the possibility that Glastonbury Abbey was a code in stone and began the study of gematria, the qabalistic relationship between words and numbers. In 1916, he gave a lecture to the Somerset Archaeological Society entitled: 'The Lady Chapel of Glastonbury Abbey: A study of measures and proportions' about his theory of secret meanings. His audience included his sceptical 'boss', Dean Robinson, who was understandably irritated.

And finally, Bond could bear the secrecy no longer. He decided to tell the whole story – everything that had happened since that first 'sitting' in November 1908. He confessed in a book called *The gate of remembrance*, which came out in 1918. The effect was instantaneous and disastrous. Budgets were cut, a co-director was appointed, Bond found himself obstructed in every possible way and was made the victim of red tape. In 1921 he was reduced to cataloguing and cleaning his earlier finds for £10 a month. In 1922 he received a letter that stated: 'The Council of this Society informs you that you are no longer responsible for the excavations at Glastonbury Abbey and that the Excavation Committee appointed by them is therefore dissolved. . . .'

*Why was the Church of England so opposed to Bond's methods? See page 1046*

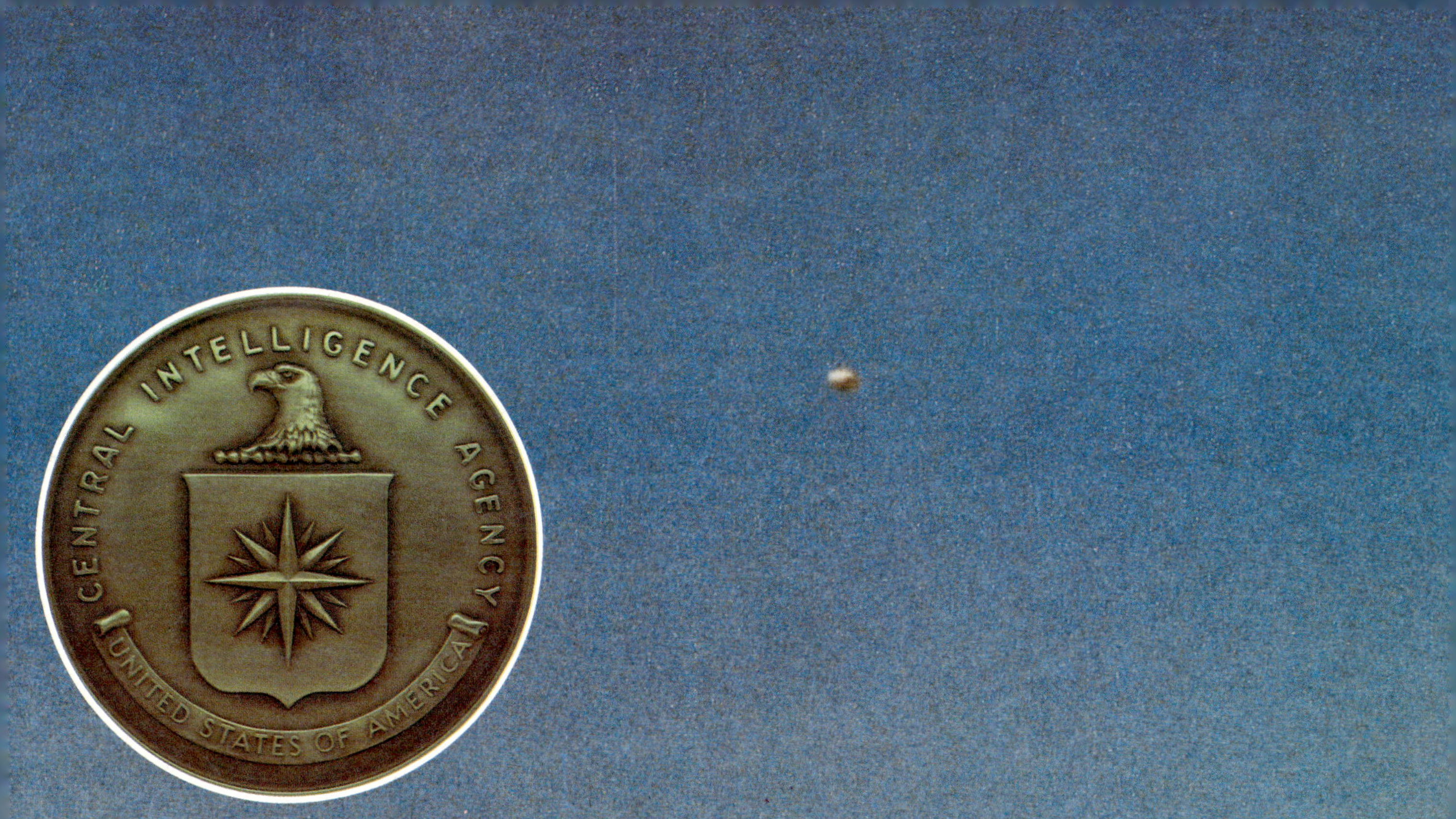


# UFOs: the case for a cover up

**The US government has long denied any interest in UFOs, yet keeps thousands of UFO documents on the secret list. WILLIAM H. SPAULDING tells how the cover was blown – and reveals a bizarre CIA plot to mislead the public**

UFO RESEARCHERS HAVE long maintained that their governments know more about the UFO phenomenon than they officially admit. One reason for thinking this has been the unfailingly sceptical attitude taken by government officials when questioned about any particular sighting – even the best-documented reports are greeted with cries of 'weather balloons' or 'the planet Venus seen under unusual conditions'. Another cause for suspicion has been the peculiar interest that UFOs take in military establishments from time to time. Some, at least, of the infamous men in black (see page 510) may have been genuine government agents, and the thought may linger in many ufologists' minds that the MIB's elusive nature is only the smoke of folklore behind which lurks the sinister fire of clandestine operations. In the United States the idea of a deliberate government attack on ufology was confirmed for many by the publication in 1969 of the Condon Report, widely regarded as at best complacent or at worst wilfully ignorant.

Documents obtained by Ground Saucer Watch (GSW) from the United States government under the Freedom of Information Act now confirm that there has indeed been a cover up – right from the start of the modern UFO era in the late 1940s. But what is revealed by the documents is not that there is a worldwide plot to hide the true nature of UFOs – involving secret contact with extraterrestrials or some gruesome conspiracy against humanity, or some other outlandish suggestion. What is indicated, rather, is that the US government wishes to maintain a certain public *attitude* toward UFOs.

This atmosphere of doubt and derision has been created in a number of ways. Anyone can offer more or less plausible explanations for a UFO sighting: bright planets, unusual atmospheric conditions, meteorites, aircraft and so on. This approach

An unidentified flying object skims over the desert outside Phoenix, Arizona, on 12 September 1972. Checked by computerised enhancement techniques, the photograph has been declared genuine by Ground Saucer Watch. Despite evidence like this, secret government agencies like the CIA (inset: the agency's official seal) deny the existence of UFOs

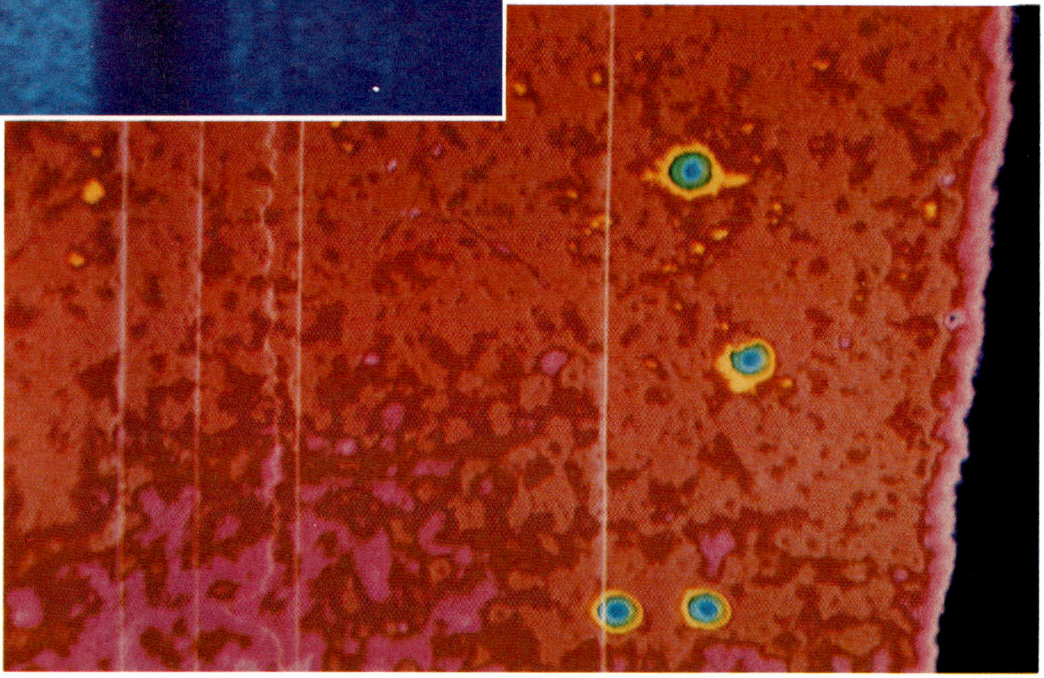

Above: a still from the film shot by Delbert C. Newhouse on 2 July 1952, 7 miles (11 kilometres) north of Tremonton, Utah, USA. Newhouse saw 'gunmetal-coloured objects shaped like two saucers, one inverted on top of the other' near the eastern horizon. Mystified, he shot some 16-millimetre film of them. A few frames have been released to the public, but many more remain in CIA hands. Ground Saucer Watch analysed the available frames with a range of techniques that included colour contrasting (right) – which demonstrated that the objects were indeed solid. Sceptics have claimed the UFOs were birds or planes, but computerised images of these at comparable distances (centre right: a bird; far right: a plane) show quite different characteristics of shape, reflectivity and density. GSW concluded that the images represented craft about 50 feet (15 metres) in diameter and 5 to 7 miles (8 to 11 kilometres) distant

cannot help but be successful, since as many as 95 per cent of alleged UFOs are indeed misinterpretations of known objects. Some sceptical investigators maintain that if these statistics are valid, then *all* UFO reports must represent objects that could be identified, were sufficient information on each sighting available. How can the man in the street argue with logic like that?

The debunking campaign has been successful too because well-known military or government figures have weighed in against the UFO. Most people have an automatic respect for public figures, whose statements are easily accepted. The few researchers who believed that they saw through the screen of official denials were easily dismissed as mavericks or cranks. There was, according to the official line, nothing to research. The government knew about everything there was to be seen in the sky.

But perhaps the cover up was so successful because no one could prove it was going on. There was no hard evidence to back the claim that the government was not being completely honest with the public.

And if the government knows so much, why haven't ex-employees come forward with their stories – revelations far more explosive, potentially, than any political scandal. Yet fewer than a dozen such individuals have come forward.

Despite all this, one's suspicions remain. Over the years GSW has encountered numerous incidents that showed every sign of direct or indirect government interference. Photographs went missing. Ground markings were ploughed under. Occasional witnesses talked about visits from military or intelligence officers who wanted to suppress the story of their UFO encounter. Too many cases came to an abrupt halt because some of the evidence was missing, making it impossible to reach a firm conclusion.

Largely at the insistence of Todd Zechel, GSW's director of research (and himself an ex-member of the intelligence community), it was decided to attack the issue head on – and approach the government directly. In the first place, GSW questioned the US Air Force – with predictable results. Typical replies were that 'the phenomenon does not represent any advanced technology beyond our present capability and . . . poses no direct threat to the United States.' And that 'there is no evidence indicating that sightings categorized as "unidentified" are extraterrestrial vehicles.' This was no more than expected; the next step was to confront the CIA – the agency most likely to be involved in suppressing UFO material. The CIA's reply – in a letter to GSW dated 26 March 1976 – is intriguing in the light of later events:

> In order that you may be aware of the true facts concerning the involvement of the CIA in the investigation of UFO phenomena, let me give you the following brief history. Late in 1952, the National Security Council levied upon the CIA the requirement to determine if the existence of UFOs would create a danger to the security of the United States. The Office of Scientific Intelligence established the Intelligence Advisory Committee to study the matter. That committee made the recommendations [in] the *Robertson Panel Report*. At no time prior to the formation of the Robertson Panel and subsequent to this issuance of the panel's report [in January 1953], has the CIA engaged in the study of UFO phenomena. The *Robertson Panel Report* is the summation of the Agency's interest and involvement in this matter.

The Robertson Panel's conclusions – after an intensive briefing by top airmen, astronomers and several CIA men – were simple. There was no cause for alarm militarily or scientifically, but – significantly for our case – the panel concluded that 'the continued emphasis on the reporting of these phenomena does, in these perilous times, result in a threat to the orderly functioning of the protective organs of the body politic.' Their recommendations were framed accordingly – debunk UFOs and educate people to recognise aerial phenomena.

Above: research director Todd Zechel (left) and director William H. Spaulding (right) of Ground Saucer Watch, discussing the UFO problem

In fact, the CIA did not let the matter drop there and then in 1953. Searches through the National Archives had shown that many reports were missing from the files. Dozens more letters to other agencies and even to the White House simply elicited the same official response – essentially, that UFOs did not exist. Why, then, the missing documents? When GSW made specific requests under the Freedom of Information Act a few papers were released – and so highly 'sanitised' that only a mind reader could have made sense of some of them. GSW then decided to attack in the courts. After 14 months of gruelling legal action the government released, on 15 December 1978, close to 1000 pages of documents. It was a major victory for GSW and ufology in general. What do the papers show?

First, that CIA involvement in UFOs actually pre-dates the National Security Council directive to set up what became the Robertson Panel – indeed it was the CIA that urged an investigation on the Council! Second, the implications for psychological warfare attract considerable attention. As one memo puts it, 'a fair proportion of our population is mentally conditioned to the acceptance of the incredible. In this fact lies the potential for the touching-off of mass hysteria and panic.' The third concern is with the vulnerability of US air defences: 'At any moment of attack . . . we cannot . . . distinguish hardware from phantom. . . .' The use of the word 'phantom' is interesting here. For another memo, from the Deputy Director for Intelligence, CIA, dated November 1952, says bluntly:

> Sightings of unexplained objects at great altitudes and traveling at high speeds in the vicinity of major US defense installations are of such a nature that they are not attributable to natural phenomena or known types of aerial vehicles.

In the light of that it is not surprising that when Edward Tauss, then Acting Chief of the Weapons and Equipment Division of the Office of Scientific Intelligence, recommended that the CIA 'continue' (*not* 'begin') coverage of the subject in August 1952, he should add:

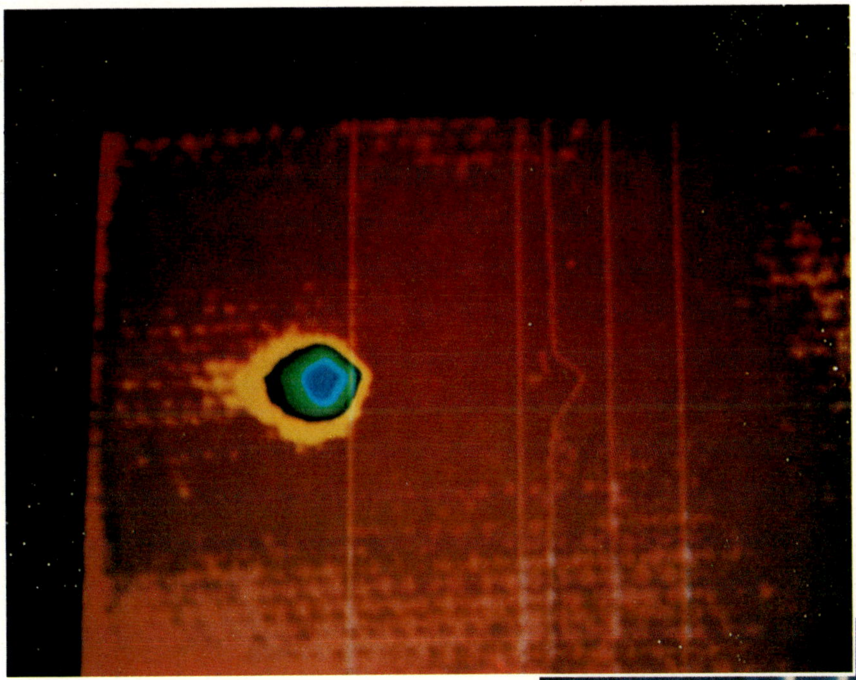

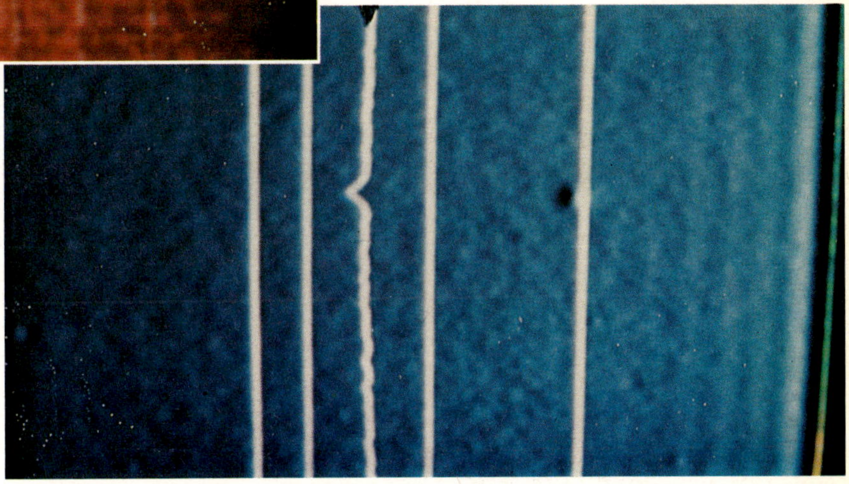

> It is strongly urged, however, that no indication of CIA interest or concern reach the press or public, in view of their probably alarmist tendencies to accept such interest as 'confirmatory' of the soundness of 'unpublished facts in the hands of the US government'.

It is clear then that the government – or the CIA at least – believed in the reality of the UFO phenomenon. It was also alarmed by it. And it was determined to keep what it did know to itself.

Nor was the report of the Robertson Panel the last word, though the CIA pretended to accept its findings. The US Air Force, after all, maintained Project Blue Book until 1969, after the Condon Committee published its findings – though whether Blue Book was ever told the whole truth either by the USAF itself or by other defence agencies remains in

Right: the last members of Project Blue Book, the US Air Force's full-time UFO investigation unit, disbanded in 1969 while under the leadership of Major Hector Quintanilla (seated). The project's tiny staff was unable to deal in any depth with the thousands of UFO reports it received every year, suggesting that the USAF was dragging its feet over the UFO question. But the more likely explanation is that the real research was being done in secret by the CIA, leaving Blue Book as a public relations front

## The marine, the CIA and the UFO

One of the oddest UFO cases on record is the 1952 sighting by US Marine Ralph Mayher (top). It is odd not because of the sighting itself, which was as 'normal' as any UFO event, but because of what happened afterward to Mayher and the film he managed to take.

Ralph Mayher had heard that on the night of 28 July 1952 a couple named Goldstein had seen a flying saucer near their home. He was an experienced movie photographer and was interested in UFOs, so he arranged to meet the Goldsteins the next day and rented a camera – he had a theory that saucers sometimes appear on consecutive nights. At 9.30 p.m. on 29 July Mayher heard a woman across the street shout that a UFO was in view. The Goldsteins and another neighbour, Herman Stern, also saw the object, which remained visible over the ocean for about three minutes. Mayher managed to shoot only some 40 frames of film because his view was obscured by trees and buildings. The object was travelling horizontally toward the witnesses then 'turned' and shot away.

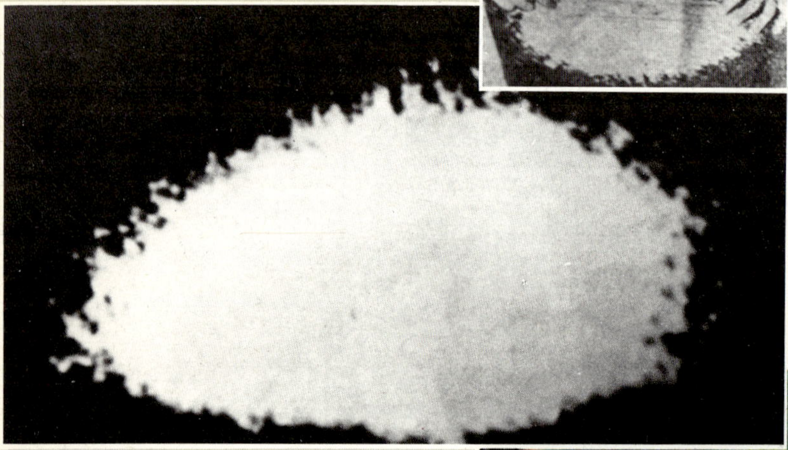

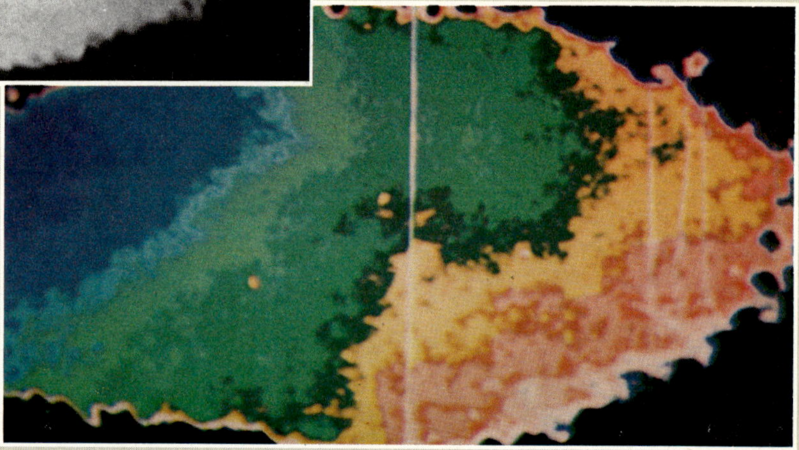

Mayher had his film processed at once and, as his unit commander had no objections, released some frames to the Miami press (centre) and even recorded a radio interview. But within 48 hours, USAF investigators were on the scene and threw a security blanket over the case. Mayher was visited by a number of men with CIA credentials, who apparently told him to keep quiet about the event. On enquiry Mayher was also told that the USAF thought the 'pinpoints of light' (*sic*) too small to analyse properly. But the film was never returned.

Perhaps the strangest part of the story is that while well-informed UFO investigators like Major Donald Keyhoe heard nothing of the film, ace debunker Dr Donald Menzel soon became familiar with it. With surreal inventiveness, Menzel said it showed a cobweb. GSW's computer analysis (bottom) indicates that the object is solid, 50 feet (15 metres) in diameter, and travelling at 2500 miles per hour (4000 km/h).

some doubt. The probable fate of the film taken by US Navy Warrant Officer Delbert C. Newhouse in 1952 – the 'Tremonton movie' that was shown to the Robertson Panel – is one indication of the CIA's true reaction to the evidence.

This film has been subject to several attempts at debunking. According to the witness, it shows a number of unusual craft travelling at enormous speed some 10 miles (16 kilometres) from the camera. Newhouse's report of the incident (he was a trained Navy photographer) is confirmed by GSW's computerised tests on the film – as it was by the USAF photo laboratory at Wright-Patterson AFB, who first analysed it. The film was then handed to the Naval Photographic Interpretation Center (NavPIC) at Anacostia, Maryland, and subjected to over 1000 man-hours of study. The Navy had no explanation for the objects but said they appeared to be 'self-luminous' spheres travelling at up to 7560 miles per hour (12,096 km/h). The Robertson Panel argued over the film for about two hours. They were also shown film of seagulls giving intense reflections of light in bright sunshine. The panel duly reported that 'the objects were considered strongly to represent birds.'

Who laid on that film of seagulls? Was it the CIA, experienced hands as they were at manipulation and suggestion? What they did not do was stop studying films of UFOs. As soon as the Robertson Panel had reported, NavPIC was dissolved. Some of its members, however, were moved to the CIA to form the National Photographic Interpretation Center (NPIC). Material dating from at least 1950 is kept there. Says GSW's Todd Zechel: 'There is a direct link between NavPIC's work on the Tremonton analysis and the decision of the CIA to place the analysis programme under its direct authority. In other words, rather than thinking the Tremonton analysis was in error, as has been purported, the CIA was impressed enough to immediately transfer the project to its headquarters.'

### A cover for the CIA

Small wonder, then, that the USAF's Project Blue Book got such short shrift. According to Todd Zechel, Blue Book was 'in reality . . . no more than a PR front, primarily covering for the secret research being conducted by the CIA. . . . to give Blue Book full support would have been a waste, since it would have been duplicating research already being conducted by the CIA. Therefore, and for the most part unwittingly, Blue Book's façade enabled the CIA to pull off the greatest propaganda fraud in history.'

The documents obtained by GSW support the view that the CIA has persisted in UFO research. Among them are numerous reports, dutifully filed by US embassies abroad, of UFO sightings: 25 cases from Spain alone in one nine-month period between 1973 and 1974, a case from Portugal, multiple events in Tunisia in 1976 with many witnesses, radar tracking and police reports. 'A very concerned Chief of Military Security, General Balma' wanted to know if the US Sixth Fleet could 'shed any light on who or what they might be'. Not only was this – and innumerable other cases – being reported in 1976, seven years after the US government had supposedly given up its interest in UFOs in the wake of the Condon Report, but all UFO reports from the embassies are sent to the CIA – and the even more shadowy Defense Intelligence Agency, the National Security Council, the Secretary of Defense and the Secretary of State.

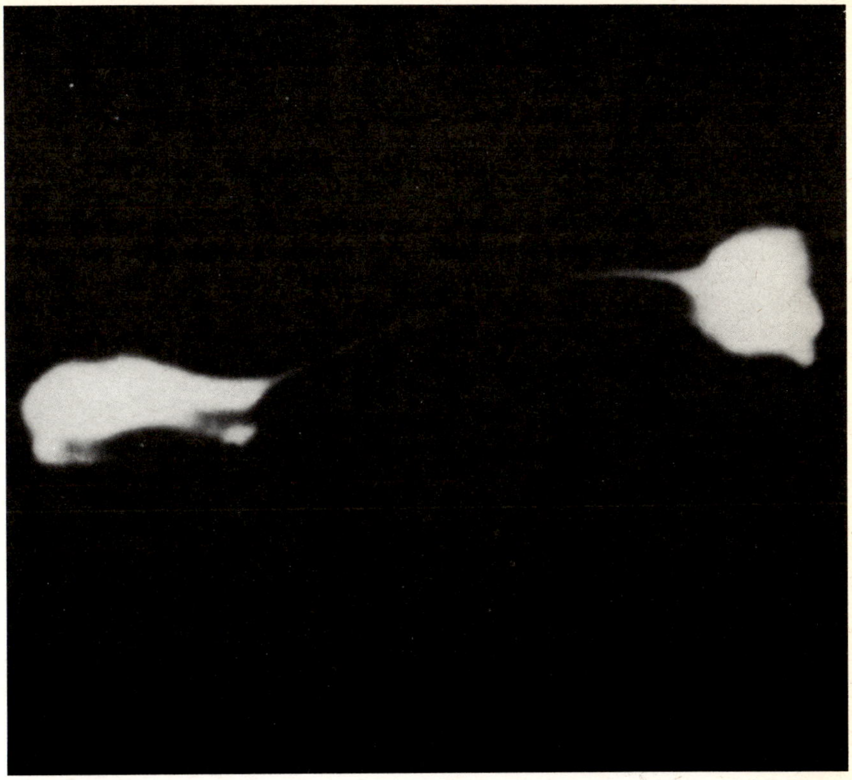

An unexplained mass of light seen over Ibiza in May 1974, which remained stationary for a brief period before rapidly climbing to a high altitude and vanishing. Reports such as this have been collected by the CIA from all over the world. Despite official claims that the agency ceased to have an interest in UFOs in 1953, documents have been obtained from CIA archives detailing sightings as late as 1976

Of course it is in the government's interests to pretend that it can identify everything in the sky: the security of the Western Alliance depends on that assumption. But the evidence indicates that the cover up does not stop at a desire to prevent alarm and despondency from spreading among the people. Just the opposite, if you happen to be a witness to a UFO: agents from the CIA Directorate of Operations (Clandestine Services) and Domestic Operations Division (sometimes called the 'Contact Division') have been known to harass, intimidate and silence people (see box).

Further to this, a more sinister game is perhaps being played out. For while the intelligence services attempt to deflate the UFO controversy, it would seem that they are also helping to feed it. It is to this aspect of the cover up, and the possible reasons for it, that we turn next.

*Are UFOs the secret weapons of the CIA's psychological warfare experts? See page 1086*

# A very strange place

**Were the messages in the Glastonbury scripts really from the spirit world – or did they, as Frederick Bligh Bond himself believed, originate in his own unconscious? COLIN WILSON assesses this strange case**

THE STORY OF THE DISMISSAL of Frederick Bligh Bond from the excavations at Glastonbury is one of the seediest tales in the history of British archaeology. The abbey trustees even ordered that all Bond's books should be removed from sale in the abbey book store, including the purely technical *Architectural handbook to Glastonbury Abbey*. The Church of England was alarmed to discover that his highly successful investigations and his remarkable discoveries were the result of 'seances' with long-dead monks, and it went out of its way to prevent Bond carrying out any further excavations.

Bond lived for almost another quarter-century; he spent much of this time in America, and did a great deal of valuable and interesting work in psychical research. But he was a lonely and embittered man, whose heart remained in Glastonbury Abbey. The trustees even banned him from the abbey grounds. In 1937 a group of American friends put up the money for more excavations at Glastonbury, to test some of the information given by the 'watchers' of Glastonbury, and the trustees gave the group permission. But the moment they heard that

agonised over the question for three years. They ended up by stating that the claims of Spiritualism are probably true, and that there is nothing in the idea of 'communication with the dead' that contradicts the ideas of Christianity. But the report ended with a curious footnote: 'The committee do not recommend that any publicity be given to this.' The Archbishop agreed, and suppressed it. The report was not finally published until March 1979.

### Depths of the unconscious

Curiously, where the unfortunate Frederick Bligh Bond is concerned, the absurdity is that he did *not* believe he was communicating with the dead. The title of his book, *The gate of remembrance*, tells us what he had finally come to believe: that his own unconscious mind had somehow gained access to a vast store of unconscious memory about Glastonbury. He wrote: 'From the depths of the subconscious mind, [the power of intuition] has evoked these images. . . .'

It was understandable that Bond should take such a view. He was a member of the Society for Psychical Research, and a friend of Sir William Barrett, who had written a classic book on dowsing. And what fascinated Barrett was that a good dowser seems to possess a form of 'second sight' (or, as Barrett preferred to call it, 'cryptesthesia'). A certain female dowser, for example, was not only able to pinpoint the exact location of an underground cistern, but was also able to

Bond was involved they cancelled it. He died, poor and forgotten, in 1945.

The situation is absurd, almost unbelievable. Between 1909 and 1920 this man proved that his unorthodox methods could lead to spectacular results. Almost single-handed, he rediscovered secrets that had been buried for four centuries. But these discoveries – such as the Edgar Chapel – utilised only a small part of the information obtained from the 'communicators'. Other communications – including some he received after leaving Glastonbury – included information about the tomb of King Arthur, secret passageways, the Holy Grail and several stores of buried treasure. There is still enough assorted information to keep archaeologists busy for another 20 years. The most fascinating part of Bond's life-work still remains to be completed. Yet the abbey trustees are apparently determined that it shall not be completed.

Why is the Church of England still so hostile to this whole notion of 'psychic archaeology'? No doubt because to accept it would imply an acceptance of some of the doctrines of 'Spiritualism'. And this is a matter about which the Church seems determined not to give any definite pronouncements. In 1936 the Archbishop of Canterbury, Cosmo Lang, commissioned a special report on Spiritualism, and his committee

Glastonbury is one of England's most ancient and mysterious sacred places – so perhaps it is not surprising that it should have been the site of an early and successful experiment in psychic archaeology. The Tor (above left) is a conspicuous landmark that is believed by many to be a centre of some kind of spiritual power. Legend has it that the Holy Thorn within the abbey grounds (above) is descended from one planted by St Joseph of Arimathea, who visited Britain with the infant Jesus, his nephew. King Arthur (left) was reputedly buried in the abbey nave; he lies sleeping, ready to come to the aid of Britain in its hour of need. The Chalice Well, at the foot of the Tor, is also part of the Arthurian legend; its cover (right), designed by Frederick Bligh Bond, carries the ancient symbol of the *vesica piscis*, which represents the source of life

## Where was Avalon?

Avalon, the Isle of Apples, elusive place of enchantments, where the soil yields crops without sowing and whose happy inhabitants enjoy eternal life, is an integral part of the Arthurian tradition. It was to Avalon, so the legend goes, that Arthur was taken after his last battle, and there he lives on, ready one day to come to the aid of the Celtic peoples and restore them to their rightful sovereignty over their land.

That, at least, is the substance of the so-called 'Breton hope' – and as long as Arthur's burial place remained unknown, this hope continued to be nurtured. But in 1191 came the discovery at Glastonbury of a tomb carrying the inscription 'Here lies the famous King Arthur, buried in the Isle of Avalon'. The Breton hope seemed dashed.

Is Glastonbury really Avalon? The group of hills surrounding Glastonbury has been known as 'the Isle of Avalon' since the opening of the alleged tomb of Arthur, and possibly for much longer. And in the early Christian period, when sea level is known to have been much higher than it is today, the hills and the high ground between them would almost have formed an island.

But the proof is not conclusive – and some people still cherish a faint hope that, after all, the magical island dreamed of by the ancients really exists.

describe exactly what it looked like, as if her eyes could see through the ground.

But some dowsers have been able to do even stranger things. The Abbé Mermet – a perfectly respectable Catholic – was able to locate all kinds of things simply by dangling a pendulum over a map. So, for example, in 1934 the Marquis de la Chevalerie asked the Abbé if he could help him locate the bones of one of his ancestors. The Abbé dangled his pendulum over a plan of the chapel, and replied that he could find no trace of the ancestor, but that under the altar there were the bones of another man at a depth of 6 feet (2 metres), together with some tin, copper and gold. The Marquis gave orders for excavation, and they discovered a coffin containing the bones of Saint Victor, presented by Pope Gregory XVI; the coffin was embossed in tin, copper and gold, just as the Abbé Mermet had described.

Mermet was also successful in locating minerals, oil, treasure and sunken ships, as well as an expedition lost at the North Pole. But the discovery of the bones of Saint Victor is relevant here because it is so similar to what Bond and Bartlett did. And if we can accept – like Sir William Barrett – that dowsing is a peculiar faculty of the unconscious mind, then there really seems no reason why Bond and Bartlett should not have used some form of unconscious dowsing to find the Edgar Chapel.

But anyone who reads *The gate of remembrance* will see that this raises an interesting problem. For the various monks who communicated with Bond are all very distinct personalities. There was Ambrosius the cellarer, who told charming stories about the

Above: Cosmo Lang, Archbishop of Canterbury, who, in 1936, commissioned a report on Spiritualism. The findings were, surprisingly, not unfavourable – but the report ended with the curious recommendation that no publicity be given to the investigation

Left: the Abbot's Kitchen, built 'to make feast on grete feast-days', according to a communicator named Ricardus. Another monk, Ambrosius the cellarer – who, Ricardus remarks pointedly, 'isne a scholar' – tells how one of the monks drank himself unconscious in front of Henry VIII (right), when he was being entertained by the Abbot. The abbey was subsequently destroyed by Henry

alcohol drunk by the monks (and how one of them drank himself unconscious in front of Henry VIII); Peter Lightfoot, the clock-maker, who told how the abbey clock came to be built because the monks of Glastonbury became jealous when they heard about the one in Wells Cathedral; Johannes Bryant, who has beautiful descriptions of nature and of the abbey's mint garden. Then there was Abbot Bere, who described how he decided to build the Loretto Chapel. He was a huge, fat man and, as he was riding along on his mule, he was attacked by 'rude men', and he rolled down a steep slope. He said a hasty prayer to Our Lady, and his cloak caught on a thorn bush, preventing him rolling over the edge – whereupon he made a vow to build the Loretto Chapel to the Virgin. . . . The 'watchers' also told the sad story of the miscalculation that led to the downfall of Glastonbury Abbey. When Abbot Bere died, the King's adviser Cardinal Wolsey appointed Richard Whyting Abbot, and advised him to invite the King to Glastonbury to try to gain his goodwill. It was a disastrous mistake. The King was royally entertained; but when he saw the abbey's treasures and its lands and farms, he licked his lips and calculated how much all this would add to the royal treasury. So after Henry's break with Rome, Thomas Cromwell had no difficulty 'framing' the monks on a number of false charges; and Henry seized the abbey and destroyed it.

As we read stories as circumstantial as this, it becomes very difficult to swallow the theory that they originate from some kind of 'racial memory'. Either the story is an amusing invention of Bond's unconscious mind, or it is a genuine communication from someone who was there at the time.

Yet the Glastonbury scripts contain one clue that implies that the truth may be even more fascinating and complex. At one point the monk Johannes says,

> Why cling I to that which is not? It is I, and it is not I, butt parte of me which dwelleth in the past and is bound to that which my carnal soul loved and called 'home' these many years. Yet I, Johannes, amm of many partes and ye better parte doeth other things – *Laus, Laus Deo!* – only that part which remembereth clingeth like memory to what it seeth not. . . .

## Multiple personalities

'I, Johannes, amm of many partes. . . .' This is a puzzling statement, yet one that is supported, for example, by the baffling evidence of so-called 'multiple personalities' – people like the heroine of *The three faces of Eve*, who periodically lose their memory and become a completely different person. Perhaps our greatest error is in thinking of ourselves as 'individuals', single and indivisible. Perhaps every one of us contains a whole crowd of different people. And perhaps the ghosts that haunt the scenes of old tragedies are disjointed personality fragments, left behind like a fragment of tape recording.

But in assessing the evidence about the 'watchers', the 'Company of Avalon' that spoke to Bond through automatic writing, we should also bear in mind that Glastonbury is a place of power, a religious site chosen because the ground seems to concentrate some unknown force – possibly something as simple as a vortex in the Earth's magnetic field. If the late T. C. Lethbridge was correct to believe that 'ghosts' are some kind of tape-recording (see page 654) then perhaps Glastonbury is a vast repository of recordings from the past. If so, it seems reasonable to suppose that other ancient sites conceal similar stores of information – and, on this hypothesis, it might be worthwhile for archaeologists to consider trying to develop methods of 'tuning in' to this secret knowledge. Perhaps Bond's real importance is that he was the first man to stumble on a treasure house that will be explored, documented and catalogued by a new generation of researchers.

Above: the cathedral clock at Wells. The monks told how improvements were carried out at Glastonbury to rival the beauty of Wells, 'new and faire with carven stone'

**Further reading**

Frederick Bligh Bond, *The gate of remembrance*, Blackwell 1918

Frederick Bligh Bond, *The Company of Avalon*, Blackwell 1924

# The journey of the soul

**Do the souls of the dead live on? Do they go to heaven, hell, purgatory – or to some other, as yet unknown, plane of existence? And if they do continue to exist, how do we know about their experiences? PAUL BEARD surveys the evidence for the afterlife**

EVEN AMONG PEOPLE who believe in some kind of an afterlife, alleged communications from the 'other side' are frequently regarded with suspicion. Perhaps it is natural to ascribe such accounts to the result of wishful thinking or unjustified hopes and fears (see page 681). For this reason most people are unaware of the enormous amount of material purporting to describe the next world from people *who are now there*. But if, for a moment, we suspend our disbelief, what emerges from this material is not only evidence for an afterlife but an amazingly consistent description of what it is like to be dead.

Obviously these accounts cannot be checked, and examining them in an open, unprejudiced way is not easy. The basic issue is one of testimony: who are the witnesses – the communicators and the living people who receive their messages?

### Bearing witness

Although there are many 'communicators' and just as many 'mediums' or sensitives, not all bear the marks of good witnesses. If the dead speak to us at all, their task cannot be easy; but this does not mean that we should feel obliged to accept any communication no matter how garbled or trivial. We are entitled to listen to only the best – the most balanced, consistent and rational – accounts. In England the Society for Psychical Research (SPR) and the College for Psychic Studies have accrued a vast amount of material, which seems to emanate from intelligent and honest sources, that has been given to reputable mediums over the past 100 years or so. In the end we ourselves have to judge the communications on their own merits and on the responses they awaken in us. But a good witness is worthy of a good listener. So what do the majority of these accounts tell us?

If we do indeed survive death, then by definition the surviving part of us must already be present within us during our life on earth. The first feature of the accounts is that we do indeed take with us the same memory bank, and the same emotions and mental concepts that we had before death. We start from where we left off. But which of us survives: the tired elderly man, or the one in vigorous prime, or even the one full of illusory youthful ideals? The answer, judging by the mass of evidence, points to our having available the private, inward contents of *all* these various 'past selves'; we can reside in them temporarily, or hold on to one aspect or the other. All these imperfect selves have made us what we are; we are said to meet them all in turn again after death, in order to understand them as they really were, and profit by re-experiencing them.

A good witness is Mrs Winifred Coombe-Tennant, known in psychic circles as 'Mrs Willett'. In life she was one of the first English women JPs and a delegate to the League of Nations. She also took part as a non-professional sensitive in the cross-correspondences, which form a highlight in the multiplicity of evidence collected by the SPR (see page 478). After her death, medium Geraldine Cummins received an enormous amount of material (in the form of automatic writing) purporting to come from the discarnate Mrs Coombe-Tennant. Much of this describes the afterlife as she had experienced it. Of the 'many selves' enigma she says:

> A human being consists of a number of selves or aspects with a primary self, the total of a sum in arithmetic. . . . We only become unified in spirit on the higher level.

Dying, it seems, is not the absolute event most people fear; largely, it appears to be a state of altered consciousness. Evidence points to it being harder after death to get rid of the old earthly self than we had supposed. The same personal limitations continue until we resolve them. Death does not in itself change us; it gives us a different kind of opportunity to change ourselves.

### In the seventh heaven

In spiritualistic communications, life after death is often described as a progress through seven spheres, each of a more rarified and spiritually invigorating nature than the last. The seven spheres – or mansions, or staging posts – basically represent levels of consciousness, and any of these levels is reached only by a widening and deepening of the moral nature. One is helped by teachers of superior moral stature who have progressed, so to speak, beyond the scope of recent arrivals, but who adapt themselves temporarily to make themselves understood. After death one must realise that life continues as a process of learning.

The great majority of communicators describe the death process itself as one of peacefulness and freedom from pain, even if, during the last hours, the physical body had shown every outward appearance of distress. Communicators often say this apparent pain

Left: *The garden of earthly delights* by Hieronymus Bosch. He saw the average man's ideal world as totally physical – and, ultimately, totally degrading

Below: the traditional Christian belief in a day of reckoning, as portrayed in Fra Angelico's *The day of judgement*

Bottom: T.E. Lawrence, better known as 'Lawrence of Arabia', who died in 1935. In life a brilliant yet difficult man, he was obliged to confront certain unappealing aspects of his character – 'the monk and the prig' – in the afterlife, in order to progress to higher planes

did not register with them. They say death is a gradual withdrawing, often accompanied by alternating periods of sleep or unconsciousness. Then they describe 'waking up' and being greeted by those they had deeply loved who had died previously – and also by others, familiar or not yet familiar, who will be found to know them intimately, even their secret selves. These are not angels sitting in judgement, but more highly developed spirits. Frequently an encounter with them is found to be disturbing. As one newly dead doctor of divinity is purported to have said of such a meeting:

> He evidently regarded my whole life on earth – which hitherto I have thought of as being so important – as mere preparation, a preliminary to the real work I have to do here. That has been one of the greatest surprises.

Experiences are, apparently, by no means uniform, and naturally enough are partly determined by old patterns of behaviour and thinking. This first plane of experience is

exactly – and literally – what you make of it. According to all communicators, the imagination is supreme; just by thinking of something it appears. Some have given this plane the term 'ideo-plastic', meaning creation through ideas alone. Some create around them past environments of home and possessions that they are unwilling to relinquish. The important key to understanding this plane is that matter is now reported to be of a finer texture, highly malleable to thought. Some, who had not believed in an afterlife, even fail to recognise they are dead. They feel they must be in a vivid dream.

But willing pupils in this environment – called the *summerland*, says the posthumous Frederic Myers – can create what they most desired on earth. But this is not 'heaven' as more enlightened communicators hasten to point out. Summerland in time shows that these 'dreams' are after all not wise enough, nor spiritual enough; they are gradually found to be too selfish and materialistic. People may find that they are seeking little more than a kind of perpetual summer holiday. Yet many accounts stress that the purpose of summerland is to enable its inhabitants to find that much of what they thought valuable is valueless.

But what sort of world does a man find around himself, if his life has been devoted to selfish gain, or if he has fallen prey to crime and violence? The habits of his mind remain the same and so, as in life, he finds he can contribute very little to his after-death environment. His self-absorption has cut him off from being able to enjoy any wider, disinterested feelings, which make up true companionship. As in the summerland his environment reflects himself – and his poverty of soul assumes an awful 'reality'. Many accounts tell of darkness, mist, bare earth and a hovel to live in. This is *winterland.*

In his continuing selfishness such a spirit often feels anger and indignation for his lot. Neither he nor others in that condition can please one another, for all are equally selfish. More unfortunately, he often treats with contempt those who enter his world from their own superior realms of freedom, who wish to help and teach him how to change. But frequently such a person is said to stop his ears, much as he often stopped them in life to the promptings of his conscience.

Yet it would be hard to find a man who is totally degraded, and each of these unfortunates who finds himself in winterland is there for only as long as he refuses to listen to the other, higher part of himself. Those who try to help him are really looking for this better self, however deeply overlaid. It is stressed that these individuals are not being 'punished'; their suffering stems only from their own nature as they have created it; and it is fully in their power to regenerate it. They can discover and build on their latent qualities, just as can those who find themselves in the summerland. And just as summerland is not 'heaven', neither is winterland 'hell'. Both states exist because of the individual's inner self. When he becomes more spiritual they are transcended.

Those who have outgrown the summerland state pass on to the *first heaven.* Here selfless ideals can be developed in a life shared with those who also wish to serve others. Its joys are not passive, however; they are certainly to be enjoyed, yet used strenuously to obtain growth of spiritual stature. But this level of consciousness is superior to that of the summerland. The soul is shown, step by step, its nature as it was when on earth. This self-knowledge includes the revelation and re-evaluation of all faults, errors and blindnesses – many of them, even at this stage, hard to accept. Faults easy to excuse on earth, or to hide from oneself, now show up in their true shape.

The prophet Mohammad journeys to the seven heavens, as depicted in an early 16th-century Persian painting. The idea that the afterlife is a continuing process, involving the soul's ascent through various stages of enlightenment, is a belief common to many different religions

## As others see us

This process is usually named the *judgement*. It is widely reported by communicators that the judgement is not made by God (as in the popular idea of 'the day of judgement'), nor by some superior being sitting in condemnation, but is in some way self-induced. To see, and then to have to condemn oneself, is painful, the more so since many faults now revealed were formerly unsuspected. The posthumous T.E. Lawrence is said to have recognised the monk and the prig in him, which had led him to reject women's values, and brought about what he now says is a travesty of the man he could have been. The judgement shows what one has made of oneself, and it is more often than not a painful experience. But once recognised these faults can be transcended, creating a different self.

The judgement usually extends over a considerable period of experiences and adjustments; it also of course includes recognition of those qualities and actions that are worthy – in this sense life in the first heaven is part of the judgement. Though judgement is carried out by oneself, loving companions are there to explain, support and give guidance for necessary corrective steps. W. V. Blewett, a former agricultural scientist, is believed to have said, 'Here we receive absolute justice, such as can never be possible on earth.'

Motive is shown to be paramount. Hence one's actions are shown as they really were, not as one preferred to think them; and whatever joy or suffering they brought about in others is now exactly felt and experienced oneself. This can be very painful without the deadening effect of the physical body, in the same way that emotions felt in dreams – love, fear, disgust – are sharply defined as if suddenly in focus, whereas the same emotions felt in our everyday lives are muffled by the demands and stimuli of the outside world. Here there is no 'outside world' – it is all 'inside', all experienced with the awful, or beautiful, clarity of dreaming.

From what we can piece together, the various 'stages' of the afterlife can be experienced one after the other – and most frequently are – but sometimes the discarnate spirit can work at several tasks at the same time or go from one to the other alternately. There seems to be no rigid plan to which every person must adhere; as on earth, all people are individuals with different needs, and these are allowed for.

But most communicators express difficulty in conveying to us that their surroundings, seemingly much as on earth, are actually part of a wonderful mental world, and are much more malleable to thought than dense earth matter. All is permeated by the thoughts, feelings and beliefs of those at a common level of consciousness. The mental-emotional environment to which one belongs is not isolated, however; it is also influenced or 'played upon' by the consciousness of those at higher levels, in a way that is as sustaining and invigorating as sunlight.

Above: a Hindu statue of an *apsaras*, who is believed to gratify men's sexual desires in paradise. Most ancient religions – with the exception of puritan Christianity – imagine paradise, or heaven, to comprise endless feasting, drinking, idleness and sex in scented gardens. The indications are that the first stage of the afterlife is indeed a place where one's dreams come true

Left: William Blake's illustration for Robert Blair's *The grave*, 1813, showing the newly freed spirit rising from the shrouded corpse, keys in hand, to open the way to a blissful future

How far and how much we can see is, as always, bounded by our own limited consciousness; being played upon from higher levels is aimed at helping us gradually to enlarge our vision, somewhat in the way we learn on earth from a teacher's entire personality and not merely from the facts he passes on. But exactly what is learned on this plane is difficult for us to imagine. It can hardly be of a mechanical or practical nature for physical objects no longer exist. And it is unlikely, in the circumstances, to entail philosophical discussion about the 'nature of life'. Learning must be confined to lessons of a moral or spiritual nature, as indeed many communicators describe. But such a formidable course of study begins only when the student is ready – and eager – for it.

Each succeeding level is shut off from us until we are in a fit state to appreciate it. It is possible that some souls never rise above the 'summer holiday' plane of the summerland. It seems more likely, however, that everyone progresses to higher planes, but at his or her own pace.

These events – life in the summerland, winterland, the first heaven, and the process of the judgement – form what is meant by the 'astral' or 'desire' world of consciousness. Each man now begins to learn that it is necessary to leave this plane behind, to shed it in order to win the freedom to dwell in the most spiritual parts of himself.

**Surrender of the self**

The experience that many believe now awaits him is known as the *second death*. Each must now gradually become as willing to yield up his present values as, in very many cases, he was ready in the end to shed his earthly body on death. His desires in the astral world, however much they have included love of others, good fellowship and companionship, have also, as he now begins to see with certainty, really largely centred upon himself. Even when he loved others, much of this was for his own emotional satisfaction. Now in the second death he sheds all he has valued; his achievements and all the things he has won in the desire world (of which earth too is a part) have now to be given up. His gifts no longer exist for him but for the glory of God. Conan Doyle, in describing his own posthumous experience, calls this transition 'terrible and marvellous', adding that 'there are no trimmings on a man after the second death.' Yet this traumatic experience prepares the student, shorn of his most dearly held pretensions, for the next stage in his progress. Through this he can begin to find his 'true self'; a larger, more complete being – one, he discovers, for which he has always been searching.

*What happens to the soul next? And do we ever come back from the afterlife? See page 1094*

# The curse on Killakee

**From the days of the Dublin Hell Fire Club to the times of the Troubles, the history of Killakee House was stained by violence and bloodshed. FRANK SMYTH tells the story of this disturbed past and its modern legacy: hauntings by a frightening supernatural beast**

THE VICTORIAN WRITER E. Bulwer-Lytton used the phrase *Haunters and haunted* as a title for a celebrated story. He implied by the phrase that there was a definite relationship between the phenomena witnessed at a haunted house and the people who witnessed them – it was not a matter of chance that one person should see a ghost while another did not do so.

This certainly seems to be true in many well-attested poltergeist cases. These disturbances frequently centre on adolescents, and several researchers go so far as to claim that in such cases the 'haunters' emanate from the minds of the 'haunted' themselves, and are simply physical manifestations of teenage traumas. In other cases the person most closely involved in the phenomena appears to act as a catalyst for an already well-established haunting, fanning its embers into flame by his mere presence.

A combination of these factors may have been present when Killakee House in County Dublin became the centre of a veritable storm of psychic activity in the late 1960s and early 1970s. The onset of the phenomena occurred when new residents moved in, and ended when they left.

A story by Edward Bulwer-Lytton (below) suggests that hauntings can be caused by their 'victims'. Did something like this happen at Killakee House?

Killakee lies in the foothills of the Wicklow Mountains, overlooking the city of Dublin. Killakee House, built in the early 18th century as the dower house of the Massey family, is a robust stone building with a small tower. Behind the house rises the steep slope of Montpellier Hill, its scrubby grass worn bare by the feet of tourists hardy enough to make the ascent to the top. On the summit stands the stone shell of a fire-ravaged hunting lodge, constructed by the Earl of Rosse in the 18th century. It was used by him and such 'bucks' as Harry Barry, first Lord Santry, and Richard 'Burnchapel' Whaley as the headquarters of the Dublin Hell Fire Club – a close imitation of the contemporary English version founded by Sir Francis Dashwood.

Rosse had a cruel sense of humour and a hatred of black cats. He used to hold court at the Eagle Tavern on Cork Hill in Dublin. On one occasion, to frighten the local inhabitants, he doused a black cat in spirits, set it alight and watched it run screaming down the hill. Dubliners swore that it was the Devil himself.

There is strong evidence that Rosse's brutal and puerile humour was given play at the hunting lodge on Montpellier Hill. On one occasion, after a black mass, he put a black cat in the seat of honour when Satan failed to turn up in person. It was also said that a half-witted dwarf with a twisted body and unnaturally large head was beaten to death by Rosse and his cronies, shortly before the lodge burned down in the 1750s.

Rosse's friends often lodged with him in Killakee House and violent scenes often took place there. The Irish rakes were addicted to pistol duelling (one of the first questions asked by a prospective father-in-law of a noble suitor was 'do you blaze?', meaning 'do you fight duels?'). At least three deaths from duelling took place in the grounds.

### Violence renewed

After a long interval that was relatively untroubled, there was again bloodshed at the house in the early 20th century. The house was then occupied by Countess Constance Markievicz, the 'Red Countess'. A friend of the mystical poet William Butler Yeats, she was the first woman to be elected to the House of Commons, although she never took her seat. The Countess participated in the 1916 rebellion, and five IRA men died in a gun battle at the house during her tenancy. All in all, Killakee House and the surrounding area were imbued with more violence and savagery than most haunted places.

Killakee House lay empty and derelict for some years after the Second World War. In the late 1960s it was bought by Mrs Margaret O'Brien, who wanted a centre in which Irish artists and sculptors could work and exhibit their art. When she moved into the place in 1968, she heard stories from locals that its grounds were haunted by a black cat the size of an Airedale dog. 'Haunted' was an appropriate term because the stories covered a period of over 50 years – much longer than the life-span of a normal cat.

Mrs O'Brien knew some of the tales related about her new property and its environs, and was rather shaken when she caught glimpses of a 'big black animal' disappearing into the thick shrubbery of her garden. She thought no more about it, however, until her friend Tom McAssey, a Dublin artist, and two colleagues had a terrifying experience one night while redecorating Killakee House in March 1968. They were working on the stone-flagged front hall, which opened onto what had been a ballroom. McAssey told a radio reporter:

> I had just locked the heavy front door, pushing a 6-inch [15-centimetre] bolt into its socket. Suddenly one of the two men with me said that the door had opened again. We turned, startled. The lock was good and the bolt was strong, and both fastened on the inside.
>
> We peered into the shadowed hallway, and then I walked forward, and sure enough the door stood wide open, letting in a cold breeze. Outside in the darkness I could just discern a black-draped figure, but could not see its face. I thought someone was playing a trick

Left: Tom McAssey's painting of the Black Cat of Killakee, which scared him and two companions one night in 1968. The picture now hangs in the house, which is an art centre

Below: the long low bulk of Killakee House stands beneath the hill on which the burnt-out ruin of the Hell Fire Club stands. A prehistoric cairn and a standing stone existed on the hill's summit before these buildings were put up

and said: 'Come in. I see you.' A low, guttural voice answered: 'You can't see me. Leave this door open.'

The men standing behind me both heard the voice, but thought it spoke in a foreign language. They ran. A long-drawn-out snore came from the shadow, and in panic I slammed the heavy door and ran too. Halfway across the gallery I turned and looked back. The door was again open and a monstrous black cat crouched in the hall, its red-flecked amber eyes fixed on me.

Beside Killakee House in a trailer in the wooded grounds lived Val McGann, a former Irish pole-vault champion who painted and showed his work at the gallery. He evinced no surprise at McAssey's story, because he had seen the huge cat on several occasions, lurking in the scraggling undergrowth of the overgrown garden.

'The first time I saw it, it frightened me stiff,' he said, 'but on subsequent occasions I have been more interested and amazed at the size of the beast. It is about the size of a biggish dog, with terrible eyes. I've even stalked it with my shotgun, but have never been able to corner it.'

For some months after McAssey's vision, apparitions were seen by workmen and artists at Killakee. They usually appeared at night, although two men saw what they thought was a nun, with her back to them, at midday in the old ballroom. When they approached her she disappeared, and a subsequent search of the house and garden failed to turn up any evidence of a real figure.

Following reports in the Dublin press and on television of the strange hauntings, a group of Irish show-business personalities persuaded Mrs O'Brien to let them try a seance in Killakee House. They included a stage conjurer who was an expert on illusions and who believed that he could rule out any 'fakery' on the part of residents.

The group arranged cards carrying the letters of the alphabet in a circle on a table and placed an upturned glass in the centre. Each participant rested one finger lightly on the glass. Those who have tried this well-known technique will know that the glass will slide around the table, from letter to letter, apparently spontaneously, with no one present applying any pressure to it – consciously, at any rate.

The group at Killakee asked any 'spirits' present to manifest themselves – but the 'replies' were gibberish. However, on two occasions the lights failed, although a subsequent check of the fuses revealed no fault, and the light bulbs and wiring appeared to be completely normal.

Two days later, however, events began to take a more frightening turn. First there were bumps and knockings in the night. Lights were switched rapidly on and off.

### Bells in the night

Throughout the whole of one night the sound of door bells, in the front and back halls, could be heard. Yet those bells had been removed many years before.

A minor but curious manifestation was the fact that none of the residents – five or six in all – was able to sleep even on 'calm' nights; after retiring to bed exhausted from a heavy day's work, they reported lying awake, tossing and turning and managing to sleep only after sunrise.

About four days after the seance, everyone in the house heard heavy crashes and went to investigate. They found large pieces of furniture – some stored in locked rooms – thrown 'like matchboxes', some upside down, some pushed into corners. One oak medieval chair had been carefully pulled apart, joint from joint; even the brass tacks holding its tapestry in place had been pulled out and placed in neat rows. On the other hand, another similar chair had been smashed into tiny slivers.

After this outbreak, peace descended again for a matter of weeks. Then the 'haunters' turned their attention to exhibits on show in the house: a potter's works were hurled all over the room and smashed, while oil paintings were torn into long narrow strips.

At this point Margaret O'Brien sought the assistance of a priest, who, after obtaining permission from his superiors, performed a Roman Catholic rite of exorcism on Killakee House. The violent outbreaks stopped, but even more bizarre incidents began to occur in their place.

Mrs O'Brien had still not completed furnishing her house, and she lacked a refrigerator. She had asked the milkman to leave the milk in a pool in a cool stream that ran

Left: Countess Markievicz, who occupied Killakee House for a period. She was sentenced to death for her part in the 1916 uprising, but this was commuted to penal servitude for life. She was actually released in 1917 and became a noted Irish politician

Below: the building used by the Hell Fire Club as it was at the height of the society's infamy. It was built about 1725 as a hunting lodge, and commanded magnificent views of the mountains and forests of the surrounding countryside. It was burned down in mysterious circumstances – supposedly during one of the club's orgies of violence

Above: duelling, then a legal activity, claimed the lives of several noblemen at Killakee House during the 18th century. A duel could be substituted for a trial: the defendant had the right to challenge his accuser. Even after the abolition of such 'judicial' duels, personal combat, regulated by strict rules, remained legal between military men until it was finally outlawed in the mid 19th century

through the grounds. After the exorcism, Mrs O'Brien found that all the tinfoil tops had been removed from the bottles, although the milk was undisturbed.

Furthermore, no trace of the foil could be found. Mrs O'Brien assumed that it had been carried off by birds, possibly magpies or jackdaws. To stop the nuisance, she had a heavy four-sided box of stone built in the stream, with a large slate lid. Nevertheless, the caps continued to disappear.

## The humour of the haunters

At this juncture, the 'haunters' showed a trace of humour as well as causing a rare psychic manifestation called an 'apport' – the sudden appearance of objects through apparently preternatural means. Following the disappearance of the caps from the bottles, 'caps' began to appear in the house itself – but these caps were types of headgear.

After the manifestations, Mrs O'Brien had made a practice of locking and checking all the doors before retiring. Despite this, a profusion of small caps began to appear all over the house. They would appear in odd places – on picture hooks or behind doors. Sometimes, rosary beads would be found, equally inexplicably.

At the end of 1970 the caps ceased to appear, although spasmodic knockings in the night continued to be heard. Then, a few months later, came a discovery that might have had a grim bearing on the whole strange series of incidents. While structural alterations to the kitchen were being made, an excavation for new plumbing was carried out. In a shallow grave a few feet under the surface was found the skeleton of a dwarf, with a skull too large for its small frame – a sinister echo of the legend told of the Hell Fire Club for so many years. In the grave, too, was a brass figurine, depicting a horned and tailed devil thumbing its nose.

Once again the priest was called, this time to conduct a proper burial service on the unknown unfortunate, and after that the manifestations ceased. Mrs O'Brien sold the premises six years later.

Was the Black Cat of Killakee – later portrayed in oils by Tom McAssey as he had seen it on that frightening night – a manifestation that was attached to the house, or had it somehow been conjured into existence by the new occupants? Were the voices, the bells and the broken furniture results of the seance, which somehow provided a focus for them? Or was the whole series of hauntings provoked by the unhappy ghost of the dwarf, brutally murdered, according to legend, by the drunken bucks of the Hell Fire Club?

It is unlikely that the answer will ever be known for sure, but we do know that all psychical phenomena ceased in 1977, when Joseph Frei took over the unfortunate house and added a restaurant to the art centre's facilities.

'Perhaps the previous owners were, shall we say, unlucky with the place,' he said. 'I and my family have been very happy here – I know about the history of it, but we have only experienced a feeling of warmth and comfort. Perhaps the "haunters" like what we are doing with their "haunt".'

# What really happened at Tunguska?

**The Tunguska explosion was the disastrous end of a visitor from space. But was that visitor a spacecraft or a fragment of a comet? IAN RIDPATH describes the latest scientific research and gives his verdict**

SIBERIA, 30 JUNE 1908: a brilliant fireball blazed through the Earth's atmosphere, exploding at a height of 5 miles (8 kilometres) above the valley of the Stony Tunguska river with the force of a $12\frac{1}{2}$-megatonne nuclear bomb. According to one popular theory, the Tunguska explosion really was a nuclear blast, caused by the burn-up of a nuclear-powered alien spacecraft. But another leading theory says the Tunguska object was the head of a small comet. What evidence is there to back up these rival theories?

Important clues to the nature of the Tunguska explosion were obtained on three expeditions to the site, in 1958, 1961 and 1962, led by Soviet geochemist Kirill Florensky. His 1962 expedition used a helicopter to chart the disaster area. Instead of looking for large meteoritic fragments, as Leonid Kulik had done in the late 1920s, Florensky's team sifted the soil for microscopic particles that would have been scattered by the burn-up and disintegration of the Tunguska object. Their search proved fruitful. The scientists traced a narrow tongue of cosmic dust stretching for 150 miles (250 kilometres) north-west of the site, composed of magnetite (magnetic iron oxide) and glassy droplets of fused rock. The expedition found thousands of examples of metal and silicate particles fused together, indicating that the

Below: Willard F. Libby, one of a team who thought they had found an increase in atmospheric radioactive carbon-14 following the Tunguska explosion

Bottom: within a year of the explosion, Tunguska looked like this: fresh green growth pushing through the dead timber

Tunguska object had not been of uniform composition. A low-density stony composition containing flecks of iron is believed to be typical of interplanetary debris, particularly meteors ('shooting stars'), which are themselves composed of dust from comets. The particles spread north-west of the Tunguska blast were apparently the vaporised remains of a comet's head.

These actual samples of the Tunguska object should have been enough to settle the controversy once and for all. Florensky wrote about his expeditions in a 1963 article in the magazine *Sky & Telescope*. The article was entitled, 'Did a comet collide with the Earth in 1908?' Among astronomers, the comet theory has always been the front runner. In his article, Florensky said that this viewpoint 'was now confirmed'.

### Radiation check

Florensky's expedition carefully checked for the existence of radiation at the site. He reported that the only radioactivity in the trees from the Tunguska area was fallout from atomic tests, which had been absorbed into the wood. Florensky's party also looked in detail at the acceleration of forest growth in the devastated area, which some had put down to genetic damage from radiation. Biologists concluded that only the normal acceleration of growth after a fire, a well-known phenomenon, had taken place.

But what of the 'scabs' reported to have broken out on reindeer after the blast? In the absence of any veterinary report one can only speculate, but most likely these were not

caused by atomic radiation but simply by the great flash of heat given out by the blast, which also set fire to the trees. Humans near enough to have felt the heat of the fireball showed no signs of radiation sickness, and remained alive and healthy when Leonid Kulik visited the site over a dozen years later.

Believers in the nuclear explosion theory quote investigations in 1965 by three American physicists, Clyde Cowan, C.R. Atluri, and Willard Libby, who reported a 1 per cent increase in radiocarbon in tree rings following the Tunguska blast. A nuclear explosion releases a burst of neutrons, which turn atmospheric nitrogen into radioactive carbon-14 that is taken up by plants along with ordinary carbon during their normal photosynthesis. If the Tunguska blast were nuclear, excess radiocarbon would be expected in the plants growing at the time.

To test this prediction, the American scientists examined tree rings from a 300-year-old Douglas fir from the Catalina Mountains near Tucson, Arizona, and also from an ancient oak tree near Los Angeles. They found that the level of radiocarbon in the rings of both trees had jumped by 1 per cent from 1908 to 1909. The picture is confused by erratic fluctuations of up to 2 per cent that exist in the levels of radiocarbon measured in the tree rings from year to year. Therefore a 1 per cent radiocarbon increase is not outside the range of normal fluctuations caused by natural effects. An important double-check was made by three Dutch scientists on a tree from Trondheim, Norway – much nearer the blast, where the radiocarbon effects would be expected to be more noticeable. Instead of a radiocarbon rise in 1909, they found a steady decrease around that time. Therefore the increase in American trees found by Cowan, Atluri and Libby must be due to local effects – and not to the Tunguska blast.

### Pattern of destruction

Lastly, what about the clump of trees left standing at the centre of the Tunguska blast area, as were trees under the explosion point of the Hiroshima bomb, and the 'fiery pillar' seen after the explosion? In fact, these effects are not unique to a nuclear blast. Any explosion is followed by an updraught of heated air and a puff of smoke. Brilliant exploding fireballs happen frequently as chunks of solar system debris plunge into the atmosphere; fortunately for us, most of them are far smaller than the Tunguska object.

The clump of standing trees would be left behind by an aerial explosion of any kind, as shown by the scale-model experiments of Igor Zotkin and Mikhail Tsikulin of the Soviet Academy of Sciences' meteorite committee. They set off small explosions over a field of model trees, and found they were able to reproduce the pattern of felled trees including the central standing clump.

Therefore it seems that all the 'evidence' adduced for a nuclear explosion at Tunguska is either misinterpretation or mischievous distortion.

The healing processes of the Siberian forest have not yet obliterated the scars of the 1908 explosion. Within a few years saplings had grown between the trunks strewn on the ground (top). But even today the fallen trees are still evident beneath a covering of moss and foliage (above)

Remarkably, the Tunguska event was repeated on a smaller scale over North America on the night of 31 March 1965. An area of nearly 390,000 square miles (1 million square kilometres) of the United States and Canada was lit up by the descent of a body that detonated over the towns of Revelstoke and Golden, 250 miles (400 kilometres) south-west of Edmonton, Alberta, Canada. Residents of those towns spoke of a 'thunderous roar' that rattled and broke windows. The energy released was equal to several kilotonnes of TNT.

Scientists predicted the meteorite's point of impact and set out to look for a crater, much as Leonid Kulik had done in Siberia half a century before. Like him, they were unsuccessful. Scanning the snow-covered ground from the air, the scientists were unable to find traces of the meteorite, or of a crater. Only when investigators went into the area on foot did they find that a strange black dust coated the snow for miles around. Samples of this dirt were scraped up, and proved to have the composition of a particularly fragile type of stony meteorite known as a carbonaceous chondrite (see page 368). The Revelstoke object fragmented in mid-air, raining thousands of tonnes of crumbly black dust upon the snow. Significantly, witnesses to the Tunguska blast described just such a 'black rain'.

Clinching evidence for the cometary nature of the Tunguska object comes from the results of the latest Soviet expeditions to the site, reported in 1977. Microscopic rocky particles found in the 1908 peat layers have the same composition as cosmic particles collected from the upper atmosphere by rockets. Thousands of tonnes of this material are estimated to be scattered around the fall area. Along with these particles of rock from space were jagged particles of meteoric iron. The Soviet researchers concluded that the Tunguska object was a comet of carbonaceous chondrite composition. This comes as no surprise, for astronomers are finding that a carbonaceous chondrite composition is typical of interplanetary debris.

But if it was a comet, why was it not seen in the sky prior to impact? Firstly, it always stayed close to the Sun so that it was lost in glare; and secondly, it was too small to have ever become bright enough to see even in a dark sky. Astronomers now believe that the Tunguska object was actually a fragment broken several thousand years ago from Comet Encke, an old and faint comet with the shortest known orbit of any comet around the Sun. A Czech astronomer, Lubor Kresak, pointed out in 1976 that the orbit of the Tunguska object, deduced from the direction and angle at which it struck the Earth, is remarkably similar to that of Encke's comet. Dr Kresak estimates that the body had a diameter of only about 100 yards (100 metres) when in space, and a mass of up to a million tonnes. Dust from its disintegration in the atmosphere caused the bright nights observed in the northern hemisphere in the period following the Tunguska event.

'The identification of the Tunguska object as an extinct cometary fragment appears to be the only plausible explanation of the event; and a common origin with Comet Encke appears very probable,' concludes Dr Kresak.

What is more, an event like Tunguska can happen again. Astronomers have found a number of small asteroids whose orbits cross the path of the Earth. For instance, in 1976 a direct repetition of the Tunguska event was avoided by hours as a previously unknown asteroid with a diameter of a few hundred yards swept past the Earth at a distance of 750,000 miles (1.2 million kilometres). Astronomers estimate that an object the size of the Tunguska comet hits the Earth once in about 2000 years on average. So it is only a matter of time before we are hit again – and next time it could do a lot of damage.

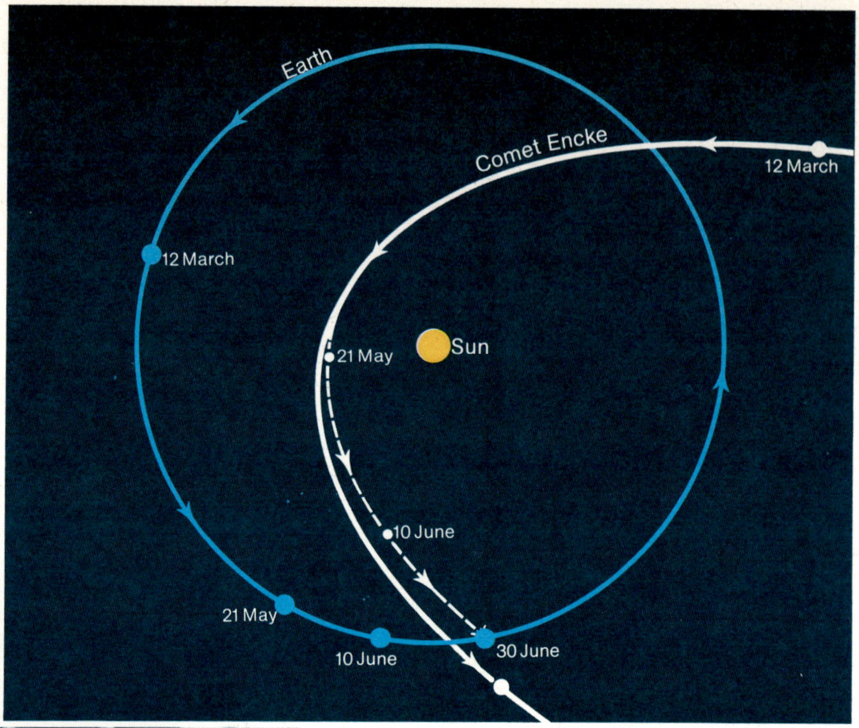


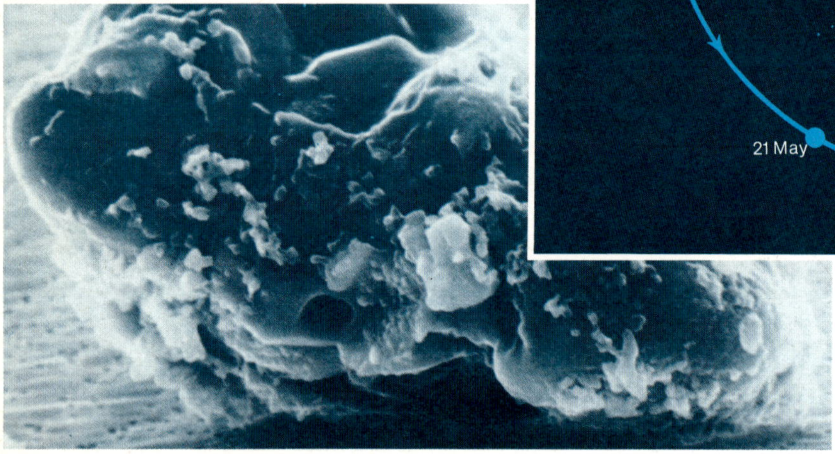

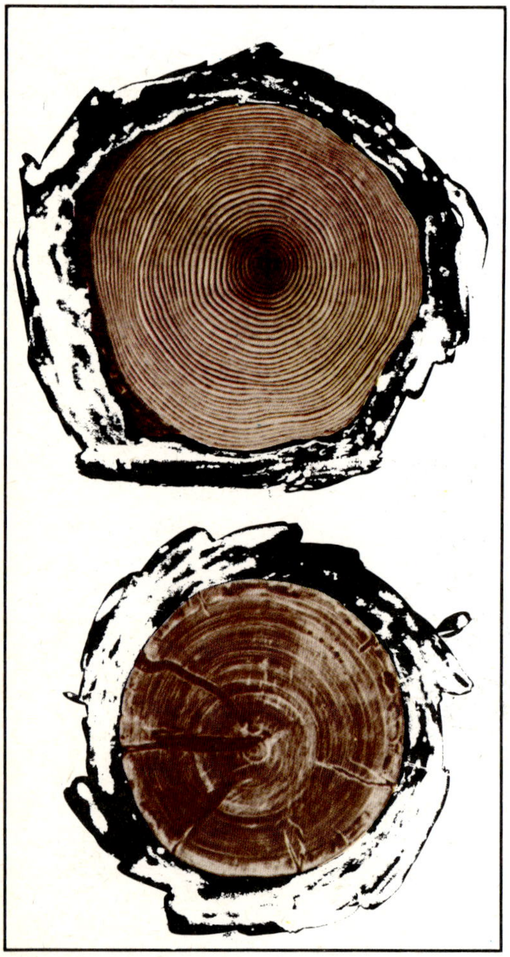

Top: how the Tunguska explosion may have happened. The comet Encke could have shed a rock fragment that was captured by the Earth

Above: this dust grain, magnified 10,000 times, was collected in the stratosphere. It is thought to have come from a comet

Left: the rings of recent Tunguska trees (top) are thicker than those of trees killed in the disaster (bottom). Some scientists claim that radioactivity from the explosion caused a spurt in plant growth


**Further reading**

John Baxter and Thomas Atkins, *The fire came by*, Macdonald and Jane's 1976

Jack Stoneley, *Tunguska, cauldron of hell*, Star 1977

Ronald D. Story (ed.), *The encyclopedia of UFOs*, New English Library 1980

# Africa's secret cities

**In many parts of the world civilisations that flourished for centuries have left only meagre traces to baffle the historian. BRENDA RALPH LEWIS begins a new series with an account of two vanished African societies**

'THE DARK CONTINENT' was a phrase coined by Europeans to suggest not only their ignorance about the interior of Africa and its past but also a belief that there was no civilisation worth knowing about, nor any history deserving the name. The darkness was not, they believed, due to the myopia of outsiders, but was a gloom that shrouded the minds of the continent's peoples, sunk in barbarism, idolatry and poverty since time immemorial.

In large measure this view of the African past was able to persist because a continuous history of events and personalities of the kind that existed in literate Europe had not been recorded in Africa, except in those areas that became Muslim. No written accounts survive from ancient African societies. The inscriptions on stone that provide archaeologists with much valuable information elsewhere are lacking in Africa south of the Sudan. To compound the lack, the ancient Egyptians had little to say about Africa beyond the Nile.

The African archaeological record is also scanty and distorted. It is impossible to say how much evidence has been destroyed at ancient sites by those natural enemies of historical knowledge, the legions of insects and relentlessly erosive climates.

Another factor responsible for the obscurity of ancient African history may be the virulent diseases of the continent. It proved impossible in most of Africa south of the Nile to rear draught animals that were resistant to disease, except in Ethiopia, where the healthy highland climate permitted the breeding of horses. In the rest of the continent, the absence of draught animals denied ancient Africans the use of the plough, and that, in turn, denied them a settled, prosperous agriculture. Many were forced to move on constantly, seeking new and better pastures. As always when life is little more than a struggle for survival, they left little or no trace of their passing, and had no chance to develop writing.

Above: an African view of European explorers. Two Portuguese seamen are shown in this 16th-century bronze from Nigeria

## Empires of Africa

Yet despite these obstacles, some regions did develop rich and settled societies. Powerful empires arose, extending over vast areas; they flourished and declined, unknown to the chroniclers of Europe. Trade routes stretched across forests and deserts to the coasts and the continents beyond. Even evidence of contact between Africa and China has been found in the form of Chinese-made objects unearthed in East Africa. African slaves were owned by rich Cantonese in the 12th century.

From West Africa, Muslim travellers in medieval times sent reports of the rich state of Ghana, known to them as the 'land of gold'. Later the kingdom of Mali flourished, where the Muslims described their shock at seeing women and girls go naked in public.

In the 16th century the Portuguese established trading posts on the East African coast, after pioneering the sea route from

Most of the tombs of the Kushite kings, in the period when Meroë had become its capital, were built on a ridge above the city (inset). This superbly preserved example (left) shows the influence of the more ancient and far more grandiose Egyptian models

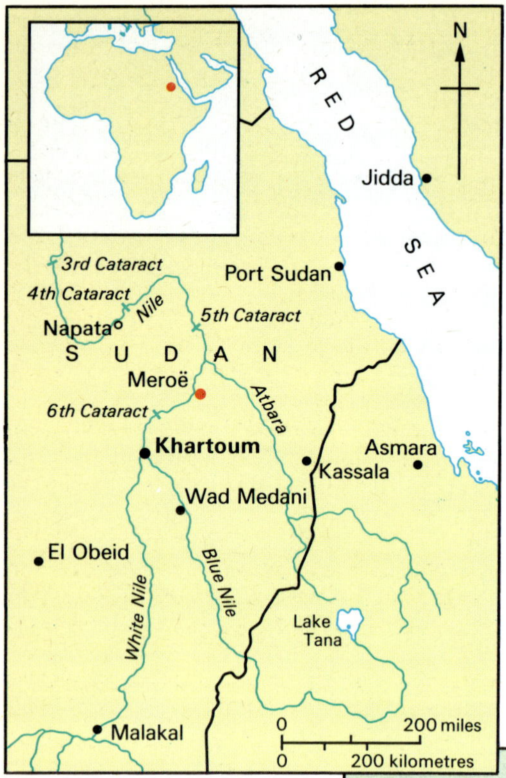

Above: Napata, capital of Kush during the period of the kingdom's greatness, and Meroë, the later capital, both lay on the Nile in what is now Sudan

Above right: ruins of one of the several temples below the hill of Barkal, at Napata. This city – really a grouping of towns – was sacked by the Egyptians in 590 BC. Although Meroë was henceforth the capital of Kush, Napata continued as a religious centre, and Kushite kings were still buried there. A number of them are represented on this stela, or inscribed slab (inset)

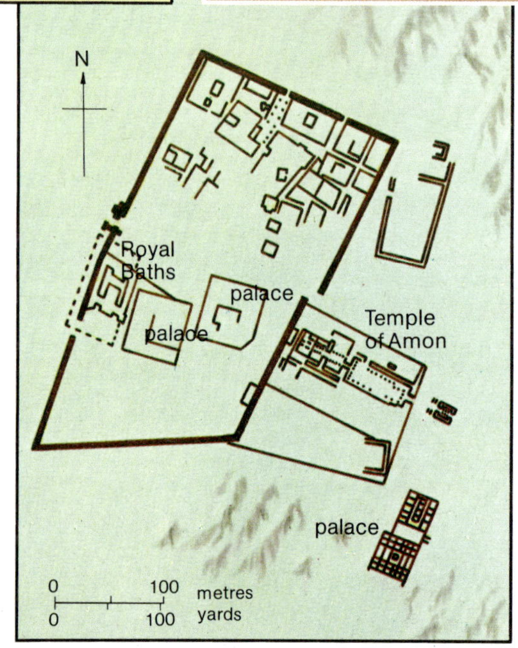


Right: the ground plan of ancient Meroë, imperfectly known from modern excavations. In its prime the temple of Amon was bright with colours, painted on the white stucco covering pillars, walls and altars. The baths were copies of Roman originals. Some distance to the east of Meroë lay several cemeteries, groups of royal pyramid tombs, and yet more temples

Europe to India around the Cape of Good Hope. They reported kingdoms such as the kingdom of Kongo in the area around the great lakes of East Africa.

Many of the kingdoms reported by the Portuguese proved transitory, possibly through lack of resources or the limited power of their rulers. It is impossible to say how many of them had broken up and disappeared by the time Africa was effectively penetrated by European explorers.

The gaps in African history have been imperfectly filled by dramatic oral traditions, liberally laced with many colourful myths and legends. One instance is a story from Ghana. This asserts that in about 1680, when the Ashanti chief Osei Tutu determined to unite his people against their powerful neighbour Denkera, his minister-priest Anokye caused a golden stool, henceforth to be the sacred symbol of Ashanti unity, to descend from the sky and come to rest on Osei's knees. Legends such as this, which give a magical cast to events and politics, tend to stand in the way of historical assessment, much as the legends of King Arthur once obscured understanding of the history of Britain in the period immediately following the end of Roman rule about AD 426.

Another adverse factor has been that in Africa, as in pre-Columbian America, the bulk of the best-attested early evidence has been provided by outsiders. Perhaps inevitably, many of these observers have come in from the outside equipped with their own prejudices. The 'scandal' of the naked girls of Mali, as seen through puritan Muslim eyes, is only one example.

### The kingdom of Kush

An African kingdom that escaped the usual prejudices of European historians was Kush. Its cities were built in sandstone, which, though now crumbling, lasted much better than the wood, clay and straw structures of most African societies. Its language was written in two scripts, one formal and hieroglyphic, the other informal and cursive. They have yet to give up all their secrets to linguists. Most importantly, from the point of view of traditional archaeology, Kush was in close relationship with ancient Egypt, about which a great deal is known.

Kush was, so to speak, a grand-daughter of ancient Egypt. It was established by an African people who may have been of Hamitic descent, under strong Egyptian influence. Initially, it was garrisoned by Egyptians. However, by 1000 BC Kush seems to have emerged as an independent unit. Its capital at that time was Napata, just below the Fourth Cataract of the Nile. Less than three centuries later, in about 730 BC, Kush was powerful enough to sever its relationship with Egypt. The Kushite king, Piankhi, apparently aged only 20 or 21, invaded and conquered Egypt, and there founded the 25th Dynasty.

Egypt, however, was by then in a decline that the five Kushite pharaohs proved unable to halt. In fact, their dynasty lasted only about 74 years. About 656 BC the Assyrians under Assurbanipal invaded Egypt and the Kushites were ousted. In about 590 BC Kush was attacked and Napata sacked by Pharaoh Psamtik II of the succeeding, Saissan, dynasty. The Kushites were forced to move their frontier further south. At this juncture Meroë, which had been the southern administrative centre of Kush since 750 BC, became its capital. Kush subsequently became more Negroid in character and the links with Egypt and Egyptian culture began to weaken as contacts ceased.

The disastrous clash with the Assyrians, whose iron weapons completely outclassed the Kushites' bronze, may have been among the influences that led to the development of large-scale ironworking at Meroë. Fortuitously, the site provided a plentiful supply of iron ore in the surrounding hills, and timber for smelting furnaces. The smelting process was learned from the Assyrians. The earliest ironworking tools found so far at Meroë come from the tomb of the Kushite king Harsiotef and date from about 400 BC. In time, Meroë became the metalworking centre of Africa – its Birmingham, in the phrase of the early 20th-century Assyrian specialist A. H. Sayce. A dozen iron slag heaps – piled, appropriately, on each side of the modern railway line – survive as visible evidence of this ancient industry.

Below: a stool, or royal throne, of the Ashanti nation of West Africa. This forest empire extended over a large area of the modern republic of Ghana. According to Ashanti legend, the first royal stool descended from the sky onto the lap of a chief who was called Osei Tutu. The Ashanti were fine metalworkers, as shown in the embellishments on the stool and in the gold ornamentation of the chief's helmet (bottom left). The skills of ironworking may have spread all over Africa from Kush, which learned them after its defeat by the Assyrians in 590 BC. Ancient slag heaps by the modern railway line at Meroë (bottom right) attest to the activity of the Kushite ironsmiths, which made Meroë the metalworking centre of Africa

It has been assumed, not unreasonably, that the techniques of ironworking spread out from Meroë to other parts of Africa, bringing them into the Iron Age. However, the routes by which ironworking was spread are still not known. There is only patchwork evidence, most of it dating from long after Meroë had fallen, some time between AD 320 and AD 350, to invaders from Axum in Ethiopia. In the northern regions of West Africa, for instance, ironworking was probably not known until after AD 500. Carbon dating puts the use of iron among peoples of East Africa between the 10th and 15th centuries. One scholar, G. A. Wainwright, suggested in 1954 that the Bantu languages of East and Central Africa may provide a clue to the spread of ironworking from Meroë to Bunyoro and from there into East Africa: in Swahili, the word for 'iron' is the Bantu word, whereas all other metals are known by Arabic names, indicating their much later introduction by the Muslims.

### The spread of ironworking

Who carried the knowledge of ironworking? Mass migrations of peoples have been suggested, but largely rejected. The natural conditions of Africa inhibited movement in large numbers and it therefore seems more likely that the necessary skills were spread by craftsmen, like the small groups of smiths who still travel round Africa, crossing the borderlines between tribes.

The first scholar to visit and survey Meroë was Karl Richard Lepsius, a Prussian Egyptologist who explored the area from Khartoum to Syria between 1844 and 1845. Excavations, however, did not commence until early this century. Between 1909 and 1914, the British archaeologist John Garstang revealed evidence of Roman influence in Meroë, in the town proper and in the Sun temple on the nearby plain. The antiquity of Meroë is attested by this temple, which was described in the fifth century BC by the Greek writer Herodotus. The Egyptologist G. A.

Reisner excavated Meroë's cemeteries and three groups of pyramids, between 1921 and 1923.

The chief features of Meroë, apart from its iron slag heaps, are the quay on the Nile, several palaces, a large temple to the Egyptian god Amon, the equivalent of the Greek Zeus, and a copy of a Roman bath. The work could be crude: some walls consisted only of two outer skins of dressed stone, the gap between being filled with rubble.

Reisner's work on the pyramid tombs at Meroë and at the previous capital, Napata, has yielded the names of 60 Kushite rulers. However, the latest known narrative of a ruler of Meroë comes from outside evidence – an inscription at Philae, in Egypt, which tells of an embassy sent by the Kushite king Tekeridaemani in AD 253.

This is, in fact, one of the very few dates in the history of Meroë that have been fixed. Much of the city still remains to be excavated. The chronology of Meroë, how the state was ruled and run, the precise order of the reigns of its kings and queens – these are unknown.

Light may be thrown on these questions as the Meroitic script is progressively deciphered. It is not a total puzzle: the alphabet is known to contain 17 signs for consonants and four for vowels, for example. Certain Egyptian hieroglyphic signs have been identified among the Meroitic signs, in slightly altered form. These have permitted the corresponding approximate sounds to be identified. Nevertheless, this has not been enough to make the language of Meroë fully translatable, nor to tie it in with any family of present-day African tongues. The language of Kush is another of the mysteries that hang over the vanished kingdom that in its prime could master Egypt.

Far to the south, a millennium later, another African culture also built enduring monuments in stone. But the arrogant presumption of the first foreigners to study Great Zimbabwe refused to acknowledge that this royal city could be the work of a native culture.

The first non-African in modern times to see Zimbabwe was an American hunter-prospector, Adam Renders, who visited the site in 1868 and returned there in 1871 with Karl Mauch, a German schoolteacher and geologist. Renders and Mauch were astonished by the massive size of Great Zimbabwe, which is situated in the south-east of the modern state of Zimbabwe. Its Great Enclosure is over 800 feet (240 metres) in circumference, 292 feet (90 metres) long and 220 feet (67 metres) broad. It consists of roughly circular double walls, some of which are over 30 feet (9 metres) high and 14 feet (4.5 metres) wide, with large coping stones protecting the top. Inside the enclosure is a conical tower built of solid granite bricks, which stands before the court of a temple. The temple itself is oval and its walls are decorated with a frieze of delicate chevrons.

### Who built Zimbabwe?

Arguably the most remarkable feature of this impressive complex, which also includes a labyrinth of staircases, courts and monoliths, was the nature of its stonework. It was made of dry masonry, with stones shaped and fitted together without mortar, but with marvellous accuracy – a method used with equal skill by the Inca builders of Peru.

Karl Mauch, who recorded the first archaeological description of Great Zimbabwe, was convinced, as was Adam Renders, that no Africans could possibly have built anything so elaborate. It must have been the work of more obviously 'civilised', probably

Above: the Great Enclosure at Zimbabwe, built on a valley floor

Left: Zimbabwe was well-placed for trade with the interior and with peoples across the Indian Ocean

Right: the scattering of ruins at Zimbabwe. Stone buildings here date from the 11th century

Below: the walls and towers of the Acropolis dominate the surrounding area

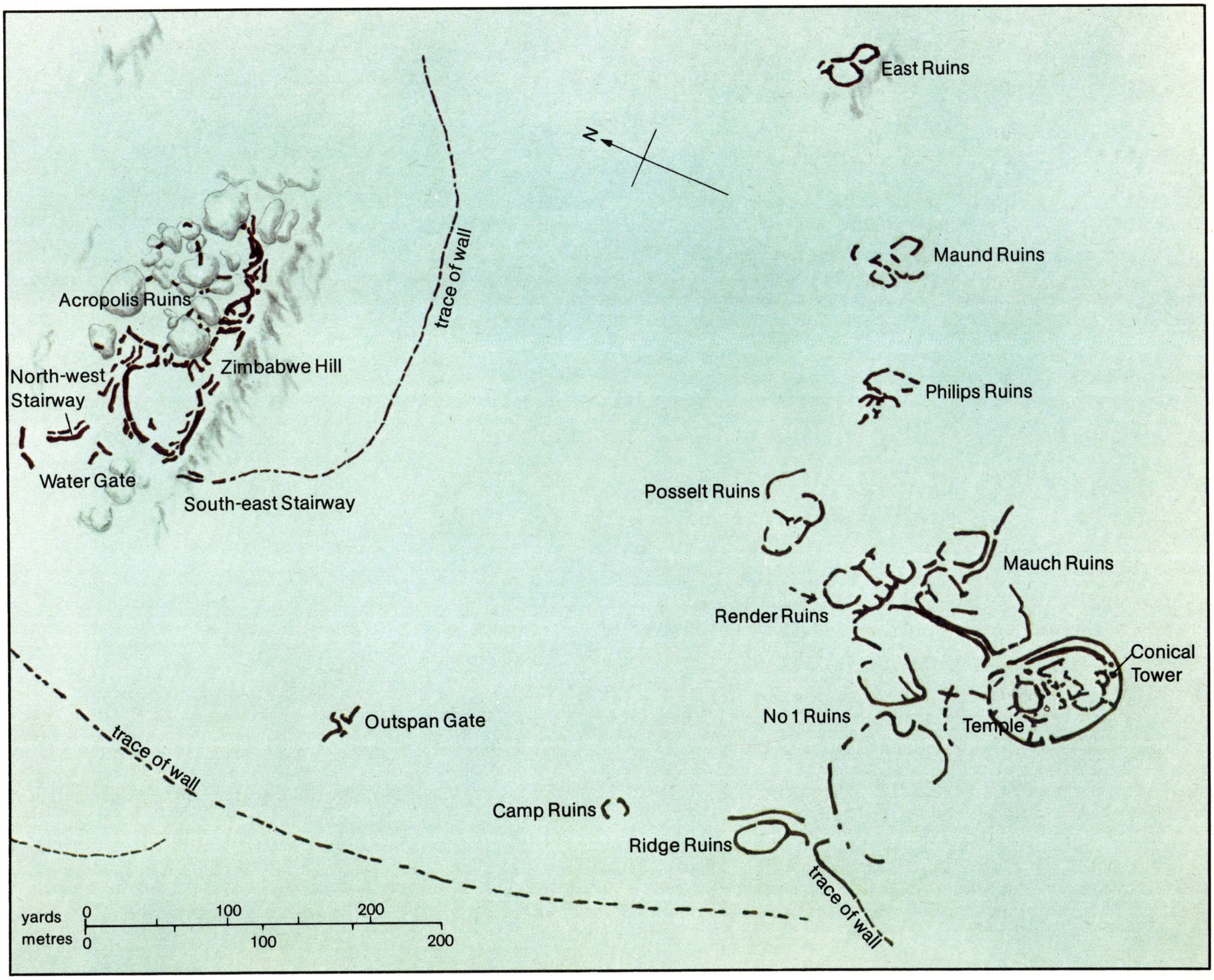

white-skinned, architects. Among the candidates were a long-vanished white race of Africa, and the fortress builders of King Solomon. Others were Phoenicians – especially favoured by Karl Mauch – or the architects of the Queen of Sheba. Mauch thought that the temple of Great Zimbabwe might well be a copy of King Solomon's palace, where the Queen of Sheba was a guest, and that the complex itself was the capital of gold-rich Ophir, a biblical El Dorado, which the book of Genesis places somewhere in the region of Arabia.

In formulating these theories, now recognised as ridiculous, Renders and Mauch observed the conditions of the local Makalanga people, not much above those of the Stone Age, and assumed that they had always lived like that. What they did not take into account, when reasoning thus, was the well-known pattern of rise and decline of civilisations. The Makalanga, the 19th-century descendants of the advanced society that had built Zimbabwe, had reverted to a more primitive cultural level.

More knowledgeable and less arrogant archaeologists have since established that the 'long-vanished race' that built Great Zimbabwe was more likely to have been black than white or Semitic. Zimbabwe was, in fact, only part of a larger culture, named Azanian, which also dug canals, built wells and worked gold mines. This Azanian state has left behind these, the only large ancient stone buildings in southern Africa, and its gold probably enabled it to prosper for some 300 years, until about AD 1500. From around 1400, Great Zimbabwe appears to have been a royal capital, a ceremonial centre for worship and the repository of the royal tombs. Zimbabwe's earliest structures date from the eighth century and the splendid edifices that so impressed Mauch and Renders date from the 16th and 17th. Great Zimbabwe survived the Azanian state by more than 300 years. It succumbed to the depredations of African invaders, probably Zulus, in about 1830. After that, Zimbabwe's fame faded quickly: no memory of it survived when the first Europeans came upon it 50 years later.

*The world's earliest experiments in city-dwelling ended abruptly. The reasons why are explored on page 1110*

# The closest encounter ever

**One of the puzzling features of so many UFO incidents is their apparent pointlessness. Yet in 1957 a young Brazilian farmer was allegedly abducted by humanoids for a startling purpose: to have sex with a being from another planet, as if he were 'a good stallion' who would improve their stock. CHARLES BOWEN documents what has been dubbed 'the most amazing case of all'**

ONE OF THE EARLIEST reports of an alleged abduction by humanoids was kept secret for over three years because it was deemed too 'wild' by those who first interviewed the abductee. And in the early reports the witness was known only as 'A.V.B.' to preserve his anonymity.

This amazing case first became known when the victim wrote to João Martins, a Brazilian journalist, and his medical friend Dr Olavo T. Fontes towards the end of 1957. Apparently, the man with the strange story was a young farmer who lived near the small town of São Francisco de Sales in Minas Gerais, Brazil. Intrigued, Martins and Fontes sent the farmer financial aid to make the long journey to Rio de Janeiro, where the investigation began on 22 February 1958 in Dr Fontes's consulting room.

The story that unfolded was, the investigators felt, so astonishing that they decided to 'keep it on ice' in case a similar incident occurred that might corroborate any of the details. And they feared that if the account became widely known there would be a rash of 'copycat' cases, which would end up invalidating this story. But a few details did leak out – fortunately in the right direction, for the outline of the tale reached the ears of Dr Walter Buhler in 1961, and he began to make his own detailed investigation.

The Buhler report eventually appeared as a newsletter and this, translated by Gordon Creighton and supplemented with editorial comments, appeared in *Flying Saucer Review* in January 1965. Very soon after, João Martin's account was published in the Spanish language edition – not the Portuguese as might have been expected – of the Brazilian magazine *O Cruzeiro*. Finally the full case, including the results of various detailed clinical reports, was included in *The humanoids*, a collection of accounts of encounters with UFO occupants, in 1969. At last the story that had been thought too 'wild' to be made known to the public was in print, and 'A.V.B.' was revealed to be 23-year-old Antônio Villas Boas.

## 'I am going to bear our child'

**Close encounter of the third kind: São Francisco de Sales, Brazil, 15 October 1957**

Antônio Villas Boas: his remarkable experience was at first concealed by UFO researchers because they considered it too wild

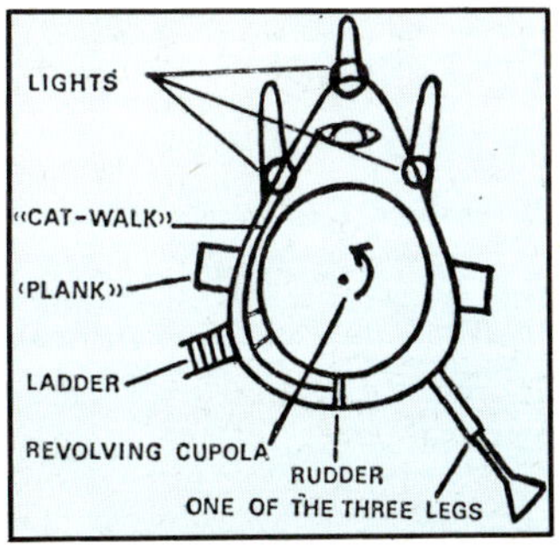


These sketches of the UFO were made by Villas Boas in February 1958 (above) for Dr Olavo Fontes, and in July 1961 (below) for Drs Buhler and Aquino of the Brazilian Society for the Study of Flying Saucers

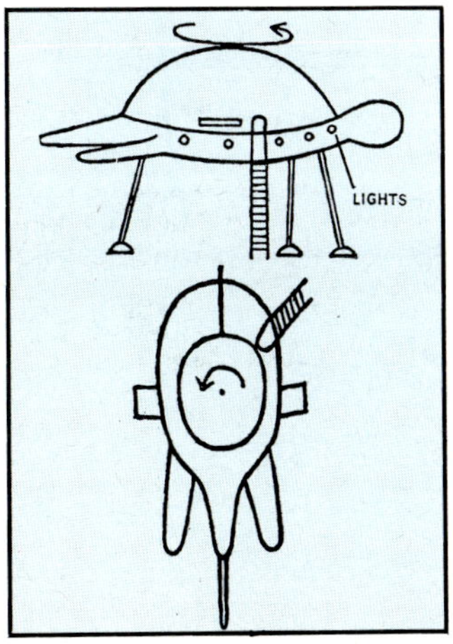


The actual abduction of Antônio Villas Boas was heralded by two unusual events. The first took place on 5 October 1957 when he and his brother were retiring to bed at about 11 p.m. after a party. From their bedroom window they saw an unidentified light in the farmyard below. It moved up onto the roof of their house, and together they watched it shine through the slats of the shutters and the gaps in the tiles (there being no ceiling proper) before it departed.

The second strange incident occurred on 14 October at about 9.30 p.m. when the Villas Boas brothers were out ploughing with their tractor. They suddenly saw a dazzling light, 'big and round', about 100 yards (90 metres) above one end of the field. Antônio went over for a closer look, but – as if playing games with him – the light moved swiftly to the other end of the field, a manoeuvre it repeated the two or three times the young farmer tried to get a closer look at it. Then the light abruptly vanished.

The following night, 15 October, Antônio was out in the field again, ploughing alone by the light of his headlamps. Suddenly, at about 1 a.m., he became aware of a 'large red star' that seemed to be descending towards the end of the field. As it came nearer he saw that it was in fact a luminous egg-shaped object. The UFO's approach brought it right overhead, about 50 yards (45 metres) above the tractor. The whole field became as bright as if it were broad daylight.

Villas Boas sat in his cab transfixed with fear as the object landed about 15 yards (15 metres) in front of him. He saw a rounded object with a distinct rim that was apparently clustered with purple lights. A huge round headlamp on the side facing him seemed to be producing the 'daylight' effect. There was a revolving cupola on top, and as he watched, fascinated, he saw three shafts – or 'legs' – emerge and reach for the ground. At this the terrified farmer started to drive off but after a short distance the engine stopped, despite the fact that it had been running smoothly. Villas Boas found he count not restart it and in a panic he leapt from the cab and set off across the heavily ploughed field. The deep ruts proved a handicap to his escape and he had gone only a few paces when someone grabbed his arm. As he turned, he was astonished to see a strangely garbed individual whose helmeted head reached only to Villas Boas's shoulder. He hit out at his assailant, who was knocked flying, but he was quickly grabbed by three other humanoids who lifted him from the ground as he struggled and shouted. He later said:

> I noticed that as they were dragging me towards the machine my speech seemed to arouse their surprise or curiosity, for they stopped and peered attentively at my face as I spoke, though without loosening their grip on me. This relieved me a little as to their intentions, but I still did not stop struggling. . . .

He was carried to the craft. A ladder descended from a door, and his captors hoisted him up this with great difficulty – especially as he tried to resist by hanging on to a kind of handrail. But in the end they succeeded.

Once inside the machine Villas Boas found himself in a square room with metallic walls, brightly lit by small, high lamps. He was set down on his feet, and became aware that there were five small beings, two of whom held him firmly. One signalled that he should be taken through to an adjoining room, which was larger, and oval in shape, with a metal column that reached from floor to ceiling, together with a table and some swivel chairs set to one side.

A 'conversation' ensued between his captors, who made sounds like dog barks:

> Those sounds were so totally different from anything I had heard until now. They were slow barks and yelps, neither very clear nor very hoarse, some longer, some shorter, at times containing several different sounds all at once, and at other times ending in a quaver. But they were simply sounds, animal barks, and nothing could be distinguished that could be taken as the sound of a syllable or word of a foreign language. Not a thing! To me it sounded alike, so that I am unable to retain a word of it . . . I still shudder when I think of those sounds. I can't reproduce them . . . my voice just isn't made for that.

### Handled by humanoids

This strange communication ceased abruptly, when all five set about him, stripping him of his clothing while he shouted and struggled – but to no avail. (Apparently they stopped to peer at him whenever he yelled, and, strangely, although they seemed to be using force, at no time did they hurt him.)

The beings were all dressed in tight-fitting grey overalls and large, broad helmets reinforced with bands of metal at back and front. There were apertures through which Villas Boas could see light-coloured eyes. Three tubes emerged from the top of each helmet, the central one running down the back and entering the clothing in line with the spine; the other two curved away to enter the clothes, one beneath each armpit. The sleeves ended in thick gloves, which seemed difficult to bend at the fingers. The trouser part fitted closely over seat, thighs and lower legs, and the footwear seemed an integral part of this section, the soles being very thick – perhaps as much as 2 inches (5 centimetres). On his chest each being had a kind of breastplate or 'shield' 'about the size of a slice of pineapple', which reflected light, and the shield was joined to a belt at the waist by a strip of laminated metal.

The naked and shivering farmer – it was a

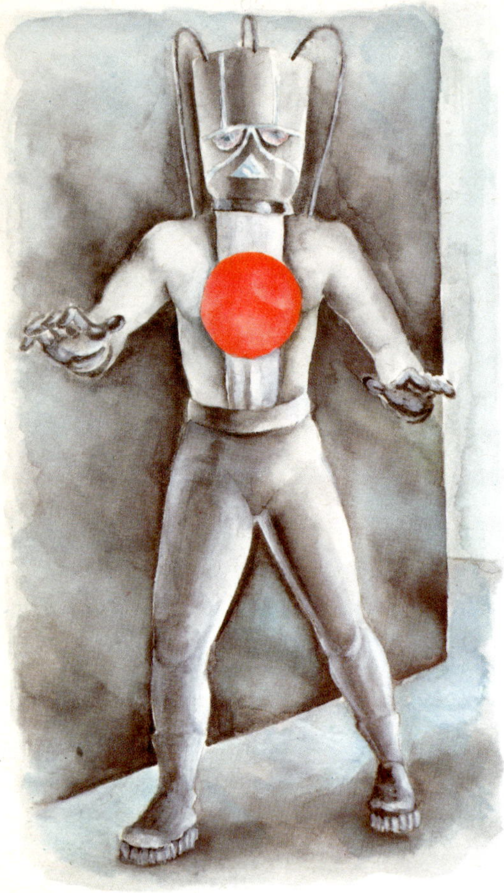

Below: Villas Boas's impression of the inscription above a door in the humanoids' craft. In the statement he made to Dr Fontes, Villas Boas said it was 'a sort of luminous inscription – or something similar – traced out in red symbols which, owing to the effect of the light, seemed to stand out about 2 inches (5 centimetres) in front of the metal of the door. This inscription was the only thing of its kind that I saw in the machine. The signs were scrawls completely different from what we know as lettering'

chilly night outside, and no warmer in the craft – stood there quaking and 'worried to death'. He wondered what on earth was going to happen to him. One of the little creatures approached him with what seemed to be a sort of wet sponge, which he rubbed all over Villas Boas's skin. He said: 'The liquid was as clear as water, but quite thick, and without smell. I thought it was some sort of oil, but was wrong, for my skin did not become greasy or oily.'

He was now led to another door, which had an inscription in red over it. He tried to memorise this, although it meant nothing to him, being written in unknown characters. In yet another room one of the beings approached with a sort of chalice from which dangled two flexible tubes; one of these, with a capped end like a child's suction 'arrow', was fixed to his chin, while the other tube was pumped up and down. The alarmed Villas Boas watched the chalice fill with what was presumably his own blood. The creatures then left him alone. He sat on a soft couch contemplating the nightmarish situation in which he found himself.

Suddenly he smelt a strange odour, which made him feel sick. He examined the walls and saw metallic tubes at just below ceiling level. Grey smoke was coming through perforations in the tubes. Villas Boas rushed to a corner of the room and vomited, and after that he felt a little less frightened. Moments later there was a noise at the door, which opened to reveal a woman standing there. As Villas Boas gaped, the woman walked towards him. Flabbergasted, he realised she was as naked as he was.

The woman, said Villas Boas, was more beautiful than anyone he had met before. She was shorter than he, her head reaching only to his shoulder – he is 5 feet 5 inches (1.6 metres). Her hair was smooth, and very fair, almost white, and as though bleached. Parted in the centre, it reached halfway down her neck, with ends curling inwards. Her eyes were large, blue and elongated, 'slanted outwards'. Her small nose was straight, neither pointed nor turned up. She had high cheekbones, but – as Villas Boas discovered – they were soft and fleshy to the touch. Her face was wide, but narrowed to a markedly

pointed chin. Her lips were thin, the mouth being almost like a slit. The ears were normal, but small.

The door closed, and Villas Boas found himself alone with this woman, whose slim body was the most beautiful he had ever seen. She had high, well-separated breasts. Her waist was slender, her hips wide and her thighs large, while her feet were small and her hands long and narrow. He saw too that the hair in her armpits, and her pubic hair, was blood red. He smelt no perfume on her, 'apart from the feminine odour'.

She approached the farmer and rubbed her head against his (presumably by standing on tip-toe). Her body felt as though glued to his, and she made it quite clear what she wanted. His excitement welled up. The sexual act was normal – as was the one that followed – but then she tired, and refused further advances.

Villas Boas recalled that she never kissed him, but once gently bit him on his chin. Although she never spoke, she grunted, and that 'nearly spoiled everything, giving the disagreeable impression that I was with an animal'.

When she was called away by one of the other beings, she turned to Villas Boas, pointed to her belly, and then pointed to the sky. These gestures instilled a great fear in Antônio – a fear that was with him still, four years after the event – for he interpreted them as meaning she would return to take him away. Dr Fontes later calmed him by suggesting that she meant: 'I am going to bear our child, yours and mine, there on my home planet.' This led to speculation by the farmer that all they wanted was 'a good stallion' to improve their stock.

Then Villas Boas was told to get dressed, after which he says he was taken on a conducted tour round the craft; during this he tried to steal an instrument for a keepsake, only to be rebuffed, angrily, by one of the crew. Eventually, he was invited to go down the ladder, and back onto solid ground. From there he watched the ladder retract, while the metal legs and the lights began to glow. The craft rose into the air with its cupola turning at great speed. With lights flashing it listed slightly to one side, then suddenly shot off like a bullet.

It was by then 5.30 a.m. and the abductee's adventure had lasted over four hours.

He returned home hungry, and weakened by his spell of vomiting. He slept through to 4.30 p.m. and awoke feeling perfectly normal. But when he fell asleep again he slept badly, and woke up shouting after dreaming of the incident. Next day he was troubled by nausea and a violent headache. When that left him his eyes began to burn. Unusual wounds, with infections, appeared on parts of his body. When they dried up they left round, purplish scars.

Villas Boas was examined by Dr Fontes in February 1958, four months after the alleged abduction. The symptoms he described suggested 'radiation poisoning or exposure to radiation', but it was too late for this diagnosis to be confirmed

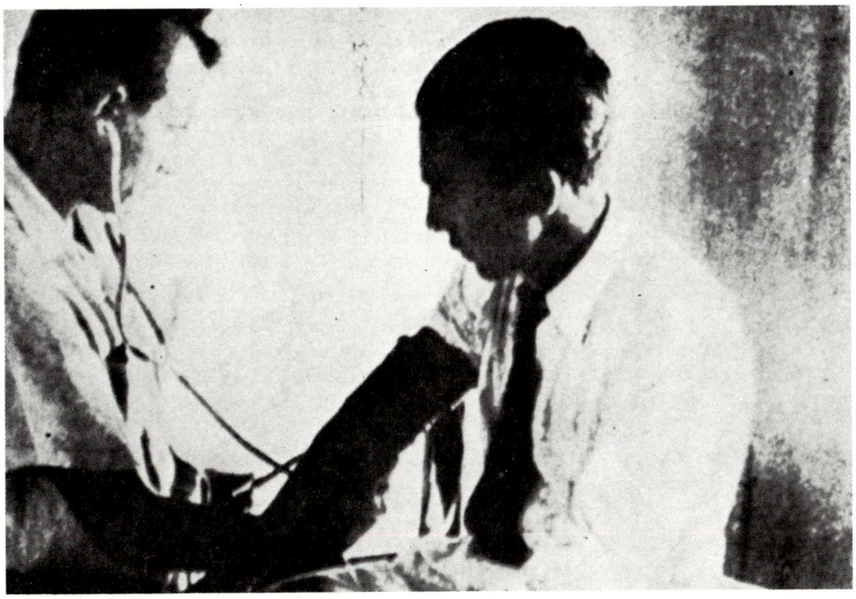

## Mysterious scars

When Dr Fontes examined Villas Boas, he observed two small patches, one on each side of the chin. He described these as 'scars of some superficial lesion with associated subcutaneous haemorrhage'. Several other mysterious scars on his body were also noted.

In a letter to *Flying Saucer Review* Dr Fontes suggested that the symptoms described pointed to radiation poisoning, or exposure to radiation. Wrote Dr Fontes: 'Unfortunately he came to me too late for the blood examinations that could have confirmed such a possibility beyond doubt.'

On 10 October 1971 João Martins was at last officially cleared to write about the case for the Brazilian public. His account appeared in the Rio de Janeiro Sunday review *Domingo Illustrado*. His abridged account concluded with a statement that:

> A.V.B. was subjected by us [Martins, Dr Fontes, and a *military officer* – whose presence was not revealed in the earlier reports] to the most sophisticated methods of interrogation, without falling into any contradictions. He resisted every trap we set to test whether he was seeking notoriety or money. A medical examination . . . revealed a state of completely normal physical and mental equilibrium. His reputation in the region where he lives was that of an honest, serious, hardworking man.

Martins also revealed that the interrogation at times bordered on harsh and cruel treatment, just short of physical violence, but Villas Boas never veered from his original story in any detail. The journalist concluded: 'If this story be true, it may well be that, somewhere out there in the Universe, there is a strange child . . . that maybe is being prepared to return here. Where does fantasy end? Where does reality begin?'

# Hitler and the holy lance

**The holy lance, which pierced Christ's side at his crucifixion, became a talisman for the Teutonic warlords of Europe. In the 20th century it was plundered by Adolf Hitler, who knew its mystical significance all too well. FRANK SMYTH tells how the would-be conqueror of the world linked his destiny with the lance**

IN THE STREETS OF VIENNA in 1913, a down-and-out former art student vainly tried to make a living by selling postcard-sized watercolours. Occasionally, driven off the streets by cold, he would wander through the corridors of the Hofburg Museum. Here he was particularly fascinated by a number of valuable pieces known as the Habsburg regalia. And among these the unprepossessing young vagrant, Adolf Hitler, paid special attention to the Holy Lance – reputed to be the spear that pierced Christ's side when he had given up the ghost on the cross.

The legend of the Holy Lance takes its origin from John 19 : 33–37:

> But when they came to Jesus, and saw that he was dead already, they brake not his legs: But one of the soldiers with a spear pierced his side, and forthwith came there out blood and water. And he that saw it bare record, and his record is true: and he knoweth that he saith true, that ye might believe. For these things were done that the scripture should be fulfilled, A bone of him shall not be broken. And again another scripture saith, They shall look on him whom they pierced.

The verse following this tells how Joseph of Arimathaea gained permission to take the body of Jesus and, helped by Nicodemus, laid it in a tomb on the night of Good Friday.

Other oral and written traditions, beginning with the earliest Christians and continuing to the Middle Ages, depict the rich Jewish philanthropist as obsessed with the artefacts associated with the dead Christ. He is said to have preserved the cross itself, the nails, the crown of thorns, and the shroud from which Christ rose on the third day. Through clues left by Joseph, Helena, mother of the first Christian emperor, Constantine, was able to rediscover these relics.

But even before Christ's death, according to the same traditions, Joseph had begun collecting: after the last supper he took charge of the cup in which Jesus had consecrated the bread and wine. After the resurrection, Joseph kept this cup alongside the spear of John's Gospel: the Holy Grail and the Holy Lance.

Joseph's subsequent travels with the Grail

Far left: the blade of the Habsburg spear, reputed to be the lance that pierced Christ's side while he was on the cross. Because it was a holy relic, the iron blade has been extensively repaired with gold and silver during its long history. It is now bound together with wire and an inscribed 'sleeve'

Left: a Roman soldier confirms that Christ is dead by plunging a spear into him, in a painting by Rubens. According to tradition, it was revealed to the soldier at this moment that Christ was truly the Son of God, and the spear acquired enduring magical potency

Right: just one face in the crowds of Germans who exulted at the outbreak of the First World War: Adolf Hitler, poverty-stricken and obscure, but dreaming already of leading the Nordic 'master race' to supremacy

Below: by selling watercolours like this, Hitler scratched a living in Vienna in 1913

and the Lance are the subject of folk tales and legends in almost every country in Europe. In Britain he is said to have hidden the Grail at Glastonbury. Afterwards he thrust his staff into the ground, where it sprouted to become the still-surviving Glastonbury Thorn, which blooms only at Christmas.

Romantic writers, beginning with the French poet Chrétien de Troyes in about 1180, bound up the fate of the Holy Grail and the Holy Lance with the adventures of King Arthur and the Knights of the Round Table, notably with Lancelot, Gawain and Perceval.

Alongside these stories – themselves based on Celtic tradition and scraps of historical fact – there ran a thin thread of evidence that the Lance, at least, had survived the centuries, passed down sometimes through good hands, sometimes through unworthy ones. With its ownership came power, to be used for great good or for terrible evil.

At least four 'Holy Lances' existed in Europe during the early part of the present century. Perhaps the best-known was in the keeping of the Vatican, although the Roman Catholic Church seems to have regarded it as no more than a curio. Certainly no preternatural powers were claimed for it by the papal authorities.

A second lance was kept in Paris, where it had been taken by St Louis in the 13th century, after his return from the crusades in Palestine.

Another lance, preserved in Cracow, Poland, was merely a copy of the Habsburg lance. The latter probably had the best pedigree of them all. It had been discovered at Antioch in 1098, during the first crusade, but mystery – and possibly imagination – obscured the manner of its finding. Crusaders had mounted a successful siege of the city and had taken control, when a more heavily armed band of Saracens rode up and turned the tables, shutting up the crusaders within the walls in their turn. After three weeks water and food were running low and surrender seemed the only course. Then a priest claimed to have had a miraculous vision of the Holy Lance, buried in the church of St Peter. When excavations at the spot revealed the iron spearhead, the crusaders were filled with a new zeal and rode out to rout their attackers.

Germanic tradition, somewhat at odds with these dates, claimed the Habsburg lance had in fact been carried as a talisman in the ninth century by Charlemagne through 47 victorious campaigns. It had also endowed him with clairvoyant powers. Only when he accidentally dropped it did Charlemagne die.

The lance later passed into the possession of Heinrich the Fowler, who founded the royal house of the Saxons and drove the Poles eastwards – a foreshadowing, Hitler may have thought in later years, of his own destiny. After passing through the hands of five Saxon monarchs, it fell into the possession of the succeeding Hohenstauffens of Swabia. One of the most outstanding of this line was Frederick Barbarossa, born in 1123. Before his death 67 years later Barbarossa had conquered Italy and driven the Pope himself into exile; again, Hitler may well have admired the brutal harshness coupled with charismatic personality that drove Barbarossa to success. Like Charlemagne, however, Barbarossa made the mistake of dropping the lance as he waded a stream in Sicily. He died within minutes of this event.

### The fascination of the spear

This was the legend of the weapon now among the Habsburg regalia, which so fascinated the young Hitler. He spent his first visit to the lance studying its every detail. It was just over a foot (30 centimetres) long, tapering to a slender, leaf-shaped point, and at some time the blade had been grooved to admit a nail – allegedly one of those used in the crucifixion. This had been bound into place with gold wire. The spear had been broken, and the two halves were joined by a sheath of silver, while two gold crosses had been inlaid into the base, near the haft.

The evidence of Hitler's personal fascination with the Habsburg lance rests on the testimony of Dr Walter Johannes Stein, a mathematician, economist and occultist who claimed to have met the future Führer just before the First World War. Stein, a native of Vienna, was born in 1891, the son of a rich barrister. He was to be a polymath and an intellectual adventurer until his death in 1957. He took a first degree in science and a doctorate in psychophysical research at the University of Vienna. He became expert in archaeology, early Byzantine art and medieval history; in the First World War, as an officer in the Austrian Army, he was decorated for gallantry.

In 1928 he published an eccentric pamphlet, *World history in the light of the Holy Grail*, which was circulated in Germany, Holland and Britain. Just five years after that Reichsführer Heinrich Himmler ordered that he be pressed into service with the Nazi 'Occult Bureau', but Stein escaped to Britain.

The Second World War found him in the guise of British intelligence agent. After helping to obtain the plans for 'Operation Sealion' – Hitler's projected invasion of Britain – he acted as adviser to Winston Churchill on the German leader's occult involvements.

Stein never published his own memoirs, but before his death he befriended an ex-Sandhurst commando officer, then a journalist, Trevor Ravenscroft. Using Stein's notes and conversations, Ravenscroft published a book, *Spear of destiny*, in 1972, which first brought Hitler's fascination with the Habsburg spear to public attention.

What hold could the Holy Lance, a Christian symbol, have on the violently anti-Christian ex-Roman Catholic Adolf Hitler? Already he was given to violent anti-Semitic rantings, and already he was a devout student of Friedrich Nietzsche's *Anti-Christ*, with its condemnation of Christianity as 'the ultimate Jewish consequence'.

Part of the answer lay in a medieval occult tradition regarding the history of the Holy Lance. As the Gospel of John describes, the Roman soldier who pierced Christ had unwittingly fulfilled the Old Testament prophecies (that Christ's bones would not be broken). Had he not done as he did, the destiny of mankind would have been different. According to both Matthew and Mark the true nature of Christ was revealed to the soldier, said to be named Gaius Cassius Longinus, at that moment: 'And when the centurion, which stood over against him, saw that he so cried out, and gave up the ghost, he said, Truly this man was the Son of God.' (Mark 15:39.)

Above: Charlemagne, King of the Franks, became Holy Roman Emperor in AD 800. One of the legends that have grown up around him says that he owed his success in war to the Holy Lance

Below: the triumphal entry of Hitler into Vienna in March 1938. One of the Führer's first acts was to order the removal to Germany of the Habsburg treasure, which included the Holy Lance

To the mind of the occultist, an instrument used for such momentous purpose would itself become the focus of magical power. And as Richard Cavendish succinctly puts it, speaking of the Grail and the Lance in his book *King Arthur and the Grail*:

> A thing is not sacred because it is good. It is sacred because it contains mysterious and awesome power. It is as potent for good or evil as a huge charge of electricity. If it is tampered with, however compelling and understandable the motive, the consequences may be catastrophic for entirely innocent people.

According to Stein, Hitler was fully aware of this concept as early as 1912: indeed it was through Hitler's obsession with the legend of the lance and its power as a 'magic wand' that the two men met. In the summer of 1912 Dr Stein purchased an edition of *Parsival*, a Grail romance by the 13th-century German poet Wolfram von Eschenbach, from an occult bookseller in Vienna. It was full of scribbled marginal commentaries displaying a combination of occult learning and pathological racism. On the flyleaf its previous owner had signed his name: Adolf Hitler. Through the bookseller Stein traced Hitler and spent many hours with him, appalled but fascinated. Although it was to be years before the poverty-stricken postcard painter took his first steps on the road to power, there was already an evil charisma about the man. Through all the tortuous windings of his discourse one obsession stood out clearly: he had a mystic destiny to fulfil and, according to Stein, the lance held the key.

Hitler described to Stein how the spear had acquired a special significance for him:

> I slowly became aware of a mighty presence around it, the same awesome presence which I had experienced inwardly on those rare occasions in my life when I had sensed that a great destiny awaited me... a window in the future was opened up to me through which I saw in a single flash of illumination a future event by which I knew beyond contradiction that the blood in my veins would one day become the vessel of the Folk-Spirit of my people.

Hitler never revealed the nature of his 'vision'; but Stein believed that he had seen himself a quarter of a century later, in the Heldenplatz outside the Hofburg Museum, addressing Austrian Nazis and ordinary, bewildered Viennese. There, on 14 March 1938, the German Führer was to announce his annexation of Austria into the German Reich – and to give the order to carry the Habsburg regalia off to Nuremberg, spiritual home of the Nazi movement.

### A curious priority

Taking possession of the treasure was a curious priority in view of the fact that Hitler despised the house of Habsburg as traitors to the Germanic race. Nevertheless on 13 October the spear and the other items of the regalia were loaded onto an armoured train with an SS guard and taken across the German border. They were lodged in the hall of St Catherine's Church, where Hitler proposed to set up a Nazi war museum. Stein believed that when Hitler had the lance in his possession, his latent ambitions for world conquest began to grow and flourish.

If Hitler's knowledge of the Habsburg spear's history was as extensive as Stein claimed, he must have been aware of the legends concerning the fate of Charlemagne, Barbarossa and others who had wielded it as a weapon, only to perish when it fell from their grasp. The legend seemed to be confirmed by a chilling coincidence that marked the end of his connection with the Lance.

After heavy Allied bombing in October 1944, during which Nuremberg suffered extensive damage, Hitler ordered the spear, along with the rest of the Habsburg regalia, to be buried in a specially constructed vault.

Left: the closing scene of *Parsifal*, Wagner's last opera. Hitler was fascinated by the legend on which the opera is based. Here the enchantress Kundry, redeemed from a life of evil, dies as Parsifal takes the Holy Grail from its shrine. He holds the Holy Lance, which, having been used to work evil by the black magician Klingsor, is an instrument of blessing in the hands of the virtuous Parsifal

Below: the Luitpold Arena in Nuremberg, scene of the Nazis' most spectacular prewar rallies, saw an informal 'march past' by victorious US soldiers in April 1945 (inset). In the ruins of the shattered city the Holy Lance, with other war booty, was found in a bombproof vault

Six months later the American Seventh Army had surrounded the ancient city, which was defended by 22,000 SS troops, 100 Panzers and 22 regiments of artillery. For four days the veteran American Thunderbird Division battered at this formidable defence until, on 20 April 1945 – Hitler's 56th birthday – the victorious Stars and Stripes was hoisted over the rubble.

During the next few days, while American troops rounded up Nazi survivors and began the long process of interrogating them, Company C of the US Army's Third Military Government Regiment, under their commander Lieutenant William Horn, were detailed to search for the Habsburg treasure. By chance a shell had made their task easier by blowing away brickwork and revealing the entrance to the vault. After some difficulty with the vault's steel doors, Lieutenant Horn entered the underground chamber and peered through the dusty gloom. There, lying on a bed of faded red velvet, was the fabled spear of Longinus. Lieutenant Horn reached out and took possession of the spear on behalf of the United States government. It was the afternoon of 30 April 1945. That much is recorded history.

And however sceptical may be the critics – about Walter Stein, the occult in general and the Holy Lance legends in particular – it is also historical fact that a few hundred miles away in a bunker in Berlin, Adolf Hitler chose that evening on which to take a pistol and shoot himself.

*On page 1106: how the swastika, symbol of good luck, was conscripted by the Nazis*

# Signals from the stars?

**Since the earliest days of radio, mysterious and seemingly intelligible signals have occasionally been received from outer space. Are they merely chance anomalies, or are alien forces trying to make contact? MICHAEL VINTER investigates**

Among the myriad stars and planets of the Milky Way (top) it seems inconceivable that none should support intelligent life. On 16 November 1974 an immensely powerful signal was beamed out into space from the world's largest radio telescope at Arecibo, Puerto Rico (above). But this was not mankind's first attempt to send a signal to the stars: over 50 years before, Nikola Tesla had sent – and received – such messages

OFFICIAL RECORDS STATE that the first radio transmissions directed specifically at the stars were dispatched from Arecibo, Puerto Rico, in 1974. But this was not, in fact, our earliest attempt to attract the attention of other worlds. Well before the term 'extra-terrestrial intelligence' was coined, two men had received intelligent signals – at a time when theirs were the only functioning radio sets on the planet Earth.

The first man was the eccentric genius Nikola Tesla. In 1899 he was working on his own, employing dangerously high voltages in an attempt to develop a means of transmitting energy by radio and thus eliminate the need for wiring systems. Throughout that long, hot summer he loosed artificial bolts of lightning into the sky from a 200-foot (60-metre) tower at his base in Colorado Springs – in an intelligible sequence. Then began a mystery that still puzzles scientists.

Having succeeded in making the lights and other electrical equipment work without wiring, Tesla saw his radio equipment inexplicably begin to register signals – in which, he later said, he could discern 'a clear suggestion of number and order not traceable to any cause then known to me.' He was entirely familiar with the natural phenomena of solar disturbances, Earth currents and *aurora borealis*, and he dismissed them all, adding: 'The feeling is constantly growing on me that I had been the first to hear the greeting of one planet to another.'

Unfortunately Tesla's strange, mystic nature, his identification with telepathy and the growing school of modern Spiritualism led to ridicule, especially when he was unwary enough to say to a reporter, 'We cannot even with positive assurance assert that some of them [life forms from other realms] might not be present here in this world, in the very midst of us . . . their life manifestations may be such that we are unable to see them.'

It is perhaps understandable that, at the

time, this seemed to many to be merely the ramblings of a madman. But in the same summer of 1899 another genius, a man with none of Tesla's mysticism, was reaching similar conclusions. That man was Guglielmo Marconi.

At the time of Tesla's startling 'other worlds' announcement, Marconi was developing radio as a means of communication, busily sending the letter v in Morse code to his fellow workers over a 50-mile (80-kilometre) distance. And by 1921 he, too, had announced that he had received inexplicable signals, which he quickly identified as some kind of cipher. He later noticed a very strange feature. Within the cipher, there appeared a measured recurrence of the Morse v he had been transmitting to his assistants back in 1899.

In the *New York Times* of 2 September 1921, Marconi was reported as believing that the mysterious signals, or some of them, originated on Mars. Incredible as it seems, no one made the connection with the signals Tesla had received 22 years earlier.

This oversight becomes more understandable when it is realised that the only common factor in the work of Tesla and Marconi was radio. The nature of their experiments was very different: Marconi was working in Morse code on the development of communicational technology, while Tesla was entirely preoccupied with the wire-less propagation of electrical energies. It was only much later that Tesla admitted that, if it were possible to draw power from the Earth's magnetic field, it would be of such awesome intensity that it would be possible to deploy it as a signal to other worlds.

Both Tesla's and Marconi's observations were largely ignored until 1924. In that year, Mars was due to approach its closest opposition to the Earth. Mr David Todd, a prominent British astronomer, conceived the notion of using a brand-new invention to scan the red planet for traces of life. This was the Jenkins radio camera, a revolution in technology, which converted radio signals into visual images and was used for sending press photographs. Todd's imaginative project captured news headlines, and whole governments devoted their broadcasting systems to monitoring the experiment.

Above: Guglielmo Marconi in St Johns, Newfoundland, Canada, where he received the first transatlantic radio message on 12 December 1901. But he also received more mysterious signals – clearly intelligible, they could not have come from either his own or Tesla's radios – then the only two working transmitters in the world

Below: radio telescopes are continually scanning space for radio signals. Pictured here is the world's largest radio telescope system, called a 'very large array' or VLA, at Magdalena, New Mexico

The project required total silence from radio transmitters on the Earth – something that would be impossible today. But in 1924 there were few commercial stations, and radar had not been invented. It is easy to imagine the tension as radio operators waited, in total radio silence, for signals. And then, suddenly, even 'ham' operators began to register signals. This was almost incredible, for early amateur receivers would generally pick up only exceptionally strong signals originating close at hand.

The *New York Times* of 28 August 1924 reported an examination of the developed film from the Jenkins radio camera:

> a fairly regular arrangement of dots and dashes along one side, but on the other side at almost evenly spaced intervals are curiously jumbled groups, each taking the form of a crudely drawn face.

### Strange cries and voices

Freak signals continued to come in throughout the 1920s and 1930s, particularly on the 30,000-metre wavelength. And in the late 1930s a new factor entered the puzzle: a wave of reports of strange aircraft – today we would call them UFOs – seen in the skies of Scandinavia and northern Europe. During the sightings, short-wave receivers in the 'flap' area would often suddenly come alive with strange cries and voices. The language used caused many a headache for philologists, because what they heard often seemed to be a mixture of Swedish and other tongues. But, if translated setting aside rigid rules of grammar, it often seemed to have some kind of intelligible sequence, even if its actual meaning remained obscure.

The dawning of the space age brought with it more strange phenomena. On 16 May 1963, in his Mercury capsule above Hawaii, astronaut Gordon Cooper was talking to mission control on a special frequency channel when extraneous voices broke in. Later examined on tape, these were found to correspond to no language known on Earth. The phenomenon was repeated on the Apollo VIII Borman-Lovell-Anders mission on 21 December, when UFOs were seen in the lunar orbit and more voices broke into the communications channel with mission control.

This, not unnaturally, caused some consternation back on Earth. The frequency channel they were using is such that it is virtually impossible for any amateur operator to intrude. Controllers were left with a problem that they could not explain, but at the same time could hardly ignore – the

Left: astronaut Gordon Cooper arrives safely back on Earth in his Mercury capsule on 17 May 1963. On 16 May, while the capsule was orbiting the Earth above Hawaii, strange voices broke in on the special channel used for communication between Cooper and mission control. When they were later analysed, the voices were found to speak what was obviously an intelligible language

Below: the launch and return of the Apollo VIII Borman-Lovell-Anders mission of 1968. On 21 December, unidentified disc-shaped objects were sighted by the astronauts in the Moon's orbit; and the strange voice phenomena of the Mercury mission were repeated

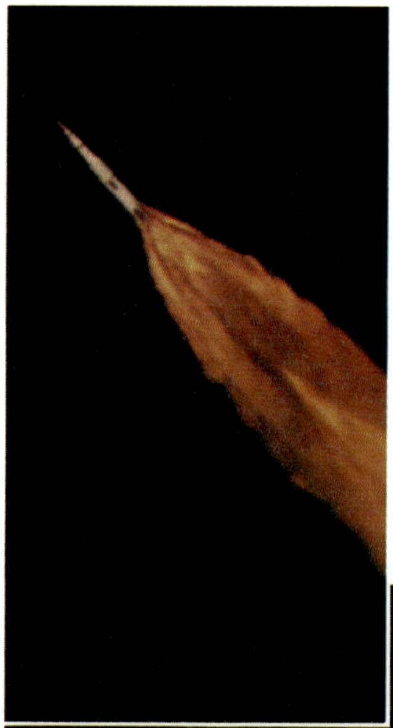

security risk was too great.

But, as far back as 1927, two Americans, Taylor and Young, had taken such phenomena seriously enough to try to locate the source of the radio signals. They had identified an echo-periodicity of 0.01 seconds originating from a distance of between 1800 and 6250 miles (2900 and 10,000 kilometres), and were comparing their observations with those of Marconi. By December 1928, a number of scientists were interested – Jürgen Hals of Philips's Eindhoven laboratories in Holland had discussed his findings with Professor Carl Stormer of Oslo, mentioning three-second delays he had experienced with an experimental radio transmitter. After another year, on 28 October 1929, Dr van der Pol, also of Philips, confirmed that he had noted further odd echoes from a planned emission of impulses at the same time every morning. It was van der Pol's analysis of the delay between emissions and the receipt of their echoes, always on the same wavelength, that effectively excluded ideas that they may have been bouncing off the Moon or the inner Van Allen belt, or that they might have been somehow stored and reflected from layers of ionised gas.

A Scottish science writer, Duncan Lunan, studied the records of these anomalous radio echoes over a period of some years, and eventually came up with the assertion that they originated from an alien space probe. He also commented on the misfortune that the signals 'happened to be received at a time when they would as a matter of course be attributed (by a majority of people) to some natural phenomenon'.

Working on the assumption that the signals constituted some intelligible message, Lunan proceeded to try to crack what he envisaged as a coded pattern. His report, published in the April 1973 issue of *Spaceflight*, is extremely complex and has to be read in the original to be appreciated. But what it boils down to is a graphical diagram of the constellations of the northern hemisphere – a picture that contains one startling incongruity: the binary star epsilon Boötis is wrongly aligned. Using astronomical measuring techniques, Lunan has deduced that the binary star appears in his diagram as it would have been 13,000 years ago – a hint that this was the time when the probe first reached our solar system.

Unfortunately for Mr Lunan, there are a number of serious objections that can be raised to his theory. First and most serious – as Robert Sheaffer has pointed out in his book *The* UFO *verdict* – Lunan's map does not correctly represent the echoes published by van der Pol, as Lunan claims. And, even allowing for the alteration in the position of epsilon Boötis that Lunan claims, the map is only a very crude approximation to the actual positions of the stars in the Boötes region. As Sheaffer says, 'one would not think it too difficult for an advanced, space-faring civilization to make its interstellar probes capable of transmitting its star maps correctly.'

But perhaps the most damning indictment of Lunan's theorising is his own reaction to criticism. If the map does not depict the stars of the constellation Boötes, then perhaps, he argues, it is the constellation Cetus – an extraordinary claim, given that Lunan once believed that the map showed the epsilon Boötis solar system down to the smallest moon, and that epsilon Boötis is a double sun whereas tau Ceti is single, something that one would expect to be apparent from so detailed a map.

But Mr John Stonely of the London *Enquirer*, at least, has taken Lunan's claims

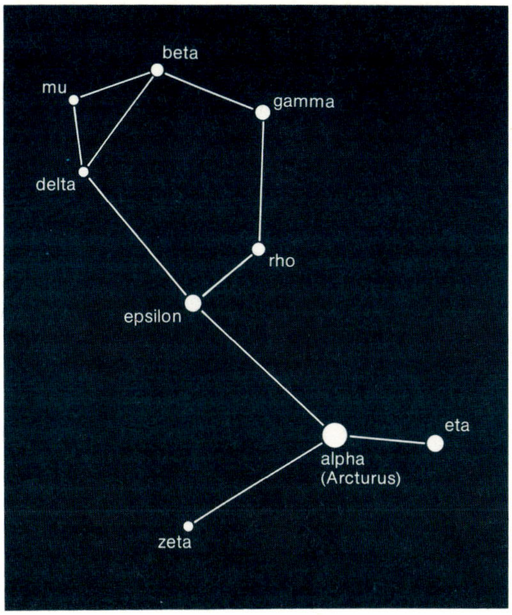


Scottish science writer Duncan Lunan has studied reports of unexplained radio echoes and put forward the idea that they are made by an alien space probe from the constellation Boötes. He claims the echoes are a coded map of the probe's home constellation, and also that he has deciphered it (below). But in fact his map bears only a superficial resemblance to the real Boötes (left); in particular, the binary star epsilon Boötis is in the wrong place – a fact Lunan explains by saying that the star appears in the position it would have occupied when the probe first reached our solar system

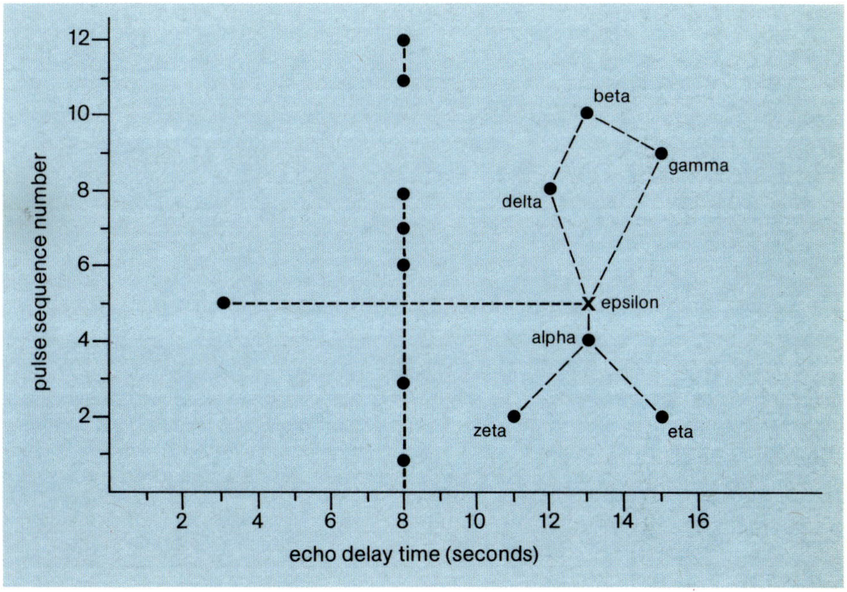


seriously enough to calculate mathematical odds, of 10,000 to 1, against delayed echoes producing such a diagram merely by chance. Of the nature of the probe, Stonely writes that it must be some kind of incomparably advanced computer. 'As soon as the existence of the probe is definitely established, we should interrogate it . . . it might lead to the release of information from its certainly immense store of data.'

### Cosmic blast

Writer John A. Keel has made an intensive study of strange signals and inexplicable broadcasts. One intriguing example took place in 1960: scientists Otto Struve and Frank Drake had just aligned the dish antenna at Green Banks, West Virginia, USA, on epsilon Eridani and tau Ceti when their recording needles were blasted off the dials by a signal of 8 pulses per second. The frequency was 1420.4 megahertz (the frequency of the radio waves emitted by hydrogen in interstellar space), and it continued coming in for five minutes. The Naval Research Laboratory later reported that it had recorded similar anomalies during the preceding six months, but tests showed that they were definitely not of cosmic origin: they seemed to come from an unidentified and unimaginably powerful terrestrial transmitter close at hand.

Signals of unknown origin (SUOS) have been with us since 1899, and may have been around for many years before we had the apparatus to detect them. The range of signals is puzzlingly wide: dot-dot-dot-dash codes and radio echoes to vocal transmissions and vibrational loudspeaker effects – it is difficult to conceive that these diverse phenomena could have a common source. But perhaps we are confusing the issue by thinking of the mysterious signals in terms of simple electromagnetic transmissions. Perhaps, in our quest for extra-terrestrial beings, we could be not so much trying to identify the wrong sources as confining ourselves to the wrong methodology.

A few years after Cleve Backster's startling discovery, in the late 1960s, that plants give out signals when attached to a polygraph lie detector, Mr L.G. Lawrence of the Ecola Institute in San Bernardino, California, USA, was testing newly developed apparatus that incorporated what he called an organic transformer. Its purpose was to transform into sound waves the electrical oscillations of the polygraph.

In 1971 Lawrence was working in the Mojave Desert, experimenting with cacti. He had prepared his instruments and was about to wire up the electrodes to the plants when, to his consternation, they began to record signals – signals that could not possibly be electromagnetic in origin, for the apparatus was completely shielded from all known electromagnetic sources by a Faraday cage. Lawrence noted that the instruments were aligned with the constellation of the Great Bear – and the only possible explanation he could think of was that the signals were some totally unknown form of energy emanating from that constellation.

No matter how often Lawrence rechecked for faults, failures and misalignment, the inflow of data from Ursa Major remained constant and continuous – seemingly intelligent signals in a rhythm that ruled out the possibility that they were the result of mere chance.

Further experiments are proceeding under controlled conditions, but a huge challenge remains: are we, as a race, sufficiently advanced to grasp the opportunity of a cosmic connection in a completely new medium – before it, like radio, becomes too clogged by our own exploitation of it?

Shall we, unlike Tesla and Marconi, be able in time to answer a strange world's greeting to us?

**Further reading**

Ian Ridpath, *Messages from the stars*, Fontana 1978

Robert Sheaffer, *The UFO verdict: examining the evidence*, Prometheus Books (New York) 1981

# Vampires: myth and reality

**Count Dracula continues to hold his audiences in a state of horrified half-belief. But whatever the truth of the vampire legend, its roots can be traced to a number of simple facts – as DANIEL FARSON explains**

AT THE END of the first stage version of *Dracula* in 1924, the actor-manager Hamilton Deane (who played the part of Van Helsing) appeared before the curtain with a little reassurance for the audience:

> Just a moment, ladies and gentlemen! Just a word before you leave. We hope the memories of Dracula . . . won't give you bad dreams, so just a word of reassurance. When you get home tonight and the lights have been turned out and you are afraid to look behind the curtains and you dread to see a face appear at the window – why, pull yourself together! And remember that, after all, *there are such things*!

It was a perfect exit line. The audience, primed to a fine degree by a background of vampire books, had spent the evening thrilling to the extraordinarily compelling tale of 'the greatest vampire of them all' – Dracula. His creator, the theatre manager Bram Stoker, knew instinctively that his story struck some chord deep in the collective subconscious of his audience. *Dracula* was both a bestseller and a box office success; that meant that it had mass appeal. And the tale of the vampire Count still has. Why?

As actor Christopher Lee explained, Dracula appeals partly because he is a superhuman figure, an immortal whose chilling presence is also sexually irresistible. Psychologists point to the clear difference between the sadistic, dominant vampire and the masochistic or subservient victim. But whatever the jargon used, Dracula is more fascinating than the atavistic werewolf (who is, after all, at least half animal, and certainly not an aristocrat) or the shadowy ghost.

Above: a still from Hammer's *Dracula AD 1972*; Christopher Lee as the Count attacks an innocent victim in a typical film interpretation of the vampire legend. The sado-masochistic overtones of the story, with its sexually irresistible attacker and willing victim, contribute to its power to fascinate

Above right: three Brahmans make incantations, accompanied by vampires, in a story from Sir Richard Burton's *Tales of Hindu devilry*. The tales are purportedly told by the Baital, Indian vampires

Right: an 18th-century representation of the day of judgement. The struggle to escape from a tomb or coffin was, all too often, a matter of grim reality at that time, when premature burial was common

But the vampire is not to be considered on a par with 'the creature from the black lagoon' or Dr Who's enemies, the Daleks. Whereas the others can be dismissed as mere stagecraft, thrilling enough during the performance but forgotten soon after, the vampire is to be taken seriously. There are masses of documents from Eastern Europe in the 18th century attesting to the reality of the 'undead'. So – are there such things?

As in many other aspects of the paranormal, all possible rational explanations must be thoroughly exhausted before a 'supernatural' explanation can even be considered. And in the case of the 'vampire epidemic' of 200 years ago there are several such rational explanations to choose from.

For example, the popular occult writer Dennis Wheatley has pointed out that in past times of great deprivation, beggars broke into graveyards and slept in the shelter of the mausoleums by day, emerging at night to forage for food; thin, pale and seen leaving tombs under cover of darkness, they were perhaps not unnaturally taken to be the legendary and terrifying vampires.

However, the mistaken identity of relatively few human scavengers does not explain those cases of corpses found to be incorrupt when their coffins were opened. This is a rare but by no means unknown phenomenon (see page 774) and various 'natural' explanations have been suggested as the cause of it. Certainly the soil in which a body is buried can make an astonishing difference to the rate at which it decomposes. On the volcanic island of Santorini, Greece, for example, corpses are found so intact after a great number of years that the local people have a saying 'send a vampire to Santorini', just as the British might speak of 'sending coals to Newcastle'.

But by far the most convincing of the rational explanations is that of premature burial. Not all cataleptics were as fortunate as the Irish soldier, in the early 1800s, who 'came back to life' when being roughly handled prior to his burial. Coma, catalepsy and other death-like states are barely understood by the modern world, let alone by superstitious peasants from 'the land beyond the forests' in times gone by.

How many poor wretches awoke to discover themselves immured in a coffin with the heavy earth pressing down on them, or perhaps, having successfully fought their way out of the coffin, found themselves locked in the family mausoleum, there to die of hunger, thirst and horror?

### Terror beyond the grave

Premature burial was common. It is said that, when an 18th-century English graveyard was being demolished to make way for a car park, a third of the corpses turned up by the bulldozer showed signs of having struggled while in their coffins. The evidence included broken fingers from scratching at the coffin lid in their – final – death agony, even hands protruding from the coffin, and blood upon the shroud where the 'corpse' had bitten his or her own flesh as suffocation, or madness, took its toll. And it was the presence of blood on an exhumed corpse that was frequently considered proof that the dead person was a vampire.

But if the newly dead was rumoured to be a vampire (perhaps feeble sounds may have been heard emanating from the grave) then the terrified 'witnesses' would take the time-honoured measures against it. And if the 'corpse's' heart was beating that was, to them, a sure sign that it must be staked. No wonder there are so many accounts of alleged vampires screaming as the stake was plunged into their living hearts.

Charlotte Stoker used to tell the young Bram a grisly bedtime story concerning a local victim of the cholera epidemic. The woman, believed dead, was thrown on the heap of corpses in the lime pit. However, her grief-stricken husband, who went to recover her body and give her a decent burial, discovered she was still breathing. She lived on happily for many years after that appalling experience. But supposing she had recovered by herself and had been seen staggering out of the pit at night – it would have been easy to mistake her for one of the 'undead'.

From time to time modern newspapers carry stories of people, certified dead, coming to life on the marble slab in the morgue or when being prepared for burial. In these days of 'spare part' surgery the controversy rages over the exact moment, and indeed, the true nature of death more than at any point in history. But the Victorians were at least aware of the possibility of premature burial; some even became obsessed with the idea. Edgar Allan Poe based several of his stories on the theme, and in both the United States and Europe various

The vampire bat, *Desmodus rotundus*, found in Mexico and South America. These creatures, only about 3 inches (8 centimetres) long, are able to feed on the blood of sleeping animals without awakening them

patents were taken out on coffins with alarm bells or emergency air supplies incorporated into their design.

Premature burial may often have arisen because the various steps of rigor mortis are commonly misunderstood. The muscles of a corpse start to go rigid, beginning in the face and neck, about an hour and a half after death. (This may set in sooner or later depending on the temperature of the surroundings.) Rigor mortis passes off roughly 36 hours later – the muscles lose their extreme rigidity and the body becomes relatively pliable. This could well be the explanation for the 'vampire' story told to the author in 1974 in the valley of Curtea de Arges, Romania. The speaker was a handsome gypsy woman, who described, through an interpreter, the shock of her family when they came to lay out her father's body for burial. For the limbs were pliable, not rigid. This news raced through the village, a village where this could mean only one thing – the old man had become a vampire. A stake was duly plunged through his heart, and the villagers were satisfied and relieved. But perhaps – if this was not simply a case of rigor mortis passing off prematurely – the old man was still alive.

There is even a logical explanation for the widespread use of garlic as a vampire repellent. Plague was frequently carried by flies, and it was noticed that certain farms were spared if they hung out garlic. There was no magic involved; garlic bulbs exude drops of moisture that flies detest. Garlic, when eaten, is also believed to be a natural antiseptic, a *blood purifier*.

And vampires were always a useful scapegoat, in certain rural communities, if animals weakened and died. These days the vet would no doubt administer a dose of antibiotics or special vitamin supplement and all would be well – in most cases. However, mysterious sicknesses and mutilations of cattle and other animals do occur, but hostile ufonauts are now the fashionable culprits.

**Demonic bloodsuckers**

There may be logical, even mundane, explanations for 99 out of 100 cases of alleged vampirism, but it is the hundredth case that sets the researcher wondering. For many years occultists have believed in the existence of demonic bloodsucking materialisations. One, the practising occultist Dion Fortune (whose real name was Violet Firth), believed that the 'astral body' can escape from a person's living body and assume another form such as a bird, animal – or vampire.

Dion Fortune also cited the case of dead Hungarian soldiers who became vampires during the First World War, maintaining themselves in the 'etheric double' – that is, halfway between this world and the next, or 'earthbound' – by vampirising the wounded. Vampirism is believed to be contagious; the person who is vampirised, being depleted of vitality, is thought to be a psychic vacuum, himself absorbing the 'life force' from anyone who falls prey to him.

Psychical research, on the other hand, deals not with beliefs but with observed facts. One of the most common of all phenomena investigated by the SPR, for example, is that of the poltergeist (see page 290) and an allied phenomenon seems to be that of the invisible attacker (such as the Reverend Neil Smith described – see page 1003). Raised scratch marks appeared on the face of poltergeist victim Eleonore Zugun of Romania, during 1926. And in 1960 a certain Jimmy de Bruin, a 20-year-old farm worker in South Africa, became the focus for a spate of poltergeist activity. On one occasion an investigating police officer heard de Bruin scream with agony as cuts spontaneously appeared on his legs and chest.

Other areas of the paranormal also involve the spontaneous appearance of wounds or blood, such as images that bleed (see page 821), and stigmata (see page 846). These, however, are commonly accepted as 'holy' phenomena, whereas vampirism is widely believed to be 'of the Devil'. It may indeed be true that these phenomena are opposite sides of the same coin, one good and the other evil. But perhaps all unexplained phenomena emanate from the same source, being neither moral nor immoral, just unusual. But until we discover what it is we can continue to thrill to the latest vampire tale and ponder on the question: are there such things?

**Further reading**

Basil Copper, *The vampire in legend, fact and art*, Robert Hale 1973
Anthony Masters, *The natural history of the vampire*, Mayflower 1974
Mark Ronson, *Bloodthirst*, Hamlyn 1980

# Under the greenwood tree

**The greenwood has always been a place where strange things happen – a doorway from the real world into the beyond. And weird things still happen in woods – as in Clapham Wood on England's South Downs. HAMISH HOWARD and TOYNE NEWTON report**

A hollow oak stands sentry to the village of Clapham – and to the forbidding Clapham Wood (inset), for hundreds of years the scene of weird incidents

CLAPHAM WOOD is a small densely-treed area nestling in the shelter of the South Downs in West Sussex, England. Travelling southwards, a sharp left turn off the busy road known as Long Furlong at Findon leads into this area of mystery and intrigue, of strange disappearances and UFO sightings. There is even an ancient hollow oak, which signposts the way to the village, adding to the general air of mystery. That there is 'something weird' in the woods has always been rumoured. But what that something is, no one seems to know.

On a hill above the village, as if protecting its parishioners from the dark woods beyond, stands the 13th-century Church of the Blessed Virgin Mary. The strange atmosphere of the woods themselves is felt immediately. Stunted trees twist and writhe as if in pain; there is a larger crater, believed to

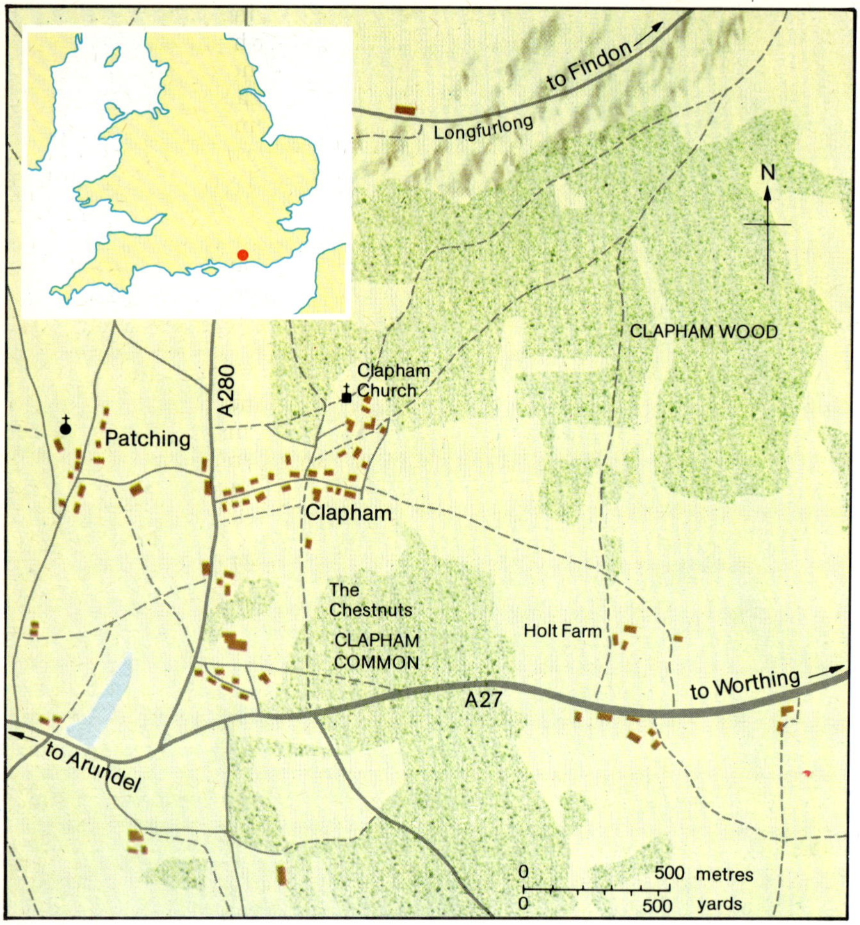


Above: the location of Clapham Wood

have been caused by a wartime bomb – although some maintain it was a meteorite and yet others say it is merely an ancient lime pit – where nothing grows; and there are mysterious little clearings containing ruins of old cottages.

Perhaps it was from one of these, a couple of centuries ago, that an old woman saw what would today be recognised as a UFO. She told villagers that one dark night she had seen a 'bright round shape like the full Moon' float down into the woods and disappear in the bushes.

The outcome of this event seems to have been that 'the woods were filled with fumes that stinketh of burning matter' and that many local folk thereafter were 'affeared to go there'. As for the old woman of the woods, she appears to have been immediately 'smitten of the palsy', and was given a wide berth by the locals; this may have been because of her sighting, but it seems more reasonable to suppose she was the victim of one of the witch hunts so prevalent in England at that time.

Since those far off days there have been many more UFO sightings – and some say landings – in the small area of Clapham Wood, and although several witnesses have given reports to the police there must be many people who are too afraid of ridicule to do so. The fact that these sightings often occur at night when few witnesses are about makes them very difficult to prove.

One such sighting concerns a telephone engineer who was driving home alone along the Findon Road after night duty when he saw a large saucer-shaped object in the sky above the woods. It hovered for some time before making a circle of the area, then veered off. That was in October 1972, when other sightings were independently reported in that area. One report came from a couple out walking near Long Furlong who thought they saw Jupiter or Venus low in the western sky – until it started to move very quickly due north, keeping in line with a ridge of the downs, as it came towards them. Suddenly, when the object was over Clapham Wood, a beam of light descended vertically from it, and then rapidly withdrew, and the object shot away north-eastwards at great speed. The beam was visible for about 10 seconds.

In fact the brief time the Clapham Wood UFOs are visible makes their verification almost impossible, as one inhabitant of the village found in 1968. It was 2 a.m. and, being unable to sleep, he was making himself a hot drink; glancing out of the kitchen window, he saw a saucer-shaped object hovering directly over the nearby woods. He promptly made an emergency call to the police; although the call was answered speedily, by the time the police arrived the UFO had disappeared.

By far the most significant sightings in this area are those reported by Paul Glover of the British Phenomenon Research Group, who was walking with a friend along the downs towards Clapham Wood one clear starlit night in the summer of 1967. At about 10 p.m. both suddenly became aware of a 'huge black mass' low in the sky blotting out the stars as it moved very quickly towards them.

The object was boomerang-shaped and made no sound. As it passed overhead the displacement of air was so great they ducked into the bushes for safety.

Below: Mr R. D. Bennett, warden of Clapham church, whose rector disappeared in Clapham Wood in 1979. Mr Bennett comments that the villagers think the wood is 'extremely weird'

They vehemently denied it could have been a cloud, for it retained its shape, was on a definite course, and there was no wind to drive it – certainly not at the tremendous speed at which it was travelling. Somewhat shaken they continued their walk, and minutes later saw two bright objects high in the sky, which they watched for several minutes. One of the UFOs released a smaller object that travelled across to the second object, seemed to enter it, and then re-emerged and veered off, disappearing from sight.

There was no denying that that night there was increased UFO activity in the area for some reason, but it was when Paul Glover and his companion were approaching Clapham Wood about an hour later that the most spectacular sighting occurred. Two yellow lights descended in the region of the woods, followed just a few seconds later by two more, and then a final pair, making a total of three groups of two. Then at the point where they seemed to have dipped down into the woods, two white beams of light shot out horizontally – quite unimpeded by the contours of the downlands – followed by the next two beams and then the final two, all travelling very fast, before disappearing into the night sky. No craft of any kind could be seen behind the lights.

**Messages from a ouija board**

During that same year, in the village of Rustington a few miles westwards along the coast, two schoolboys, Toyne Newton and John Arnold, who had never even heard of Clapham Wood, had a strange story spelled out to them on a ouija board: that Clapham Wood was a base for spacecraft, and that one

Paul Glover saw UFOs in Clapham Wood – a huge black boomerang (above) followed by small lights moving at speed (below)

had landed recently to fetch supplies of sulphur and other chemicals.

No one believed the boys, of course, but nearly 10 years later an investigation was carried out when soil samples were taken from the woods. From the report given in BBC-TV's *Nationwide* programme at the time it seems there was more than a grain of truth at least in the boys' sulphur story.

The investigation had actually been triggered off by reports of dogs disappearing in the woods in 1975. According to a local newspaper, the *Worthing Herald*, Wallace, a three-year-old chow belonging to Mr and Mrs Peter Love of Clapham, disappeared, as did a two-year-old collie belonging to Mr John Cornford. Apparently the collie, although normally obedient, suddenly rushed off into a small copse between two trees in an area known locally as the Chestnuts, and was never seen again – although its mystified owner searched the place thoroughly.

Mrs H. T. Wells, who lives at nearby Durrington, said that when her collie gets near the woods it 'becomes desperate', and a golden retriever belonging to Mr E. F. Rawlins of Worthing ran into the woods one day and returned 'very distressed'. Shortly afterwards it became paralysed and the vet had to destroy it.

Another dog owner, who wishes to remain anonymous, reported that when she took her dog to this area it ran round in circles foaming at the mouth, with its eyes bulging

Above: Clapham Wood's mysterious crater. Nothing will grow there; no one knows its cause

Right: the strange black shape seen in Clapham Wood by Dave Stringer in 1977. He later found a footprint at the site (above right) – similar to one he had seen at the meeting place of a black coven in Brighton

Below: Mr John Cornford, a local farmer, whose two-year-old collie dog went missing in Clapham Wood and was never seen again

out of its head as if in great pain, and only with difficulty did she manage to entice it back into her car and drive home, where the dog eventually calmed down.

This part of the woods is easily accessible to the public, being on the A27 dual carriageway, and it is regularly used for exercising dogs. It is also used by horse riders. One young horseman (who wishes to remain anonymous) tethered his mount firmly to a tree stump while he relieved himself in the woods, and was amazed to find the animal had disappeared during his brief absence. Although he searched the area extensively and made exhaustive enquiries, the horse was never found.

Animals are not alone in being affected by the peculiar atmosphere in this particular part of the woods, for several people have described how they have felt 'pushed over by invisible forces', while others have felt faint for no apparent reason.

Two men walking together in the woods told how they were both suddenly afflicted at the same time – one doubling over in agony and staggering, the other clutching at his head and saying that he felt as if his eardrums 'were being pulled from the inside outwards'. These painful effects disappeared simultaneously when the two men had gone about 50 yards (45 metres) further.

It seems beyond doubt that this small area encapsulates a source of electrical charge, or ray, or unknown force, which, when released into the atmosphere in small bursts, seems to affect anyone in the vicinity at the time with some kind of abnormal pressure or even mild apoplexy. But what the force is, no one seems to know.

Its strange and disturbing effects seem to be metamorphic, for – according to the local press – the body of a man who went missing in the woods was found only two weeks later in such an advanced state of decomposition that only when the body was positively identified could the short time lapse be pinpointed. Forensic evidence showed that the normally accepted rate of a decomposing corpse had, in this particular case, been greatly accelerated due to some unknown factor.

Mystifying reports such as these have a double effect in that, while keeping apprehensive people away, those given to seeking the truth of such situations are particularly drawn to the area. Among these is Dave Stringer of the Southern Paranormal Investigation Group, who, while not disbelieving the reports of so many independent witnesses, nevertheless visited the woods in August of 1977 'with an open mind' – and his Geiger counter.

He was aware of a strange silence, but the woods were beautiful and the air still as he came to the part called the Chestnuts. Everything appeared normal, but as he walked through the heavy undergrowth he had to raise the Geiger counter above his head. It was then that it began to register at an alarming rate before returning to normal.

Wonderingly, Stringer looked back at the area through which he had just passed, and saw a dark shape about 12 feet (3.5 metres) in height; while not being distinctive in outline, it was very definitely not smoke, or a smoke-enshrouded bush, but he could describe it only as a 'black mass'. Seconds later a large white disc shot out from behind nearby trees at an angle of about 45° and disappeared into the sky, and simultaneously the dark form disappeared also.

Stringer retraced his steps, not using the Geiger counter this time but looking down at the ground, which was part grass and part muddy footpath, for some evidence of a solid shape to back up what he thought he had witnessed. At the spot where the form had appeared he came upon a faint imprint of a four-toed foot, twice the width of a man's foot but very narrow at the heel.

Only on one other occasion had he seen such a mysterious footprint, and that had been at Devil's Dyke near Brighton, where there was known to be a black magic coven. Could there be a connection?

### Devil's footprint?

Part of a black coven's ritual involves the burning of sulphur, which could account for the acrid smell and fumes reported in the woods, and one particular branch of their rumoured experimentation concerns the dematerialisation of small creatures. This, it is claimed, releases the creatures' 'life spark', which escapes without form or shape.

Stringer made a quick sketch of the single footprint, which, although unknown to him at the time, coincides significantly with the footprint of the demon Amduscias, illustrated in the 1863 edition of Collin de Plancy's *Dictionnaire infernal*.

The consistency of UFO sightings over

Clapham Wood continued during 1978 and 1979, one being reported by a man standing on nearby Highdown Hill, which is higher than Clapham and overlooks the woods. The witness says he saw a large orange ball about twice the size of an aircraft, which manoeuvred above the woods for some 20 minutes before disappearing. And several independent witnesses from different vantage points reported seeing a huge light in the sky above Clapham Wood one summer's night in 1979. It descended vertically into the woods and glowed among the trees.

Could it be explained away as mere coincidence? It seems unlikely with so many people coming forward with similar stories of sightings all made at the same time.

The spate of strange reports that year concluded with the disappearance of the Reverend Neil Snelling, vicar of Clapham church. One fine morning after shopping at Worthing he decided to walk back to his Steyning home through Clapham Wood. Almost certainly he would have taken the 'Chestnuts' route. He has not been heard of since, and an exhaustive search of the area revealed nothing.

Right: a photograph taken by Paul Glover. He saw nothing at the time, although he felt intense cold – but when the photograph was developed, it showed a goat's head, age-old symbol of satanism

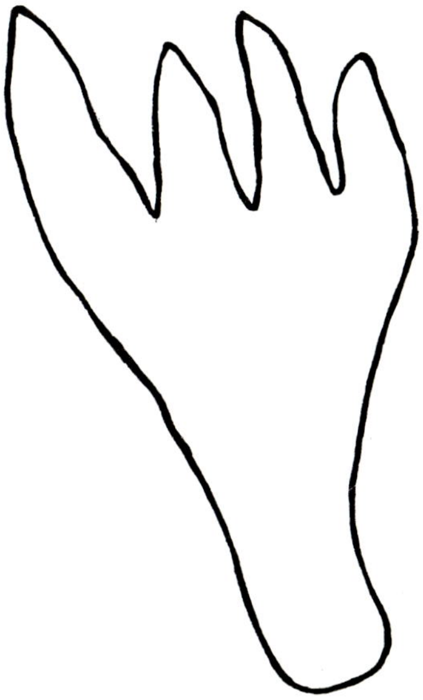

What happened to him? Why did the dogs disappear so completely within only a few yards of their unsuspecting owners? How can solid bodies vanish into thin air without leaving a trace? Is there a deadly chemical in the soil, or some unknown force that disrupts the molecular structure of organic creatures? Did a meteorite – or some unknown object from space – once fall in the area, and if so, is it giving off harmful rays or acting as a beacon for UFOs?

So many independent reports cannot be ignored, but real proof of the phenomena is not easy to come by. It was in the hope of obtaining some form of proof that Paul Glover armed himself with a camera and, accompanied by Dave Stringer and another friend, made for Clapham Wood.

It was a dark, clear evening, but there was no UFO activity. Eventually they decided to make their way homewards via the Chestnuts route, and it was as they were walking through this area that all three of them, simultaneously, had a feeling of intense cold. They hurried on, and the feeling ceased. So they walked back over the same area – three times in fact – and each time experienced this sudden and unnatural drop in temperature.

Glover decided to point the camera at what he thought was the source of this strange condition, seeing nothing, but firing the shutter purely on speculation.

When the photograph was developed, however, it showed an uncanny white mass revealing the unmistakable image of a goat's head, the age-old symbol of satanic rites. Was this confirmation of the past – or present – activities of a black coven? Or was it quite separate, adding yet another phenomenon to the enigma of Clapham Wood?

# Agents of confusion

**For decades ufology has been in a state of confusion and disarray, struggling to research a phenomenon for which there is only slender evidence, says WILLIAM H. SPAULDING. And the reason? Secret government agencies have been manipulating the evidence and the witnesses**

WHAT CONCLUSIONS can we draw from the documents that GSW has drawn from the CIA and the State Department? To answer that question, we first have to look objectively at some salient facts about the state of ufology. For that is the raw material that the CIA has used to its advantage over the years in its campaign of debunking, disinformation and calculated manipulation.

In the first place, most information about UFOs is based on the (usually unsupported) word of the witnesses. In many instances, this type of report is labelled 'authentic' by the pro-UFO community after an investigation that usually amounts to little more than a conversation with the participants. The ability of witnesses to 'identify' unusual aerial phenomena is notoriously unreliable: take for example the numerous cases of dome-shaped, spinning, saucer-like craft that perform extraordinary manoeuvres and display unusual lighting configurations reported by numerous reliable individuals – and then turn out to be aircraft towing advertising material. Lack of time, money and effective research techniques all contribute to the large element of foul-up in ufology.

On the other hand not all UFO events can be categorised as 'identifiable'. There is a small residue of events that seem to be caused by real objects (or what appear to be real objects). Blue Book estimated these at some 3 per cent of the total; civilian investigators put the figure at about 8 per cent. Probably the true figure is somewhere in between. But relatively little can be done to investigate these cases scientifically: there are few physical traces to take into the laboratory. What does seem certain is that no event represents a visitation from outer space. The mathematical odds are simply too remote for the extraterrestrial hypothesis to be taken seriously. Whatever true UFOs are, they would appear

The Goodyear blimp broadcasts its message to the world. But at some angles, could it be taken for a UFO? On 29 April 1978, Mr and Mrs S of Aurora, Illinois, reported a brilliantly lit, saucer-shaped craft 'as big as a football field' that was also seen by numerous other witnesses. With lights 'twirling round it', it followed the couple's car and allegedly caused power failures in the locality. But Allan Hendry, then investigator for the Center for UFO Studies, identified the 'saucer' as an aircraft owned by Ad Airlines of Chicago. This 'classic' UFO – and its mundane explanation – is a perfect example of the suggestibility of people. Anyone wishing to exploit such credulousness would have an easy task

to have a distinctly earthly origin.

Even so, the transparent ineffectiveness of the official investigations, the ineptitude of the special commissions, and the constant stonewalling of the government led many civilian researchers to believe that a massive conspiracy was at work to cover up the government's knowledge of contact from outer space. In the 1940s, rumours of crashed saucers and dead aliens were rife. In the 1970s there were contactee and abduction stories galore. Not only that, but odd leaks and whispers of information came the way of the research groups from seemingly well-placed military and intelligence sources. What other conclusion was there to draw? Who else but aliens could be behind these tantalising stories?

Undoubtedly the government – as embodied in the CIA – has been involved in a cover up, as we have seen in the previous article. But what we are about to suggest is that while the CIA was collecting UFO information from around the globe (though claiming to be doing nothing of the kind), it was also manufacturing the rumour that the government knew more than it was prepared to admit. This tactic was employed partly to distract ufologists' attention from what the government was actually up to, and partly to add to the disarray of ufology.

Behind the smokescreen of confusion and ignorance that it created, the CIA could proceed with its own outlandish experiments, whose real nature would be further disguised by the fact that they seemed no weirder than the rest of the whole bizarre phenomenon. And such activity would be just as intractable to scientific investigation, whether by the USAF or by civilians. In this it was fundamental that the USAF's investigations, for example, should be kept secret.

Clues to what really came to fascinate the CIA about the UFO question are scattered throughout the documents obtained by GSW. Of course, the government's conspirators of silence may not be from the CIA: they may be from the Defense Intelligence Agency, the National Security Agency, or the super-secret National Reconnaissance Organisation, or some clandestine group within any of these. Though the evidence to hand points to the CIA, the precise identity of the culprits is unimportant as long as the principles on which they seem to be working remain obscure.

From the first the CIA was intrigued by the psychological implications of the flying saucer mystery. Says part of one memorandum from 1952:

> With world-wide sightings reported, it was found that, up to the time of this investigation, there had been in the Soviet press no report or comment on flying saucers. With a state-controlled press, this could only result from an official policy decision. The question, therefore, arises as to whether or not these sightings: 1) could be controlled, 2) could be predicted, and 3) could be used from a psychological warfare

Top: artist's impression of the 'spacecraft' seen by Joe Simonton in 1961, one of whose occupants gave him a pancake (above). Was he hoaxed by a secret government agency such as the DIA or NSA (below: their official seals)? And to what extent has the US government connived at rumours of 'captured aliens'? This picture (right) almost certainly shows a monkey used in rocket tests, not (as alleged) a space visitor

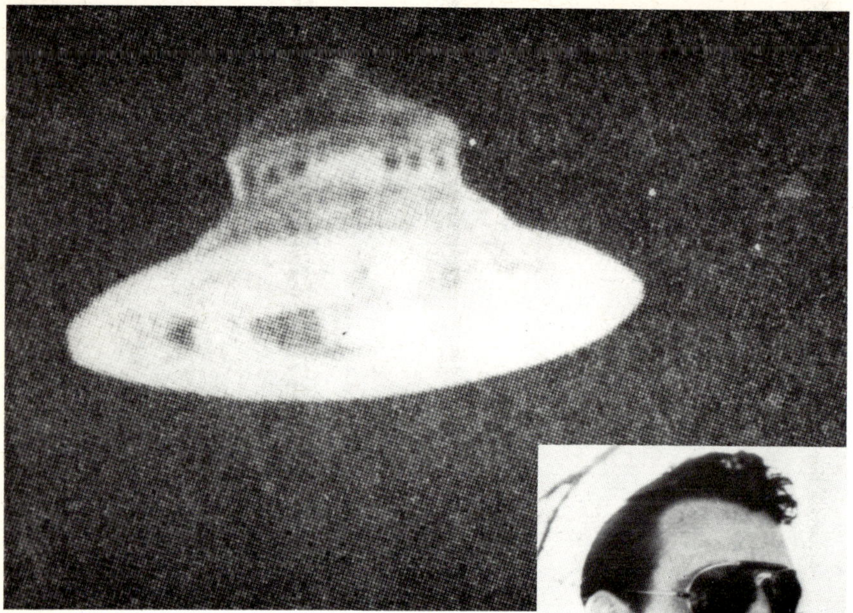

> point of view, either defensively or offensively . . . a fair proportion of our population is mentally conditioned to the acceptance of the incredible.

These concerns were echoed in the secret report of the Robertson Panel in 1953, after which the CIA took over the real business of UFO investigation. At this time, the documents show, the CIA's Office of Scientific Intelligence was privately convinced that UFOs were extra-terrestrial craft. While awaiting proof of this, a debunking campaign was designed to defuse any potential public hysteria. Everyone expected that UFOs, like any other fad, would thus be helped to evaporate from the public consciousness.

The 'spaceship' (top) that was photographed by Howard Menger (above). The ship is suspiciously similar to that seen by Adamski, and its occupants imparted a similar, banal, wisdom. Who hoaxed whom?

But at some point – perhaps when the extra-terrestrial hypothesis was discarded, or perhaps when it became indisputable that UFOs were not simply a passing craze, or perhaps with the growth of secret high-technology research – the Agency realised that it could conduct experiments in psychological warfare of its own. If the Soviets were not behind the sightings in an attempt to manipulate the populace, there was no reason why the CIA should not get behind them instead. The benefits would be manifold: the military could get on with its secret aerial projects in comfort, since anyone coming unwittingly in contact with them would fall foul of the CIA's disinformation service and public debunking routine; and the CIA would discover just how far public attitudes could be manipulated, how individuals reacted to bizarre and unprecedented events, and how the information was disseminated and what reactions it generated.

This paradoxical programme of simultaneous encouragement and discouragement of the UFO controversy would work on several fronts. The idea of a cover up would be nurtured through leaks of classified information to civilian investigators, while a number of events could, quite simply, be staged. A number of agents infiltrating the research organisations would then be able to feed disinformation to the UFO groups and at the same time monitor their awareness of secret military hardware. Friends in the press would dutifully play up UFO material whether it were hoax, misidentification or staged event.

This programme is what GSW calls the

## Anonymity guaranteed

At a UFO conference held at Fort Smith, Arkansas, in 1974 the research group APRO announced that henceforth it was intending to concentrate solely on contactee and abduction cases. Whether this was out of boredom with run-of-the-mill UFO sightings or because APRO hoped to gain publicity is not known. Some of the cases APRO has espoused are highly questionable – the Walton abduction case (see page 307) being but one instance. Here is another.

In February 1981 Ground Saucer Watch received from APRO an anonymous letter purporting to come from a US airman. It described a UFO landing near Kirtland Air Force Base, New Mexico. An individual in a metallic suit got out, got in again, and the craft flew away. A Civil Air Patrol Cadet, one Craig R. Weitzel, apparently took photographs of the landing. Later, he was (the letter said) visited by men in black, which

Coral Lorenzen, founder of APRO, which concentrates on UFO contacts and abductions. Mrs Lorenzen has said that such cases show 'a careful, methodical and in-depth study of Earth and its inhabitants is underway'

Weitzel reported to the USAF security police, who in turn notified the Kirtland AFB Office of Special Investigations. A Mr Dody then looked into the matter, though the letter-writer claimed that Dody later disavowed all knowledge of the incident. The letter-writer also claimed that his commanding officer, one Colonel Bruce Purvine, had admitted to him that OSI was investigating UFO sightings – in the greatest secrecy. Mention was also made of crashed saucers, some of which are supposedly kept in the Sandia area of Kirtland AFB.

Ground Saucer Watch did what it could to check this report, which confirmed the existence of the Sandia area and of Mr Dody of the OSI. Colonel Purvine expressed some astonishment that he should be reported as discussing classified information with enlisted men, and denied discussing UFOs at all with anyone. He also pointed out that the 'airman' had got the name of Col. Purvine's command quite wrong.

Who led APRO up the garden path?

'Federal hypothesis'. It would not require especially large resources to be effective, since only a small number – no more than the unexplained 5 per cent – of events need to be created. The network of enthusiasts would do the rest. As the ripples spread out from ufologists a segment of the public would respond with psychic experiences, fantasies, a smattering of hoaxes and numerous 'induced' misinterpretations of aircraft, birds and planets. Another flap would be under way. And a similar pattern of manipulation could be used to cover up mishaps with military equipment or explain away occasional instances of its illegal testing. Once the technique was established there would be no reason not to use it to distract public attention from political embarrassment at home or abroad.

How far can we prove the Federal hypothesis? The documents obtained under the Freedom of Information Act reveal the CIA's persistent interest in psychological warfare. Is it coincidence that several members of the board of Governors of the National Investigations Committee on Aerial Phenomena (NICAP) are former members of the CIA? One, Colonel Joseph Bryan III, USAF (Ret.), is actually reputed to have been the founder of the CIA's psychological warfare section; another NICAP officer, Nicholas de Rochefort, had come to the CIA through its predecessor, the Office of Strategic Services – and was also an expert in psychological warfare. No less telling in GSW's view is the decision by the Aerial Phenomena Research Organisation in 1974 to concentrate solely on contact and abduction cases, which may have led them straight into the hands of the manipulators (see box). How many other UFO organisations have been infiltrated? How many other publications have been fed stories?

There is evidence that Generso Pope, owner of the *National Enquirer*, is an ex-CIA member and is still an associate of the Covert Action Staff (Disinformation and Propaganda) of the CIA's Operations Directorate (Clandestine Services). And who has paid the highest sums for the most exotic and sensational UFO stories – and so helped shape American popular opinion – but the *National Enquirer*? Such a technique is standard with the CIA: in December 1977 the *New York Times* reported that in the mid 1960s the CIA 'owned, subsidised or otherwise influenced . . . more than 800 news and public information organisations and individuals'.

It is also significant that UFO stories undergo reincarnation: the crashed saucer tales of the 1940s are emerging once again in the 1980s, while the fashion for contactee experiences of the early 1950s recurred in the 1970s. In a more sinister vein, what kind of psychological manipulation may be involved in close encounter cases? How many times have we all heard a baffled researcher say in all honesty that the event was 'real in the mind of the witness', despite a total lack of supporting evidence? It is at such specific instances of the UFO phenomenon, and its manipulation, that we must look next.

*Some reasons why the CIA may have manipulated the UFO phenomenon: see page 1118*

Above: a ground marking allegedly left by a UFO near Tully in Queensland, Australia, in 1966. Hard evidence like this is rare – and is rarely investigated by qualified scientists

In its attempts to get to the truth about the UFO phenomenon, GSW made an approach to President Jimmy Carter (above), who, while campaigning for the presidency, had announced his intention to pursue the mystery and had himself filed a UFO report (left). But NASA denied Carter's request to review UFO data, and the President himself was unable to further GSW's suit against the CIA. Said GSW: 'The guests in the White House come and go every four to eight years, but the CIA goes on for ever'

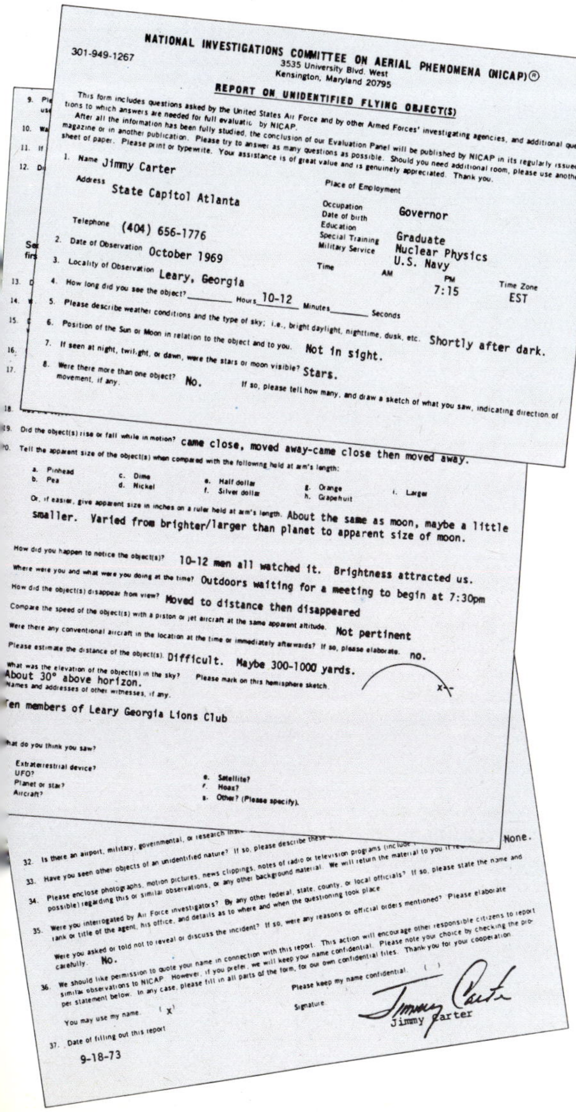

NATIONAL INVESTIGATIONS COMMITTEE ON AERIAL PHENOMENA (NICAP)®
301-949-1267
3535 University Blvd. West
Kensington, Maryland 20795

REPORT ON UNIDENTIFIED FLYING OBJECT(S)

This form includes questions asked by the United States Air Force and by other Armed Forces' investigating agencies, and additional questions to which answers are needed for full evaluation by NICAP.
After all the information has been fully studied, the conclusion of our Evaluation Panel will be published by NICAP in its regularly issued magazine or in another publication. Please try to answer as many questions as possible. Should you need additional room, please use another sheet of paper. Please print or typewrite. Your assistance is of great value and is genuinely appreciated. Thank you.

1. Name Jimmy Carter
Address State Capitol Atlanta
Telephone (404) 656-1776
Place of Employment
Occupation Governor
Date of birth
Education Graduate
Special Training Nuclear Physics
Military Service U.S. Navy
2. Date of Observation October 1969
Time AM PM 7:15 Time Zone EST
3. Locality of Observation Leary, Georgia
4. How long did you see the object? ____ Hours 10-12 Minutes ____ Seconds
5. Please describe weather conditions and the type of sky; i.e., bright daylight, nighttime, dusk, etc. Shortly after dark.
6. Position of the Sun or Moon in relation to the object and to you. Not in sight.
7. If seen at night, twilight, or dawn, were the stars or moon visible? Stars.
8. Were there more than one object? No. If so, please tell how many, and draw a sketch of what you saw, indicating direction of movement, if any.

19. Did the object(s) rise or fall while in motion? came close, moved away-came close then moved away.
20. Tell the apparent size of the object(s) when compared with the following held at arm's length:
a. Pinhead b. Pea c. Dime d. Nickel e. Half dollar f. Silver dollar g. Orange h. Grapefruit i. Larger
Or, if easier, give apparent size in inches on a ruler held at arm's length. About the same as moon, maybe a little smaller. Varied from brighter/larger than planet to apparent size of moon.

How did you happen to notice the object(s)? 10-12 men all watched it. Brightness attracted us.
Where were you and what were you doing at the time? Outdoors waiting for a meeting to begin at 7:30pm
How did the object(s) disappear from view? Moved to distance then disappeared
Compare the speed of the object(s) with a piston or jet aircraft at the same apparent altitude. Not pertinent
Were there any conventional aircraft in the location at the time or immediately afterwards? If so, please elaborate. no.
Please estimate the distance of the object(s). Difficult. Maybe 300-1000 yards.
What was the elevation of the object(s) in the sky? Please mark on this hemisphere sketch. About 30° above horizon.
Names and addresses of other witnesses, if any.
Ten members of Leary Georgia Lions Club

What do you think you saw?
Extraterrestrial device? UFO? Planet or star? Aircraft? e. Satellite? f. Hoax? g. Other? (Please specify).

32. Is there an airport, military, governmental, or research installation ... None.
33. Have you seen other objects of an unidentified nature? If so, please describe these ...
34. Please enclose photographs, motion pictures, news clippings, notes of radio or television programs (include ... We will return the material to you if requested) regarding this or similar observations, or any other background material.
35. Were you interrogated by Air Force investigators? By any other federal, state, county, or local officials? If so, please state the name and rank or title of the agent, his office, and details as to where and when the questioning took place.
Were you asked or told not to reveal or discuss the incident? If so, were any reasons or official orders mentioned? Please elaborate carefully. No.
36. We should like permission to quote your name in connection with this report. This action will encourage other responsible citizens to report similar observations to NICAP. However, if you prefer, we will keep your name confidential. Please note your choice by checking the proper statement below. In any case, please fill in all parts of the form, for our own confidential files. Thank you for your cooperation.
You may use my name. ( x ) Please keep my name confidential. ( )
Signature Jimmy Carter
37. Date of filling out this report 9-18-73

**Age-old myths tell of great birds that preyed upon human beings. Ornithologists scoff at the idea that such creatures exist in reality but, as JANET and COLIN BORD explain, some people think they have encountered such monsters – and some have felt the strength of their claws**

# Monsters on the wing

IN TIPPAH COUNTY, MISSOURI, USA, a teacher had this tragic story to tell in 1878:

> A sad casualty occurred at my school a few days ago. The eagles have been very troublesome in the neighbourhood for some time past, carrying off pigs, lambs, etc. No one thought that they would attempt to prey upon children; but on Thursday, at recess, the little boys were out some distance from the house, playing marbles, when their sport was interrupted by a large eagle sweeping down and picking up little Jemmie Kenney, a boy of eight years, and flying away with him. The children cried out, and when I got out of the house the eagle was so high that I could just hear the child screaming. The alarm was given, and from screaming and shouting in the air, etc., the eagle was induced to drop his victim; but his talons had been buried in him so deeply, and the fall was so great, that he was killed. . . .

This is not the only case of a child being carried away by an eagle. In 1838, in the mountains of Switzerland, a five-year-old girl called Marie Delex was snatched away from her friends. She was not carried to the bird's nest – a search party found two eaglets there, with heaps of goat and sheep bones, but no sign of her. It was not until two months had passed that a shepherd found her mutilated corpse, lying on a rock.

Svanhild Hantvigsen, a Norwegian, claims that when she was three years old, in 1932, she was seized by an eagle and carried to its nest. She was rescued by some people who had noticed the eagle's strange behaviour and she was lucky enough to escape without a scratch, though her dress was torn.

Such attacks are frightening, but not mysterious. Sometimes, however, there are reports of a different kind – of monstrous winged creatures that do not seem to fit the description of any bird known to ornithology. Sometimes they seem most like giant flying creatures that became extinct millions of years ago. And sometimes, as we shall see in a later article, they seem half human.

The largest living bird known to science is the wandering albatross, which is seen only in the southern oceans and has the largest known wingspan – 11 feet (3.3 metres). Very close to it in size is the Andean condor, with a 10-foot (3-metre) wingspan. The Californian condor's wings span 9 feet (2.7 metres) – but it is thought that today less than 40 of these birds survive.

Left: five-year-old Marie Delex was borne away by a large bird in 1838. Local people assumed it was an eagle – yet scientists believe eagles are capable of lifting nothing heavier than a fawn or goat kid

Below left: Svanhild Hantvigsen displays the torn dress that she was wearing in 1932 when an eagle swooped on her and carried her to its nest. The arrival of rescuers saved her from the fate suffered by Marie Delex nearly 100 years before

Below: the dog belonging to Peter Swadley, a bear hunter, attempted to fight off an eagle that attacked his master in West Virginia, USA, in 1895. The dog was carried off, while Swadley was left badly injured

Even a condor would look tiny, however, alongside the teratorn, a bird that became extinct about 10,000 years ago. It is thought to have been the largest bird that has ever lived on Earth, having a length of 11 feet (3.3 metres), a wingspan of 25 feet (7.5 metres), and a weight of 160 to 170 pounds (72 to 76 kilograms). Fossils have been found in Argentina, Mexico and the southern United States; some of them are thought to be 5 to 8 million years old.

Huge birds figure in mythology. The Illini Indians painted a picture of a monstrous bird, the *piasa* or 'bird that devours men', on a rock face overlooking a river near Alton in Illinois. They used to fire bows or guns at the picture as they passed by in their canoes. The painting was seen by missionary explorers in the 17th century, before the rock face was destroyed. In the 1970s a new *piasa* design, following the traditional one, was repainted at Norman's Landing.

According to the Illini, the *piasa* is scaly, with a long tail, horns and red eyes. It can be seen once a year, at dawn on the first day of autumn, as it emerges from the river to pick a cave for the winter. But despite vigils by students on bluffs above the Mississippi River, no one has seen the dreaded *piasa* in recent years.

However, some Indians claim to see another huge creature, the thunderbird, today. According to James Red Sky, an Ojibwa Indian from the Thunder Bay region of Ontario, Canada: 'We saw a thunderbird a few summers ago. A huge bird it was; a lot bigger than planes you see go by today. It didn't flap its wings. Not even once. It was white on the underside, black on top.'

Modern reports of giant birds in the USA began in the late 19th century. At Dent's Run, Pennsylvania, in 1882, one Fred Murray saw a flock of birds that, he said, looked like giant buzzards, with wingspans of more than 16 feet (5 metres).

In February 1895 the disappearance of 10-year-old Landy Junkins in Webster County, West Virginia, was ascribed to a giant bird. Landy was sent by her mother to a neighbour's house, but never arrived. A search party found her tracks in the snow: they left the path and went a few feet into a field. There, a number of tracks were crowded together, as if she had turned round and round, perhaps trying to avoid something. No trace of Landy was ever found.

An incident a few days later suggested what had happened to her. A bear hunter, Peter Swadley, was attacked by a massive bird, which swooped down and dug its talons in his back. Swadley was saved from death by his dog, which made for the bird. The bird turned its attention to the dog, ripping open its stomach with one stroke of its claws before flying off with the unfortunate animal. A deputy sheriff and his son also saw the giant 'eagle', which captured a fawn while they were in the forest hunting deer. They said the bird had a wingspan of 15 to 18 feet (4.5 to 5.5 metres), and a body as large as a man's.

The same monster was also thought to be responsible for the strange disappearance of a sheep from a locked shed. One morning,

Above: a carved human face peers out from a mask of a thunderbird, made by Haida Indians of the American north-west coast. The Haida believe that a human spirit can take on a thunderbird's form: this is symbolised by the closing of the mask's jaws

Above right: the *piasa*, a gigantic legendary bird, was shown in these rock paintings, which formerly existed near Alton, Illinois, USA. The bird terrorised the Illini Indians until the great chief Ouatogo offered himself as bait, while 20 warriors hid nearby. The bird was killed by their arrows, while Ouatogo was unharmed. The paintings commemorated the event

Hanse Hardrick found one sheep missing, with a hole in the shed roof showing how it had been extracted.

Some eagle – able to carry away a fawn, a hunting dog, a sheep and a 10-year-old girl, and make a bold attempt to carry off a fully grown man!

Around 1940, in Pennsylvania, an author and local historian, Robert Lyman, was in the Black Forest near Coudersport, when he saw a brownish bird standing in the middle of a road. It stood 3 to 4 feet (about 1 metre) tall and had a short neck and short legs. When it flew off, Mr Lyman saw that its narrow wings, when extended, reached across the road – a span of 20 to 25 feet (6 to 7.5 metres). He wondered how such a big bird could fly through dense trees so easily.

In 1947 farmers around Ramore in Ontario, Canada, were experiencing problems with a giant black bird that was attacking their livestock. It had a hooked beak, huge talons, and yellow eyes 'the size of silver dollars'. A few months later an outbreak of sightings of big birds occurred in Illinois. 'There's a bird outside as big as a B-29!' gasped 12-year-old James Trares as he rushed indoors to his mother. That was in January 1948, and James was the first to report seeing the monster. He lived in Glendale, Illinois, and the bird he saw, wings flapping as it flew over, was grey-green in colour.

A former army colonel, Walter Siegmund, saw something similar on 4 April. He estimated that it was 4000 feet (1200 metres) up, and from his military experience he was quite convinced that 'it could only be a bird of some tremendous size.'

More sightings followed, including some over St Louis, Missouri. Several witnesses at first believed they were seeing an aeroplane because of its size – until it began to flap its wings and to perform bird-like manoeuvres. Policemen and flying instructors were among

Above: the magnificent bald eagle of North America. Fish are its favourite prey, but it has been blamed for attacks on small animals and children

Right: the Californian condor, hideous when at rest, is majestic in flight, gliding effortlessly for long distances. One of the world's rarest birds, it can attain 9 feet (2.7 metres) in wingspan. It attacks living animals, though like other vultures it feeds mainly on carrion

Right: the imagined abduction of an Alpine peasant woman's child by an eagle. The artist entitled this picture, published in 1900, *The robber of the skies*

Left: one of the rarer hazards of the American West: in 1870 a golden eagle attacked a woman rider near the track of the Pacific Railroad and was beaten off only after severely wounding her

the witnesses. The last sighting seems to have been on 30 April 1948. Charles Dunn could hardly believe his eyes when he saw a bird 'about the size of a Piper Cub plane', flying at about 3000 feet (900 metres) and flapping its wings.

Little more was seen of monster birds for nearly two decades, although in 1957 a huge bird with a wingspan of 25 to 30 feet (7.5 to 9 metres) was seen flying at about 500 feet (150 metres) over Renovo, Pennsylvania. In 1966 there were reports from Utah, West Virginia, Ohio and Kentucky, only some of which could be explained as sightings of rare known species.

Then, in 1975, during an outbreak of mysterious deaths of animals in Puerto Rico, large birds resembling whitish condors or vultures were seen. On 26 March Juan Muñiz Feliciano, a workman, was attacked by 'a terrible greyish creature with lots of feathers, a long thick neck, bigger than a goose'.

At the end of July 1977, a big bird was seen trying to steal a young pig weighing 50 to 60 pounds (22 to 27 kilograms) near Delava, Illinois. The bird had a companion. Both resembled Californian condors and had 8-foot (2.5-metre) wingspans. But an ecologist at the University of Illinois commented that condors are rare, almost to the point of extinction, could not lift such a weight and anyway feed on dead animals, not live ones.

Right: 10-year-old Marlon Lowe, victim of an attack by a large bird in 1977, with his mother, whose cry startled the bird into dropping the boy. The incident occurred in Illinois, home of the legends of the *piasa*

Below: Juan Muñiz Feliciano, a Puerto Rican workman, fights off an attack by a 'terrible greyish creature' one night in 1975. At about this time, farm animals were being killed and mutilated in a manner reminiscent of cattle mutilation cases on the American mainland

What was it, then, that tried to abduct 10-year-old Marlon Lowe from the garden of his home at Lawndale, Illinois, on 25 July? That bird, too, was accompanied by another, and the near-tragedy took place only a few days before the abortive pig-stealing, and 10 miles (16 kilometres) away. Marlon was playing hide-and-seek when at 8.10 p.m. one of the birds snatched him off the ground. Fortunately his mother was at hand. She saw Marlon's feet dangling in the air and screamed, and the bird dropped the boy before he had been lifted very high. Mrs Lowe was only 10 feet (3 metres) away from the birds, and afterwards recalled: 'I'll always remember how that huge thing was bending its white ringed neck, and seemed to be trying to peck at Marlon, as it was flying away.' She described the birds as 'very black' except for the white rings around their necks, which were 18 inches (45 centimetres) long. They had hooked bills 6 inches (15 centimetres) long, and a wingspan of at least 8 feet (2.5 metres). She estimated they would have stood $4\frac{1}{2}$ feet (1.3 metres) tall had they landed. Six people watched the birds fly off towards Kickapoo Creek where there is heavy underbrush and thick tree cover.

But for the bird's being startled by Mrs Lowe's screams, Marlon would probably have suffered the same fate as Marie Delex, Jemmie Kenney and Landy Junkins. As it was, the Lowes suffered in other ways. They were harassed by people leaving dead birds on the front porch, and by unpleasant notes and telephone calls. At school Marlon, nicknamed 'Bird Boy', had literally to fight off the taunts of his fellows. His red hair turned grey, and for a year the frightened boy refused to go out after night had fallen.

*Have nightmarish flying creatures survived from past aeons to terrify present-day witnesses? See page 1126*

# The purpose of death

**Far from resting in peace, it is claimed that the dead lead a strenuous and purposeful existence; in fact that they are more 'alive' than we are. PAUL BEARD explains the meaning of the afterlife**

IF DEATH IS NOT the end of man's personality, but rather the beginning of a sort of 'pilgrim's progress' as many psychical researchers claim, then what are the stages of this adventure? The discarnate spirit, after meeting the loved ones who had died before him, lives first in summerland or winterland (see page 1051), both of which he creates from his own habits of thought, good or bad. These are both on the *ideo-plastic* plane and seem to serve to break him of his earthly preoccupations and make him yearn for the benefits of higher, more spiritual faculties. But he must first undergo the judgement and the second death, processes that hold a mirror up to the person he was, mercilessly stripping him of his illusions about himself and making him realise – by momentarily *becoming* other people in his life – what his actions and words had done to them.

Through experiencing the shattering but ultimately rewarding process of the second death the spirit 'earns' his entry into the *second heaven*. What has been shed in the trauma is only, he discovers, his outer self, his personality, which had seemed so essential in his earth life. Personality is derived from the Latin *persona*, meaning 'actor's mask'; having cast this away during the second death he can emerge as his real, 'undivided self'.

The purpose of the second heaven is, apparently, to enable the questing spirit to grow and develop. The process takes place in what many accounts call 'the great silence'. During this period one's former identity dissolves away and one experiences a sense of great peace. One no longer knows who or where one is, but this is not in any way distressing, any more than it is 'distressing' for a butterfly to undergo the natural process of emerging from its cocoon.

## Kinship of the spirit

At this point the spirit loses contact with all those he had known during his earth life. This is a temporary phase but apparently essential if he is to concentrate his energies on coping with the new, immeasurably broader landscape he now faces. There are now highly significant meetings with others, men and women with whom one feels a deep spiritual link and an intimate familiarity. This is reported as being like meeting old friends on earth with whom one has shared profound experiences. However, the spirits on this plane, although they are indeed old friends, belong to relationships formed over many lifetimes. And this one fact is central to the understanding of the whole nature of the afterlife. With those friends from long ago the spirit relives ancient memories, memories to which his immediately previous personality had no access. Together the members of the reunion relive past events they had shared, and as they do so they begin to see a distinct purpose and meaning emerge

Above: the Hindu deity Vishnu reincarnates for the second time – as a turtle. Belief in the transmigration of souls, or reincarnation as man or animal, is still common in the East. But, according to the alleged evidence for the afterlife, man is always reincarnated as another human being

Right: the ninth hell as described in Dante's *Inferno* and illustrated by Gustav Doré. In this wasteland of ice and desolation, the damned soul is frozen forever, unless he confesses his sins to the superior souls who visit him

experienced before, or perhaps at last the spirit has overcome a lengthy pattern of mistakes. Frances Banks said, 'It is still a continuation, a sequel. There is a definite continuing thread.'

This enrichment of the soul through the revelations of the past is the first step in the process of reassessment carried on in the second heaven. There are two other, equally important steps.

The first involves advice from wiser beings on how to deal with one's future earth life. The second step clarifies the true nature of the spirit's relationship with his peers, those 'old friends' with whom he has just been reunited. He now realises that they are all bound together for all eternity, united with the same overall purpose. Together they form part of a highly important unit known as a *group soul*. It is said that to be with its members is to feel a deep spiritual homecoming.

The members of an earth family may be spiritually close or they may simply be genetically linked – effectively strangers on

Most ancient cultures believed in a supernatural deity whose sole task was to preside over the dead. Part custodian and part judge, he is usually shown as a terrible figure, such as Yamantaka, Tibetan lord of the dead (above) or the Totonac god of ancient Mexico, Mictlantecuhtli (right)

from the apparently disparate and fragmentary personalities they had been in the past. Each soul has been reincarnated many times.

They now see that their lives are in no way arbitrary; they form part of a pattern and purpose that are still being worked out. Each is slowly awakening towards recognition of, and participating in, what is named his *causal self*. This carries within it the seeds of each former life but also contains hints of what is to come in future incarnations. The second heaven is both retrospective and prospective; a plane of insight into both past and future. As the posthumous Frances Banks, a former Anglican nun, is claimed to have said, it is 'the initial stage of a journey into light, during which the surviving entity is gradually reunited with the whole soul.' And now he sees his past earth life in its true perspective; not, as he perhaps thought as he was actually living it, that it was the 'be all and end all', but that it was only a tiny fragment of a much larger prospect.

The past life is only the latest chapter in a long book, the 'story' of which can stretch back over many earth centuries. As the spirit begins to witness the unfolding panorama of his lives he will inevitably realise that much in his past life was the direct consequence of actions from other, previous incarnations. Nothing is meaningless – now at last he knows the answer to the question every person asks at some point: 'Why me?'

There are many incarnations for most spirits, for almost everyone needs many chances to learn all the necessary lessons. All the opportunities will be there over the centuries for everyone. Not everyone will profit by his experience or learn at the same rate but there are many chances to put right mistakes made or opportunities lost. Perhaps the failures of the last life are similar to those

The statue of Justice that stands above the Old Bailey, Britain's foremost criminal court. The scales and the sword she carries represent the two aspects of justice: mercy and retribution. Absolute justice, however, is said to be found only in the afterlife – where motives are seen for what they really were in life. During the judgement the soul suffers the pain and humiliation he once inflicted on others. He learns for himself – the hard way – the effects of his every word and deed. But his kindnesses are also relived and rewarded

any deeper level. Their spiritual 'family' is elsewhere. Such people are said to be the true foundlings. But in the afterlife there are no such random or loose ties; the group soul comprises only members who are totally committed to their particular long-term spiritual assignment under the leadership of one who can perhaps best be called an elder brother. The individual members of each group are responsible to each other – and to the world – in order to fulfil the special task assigned them when their group was created.

## Life goes on

If these narratives that claim to describe conditions in the afterlife – and, indeed, the purpose of life itself – are true, then our individual lives on earth can be seen in proper perspective, as part of a much greater plan. And although these accounts seem basically in harmony with the conventional Christian belief in purgatory, hell and heaven, the approximately similar states exist, not as final punishments or rewards for a single earth life, but as stages in a continuing education. Each has to redeem those parts of himself that are bound by the chains of his own creation. Even in the second heaven the processes of self-cleansing and selfless service continue. Here the spirit learns that there are further states of bliss, but these are too intense for it yet.

It becomes plain that life on earth and life between incarnations simply provide different opportunities of 'growing up'. Each spirit will pass from hard work to refreshment and from refreshment to further tasks – and although on the planes beyond the surroundings are said to be more pleasant than on earth, basically the work is just as strenuous. It takes enormous effort for each spirit to make any lasting progress, but he is not alone and can expect the kind of help, advice and inspiration that would have been impossible on earth. Encouraged and inspired, the individual can progress towards his own ultimate maturity.

The destiny of each soul will be fulfilled, say the communicators, only when that of the


**Further reading**

Paul Beard, *Living on*, George Allen & Unwin 1980

Geraldine Cummins, *Mind in life and death*, Aquarian Press 1956

Charles Drayton Thomas, *Life beyond death with evidence*, Collins 1930

W.S. Pakenham-Walsh, *A Tudor story*, James Clarke 1963


## The man who would be king

Death is said to be 'the great leveller' and nowhere is this shown more clearly than in *A Tudor story* by the late Canon W. S. Pakenham-Walsh. This purports to tell the tale of the Canon's relationship – through several mediums – with various members of the Tudor court from the early 1920s to his death at the age of 92 in 1960. Pakenham-Walsh found that his main spiritual mission was to aid Henry VIII himself, who was angry, lost and clinging pathetically to a crown he no longer possessed, and could therefore make no progress in the afterlife.

One medium had to remind 'Henry' that he was king no longer. He was furious, saying 'I am a king. I carry royal birth and death in my hands. . . . A king does not commit acts for which he is sorry.'

The Canon enlisted the help of the 'spirits' of Anne Boleyn and Elizabeth I among others, while also praying for the King's soul himself. For a time Henry vacillated between apparent repentance and humility and outbursts of regal temperament. The breakthrough came when he was allowed to meet his sons – including the baby who had been stillborn, now grown up. Henry's last communication was: 'Know that Henry, once King of England, did repent.'

group soul is completed. This may take aeons. There are many group souls, said to range from comparatively few members to many hundreds. Frequently a person's inner urge on earth is a reflection of the quest of his group soul, his equivalent of the Holy Grail. Everyone retains his free will to depart from the group soul's set path, but the promptings of his own inner nature will, it is believed, eventually lead him back to it.

During his stay in the second heaven the spirit learns from the 'replay' of his past lives to discover his true potential and what steps he should take to fulfil it. Strengthened by the insight and love of his companions he is now ready for a yet further expansion of his consciousness, which takes place in the *third heaven*. This is, however, too intense an experience for many spirits to endure for very long, although it is open to them for precisely as long as they can endure. Although almost impossible for us to understand, communicators tell us that in the third heaven a spirit comes to the limits of his consciousness. After a brief glimpse of this plane he finds he cannot go further into it than his nature allows. Faced with his limitations he has no coice but to return to earth.

## Other lives, other worlds

However, if his next incarnation goes well and he grows spiritually as a result, he will find that he can then proceed deeper into the third heaven. This in turn will enable him to make more of his succeeding earth life, for it is in the third heaven that the true nature of the group soul's task unfolds as consciousness expands in the individual members.

But what happens when a person has little more to learn from earth? Most accounts agree that a choice awaits him. He can take a leap into the great unknown, leaving this planet and its successive incarnations altogether, and begin again somewhere else. Communications are vague on this point, but they do seem to imply a new cycle of physical lives on another planet. Few, the posthumous F.W.H. Myers says, are sufficiently strong to go the first time the chance arises. Most spirits prefer to wait, helping others if needed, even if it means being reincarnated on earth yet again. A group soul will move on only when every member is ready to go. No one will be left behind.

People frequently deplore the injustice of 'life', meaning their earthly existence. But if the accounts of the afterlife summarised above are substantially true, then there is such a thing as absolute justice, there is cause for hope, there is free will and ever-expanding consciousness. The narratives purporting to come from people in the afterlife can be examined by anyone – religious beliefs and pious hopes aside – as evidence. Perhaps the last words of Mary, Queen of Scots, 'In my end is my beginning', express the literal truth for everyone.

Above: a bark painting by the Australian Aborigine artist Bunia, showing the afterlife

Right: an early 15th-century representation of St Peter receiving three souls at the gates of heaven. In the traditional Christian view, admission to heaven was in itself a kind of judgement, although the dreadful day of judgement was still to come

Below: a wall painting at Tepantitla, Mexico, dating back more than 1000 years. It is believed to show the rain god's paradise

# Dr Lang and Mr Chapman

William Lang (left), a respected surgeon and ophthalmic specialist, died in 1937. Yet, according to medium George Chapman (far left), he continues to practise medicine in the 1980s. Chapman says that he puts himself into a trance, then Lang's spirit takes over his body and, assisted by his son Basil (below left) – himself a doctor during life – he performs operations on the 'etheric body'. Witnesses state that 'Dr Lang' appears to be using surgical instruments, yet none can be seen, and that after the operation there are no signs that any surgery has taken place. Many patients report some relief from their condition – and occasionally a complete cure – while most describe an increased feeling of well-being

**Can the spirit of one man take over the body of another, perform an imaginary operation – and effect a cure? DAVID HARVEY examines the remarkable claims made on behalf of a dead surgeon**

MORE PEOPLE know of Dr Lang today than ever before. His reputation for helping sufferers from a variety of illnesses, sometimes when all other therapies have failed, is international. He can be consulted at his surgery in Aylesbury in Buckinghamshire, England, or at one of the clinics he runs in Europe and the USA. There is nothing out of the ordinary in that until one learns that Dr Lang, or – to be more precise – Mr William Lang, a well-known surgeon and ophthalmic specialist, died in 1937 at the age of 84.

Since 1946 Dr Lang has allegedly continued his work through the medium George Chapman, and their partnership has become one of the most interesting cases in the annals of mediumship.

Chapman was brought up by his grandparents in Liverpool, and he had a number of jobs before joining the Irish Guards in 1939. He later transferred to the Royal Air Force and was stationed at RAF Halton in Buckinghamshire, where he met and married a local girl. Then, after the Second World War, he joined the Aylesbury fire brigade.

At this time Chapman was grieving over the loss of his daughter Vivian, who had died in 1945 when only a month old, and he was anxiously trying to discover whether there is indeed life after death. Then one of his colleagues introduced him to seances, with the result that he received 'messages' telling him he had been chosen to be a healer, and he went on to develop his mediumship with a small circle of friends.

At first these sittings were much like many Spiritualist sessions. Chapman would go into a trance and a number of purported spirit entities would speak through him. He was, however, aware of the problems that can arise in sifting tricks of the subconscious from genuine mediumistic ability, and he looked for the opportunity to check the facts for himself.

The chance came when a surgeon, calling himself Lang, began to 'come through' during seances. As time went by, the surgeon gave an increasing amount of information about his life on earth, sufficient for Chapman to trace William Lang, who had practised at the Middlesex Hospital in London from 1880 to 1914.

This identification enabled Chapman to check and double check the authenticity of Lang's identity with many who knew the man during his earthly existence. Members of Lang's family and several of his medical colleagues had regular sessions with Chapman during which they spoke with the dead surgeon: all vouched for his identity.

In 1947 Chapman met Lang's daughter Lyndon and, over the years, they became close friends, meeting regularly until Lyndon's death in 1977. She was in no doubt that, through Chapman, she had communicated with her dead father: 'I can truthfully say the William Lang who operates via the body of George Chapman is, without a doubt, my father.'

Lyndon Lang (left), William Lang's daughter, and Susan Fairtlough (right), his granddaughter. Both met George Chapman and spoke to him when he was in a trance; they were astounded by the sound of his voice – which was exactly like Lang's – and by the details he gave them about their personal lives. They became convinced that the spirit of William Lang lived on through Chapman. But could it be that the information the medium gave them came not from the dead surgeon, but from the ladies themselves – that Chapman picked it up from their subconscious minds through extra-sensory perception?

Mrs Susan Fairtlough, Lang's granddaughter, became convinced of the surgeon's survival almost despite her own resistance to the evidence. She travelled to Aylesbury to see Chapman, determined to expose him as a fraud. But:

> To my great horror, or rather stupefaction, the man who was in this room was indisputably my grandfather. It was not him physically, but it was his voice . . . his behaviour. It was unquestionable. He spoke to me and recalled the precise events of my childhood. And I was so impressed that all I could say was, 'Yes grandpapa. No grandpapa.'

The author has met George Chapman and has spoken through him to Dr Lang, and there is a marked difference in the tone of voice, vocabulary and mannerisms of Chapman the man and Chapman the medium controlled by Lang. But some people have given the most convincing performances intentionally, or under hypnosis; mental instability has allowed another personality to surface. All that one can say is that either Chapman is an extremely cunning actor, capable of fooling those who knew Lang intimately, or the dead surgeon really does 'come through'.

But the identity question is only part of the issue. Important though proof of survival may be, what keeps people flooding to the various clinics Dr Lang runs is the success he has had with healing a wide variety of conditions.

Chapman is a trance healer, through whom Dr Lang performs what can be best described as spirit operations, a little way above the body. Dr Lang operates, he explains through Chapman, on the spirit body, the invisible essence of each human life, which reflects ill-health in the physical body and through which the physical body can be influenced. He works with invisible instruments and is aided by an invisible team of surgeons, including his son Basil, who during life was also a doctor.

A description of what it is like to be on the receiving end of a spirit operation is given by Morton B. Jackson, a lawyer from Los Angeles, USA, who consulted Dr Lang for treatment of rheumatoid spondylitis, from which he had been suffering for 10 years.

> Asking me to lean forward slightly, while sitting erect, he placed his fingers lightly at various points up and down my spine through my shirt – my jacket having been removed. . . . The nature of the touch, while light, seemed consistent with the handling and utilisation of invisible instruments. . . . All this while . . . our conversation continued, although it tended to be somewhat more one-sided, with Dr Lang

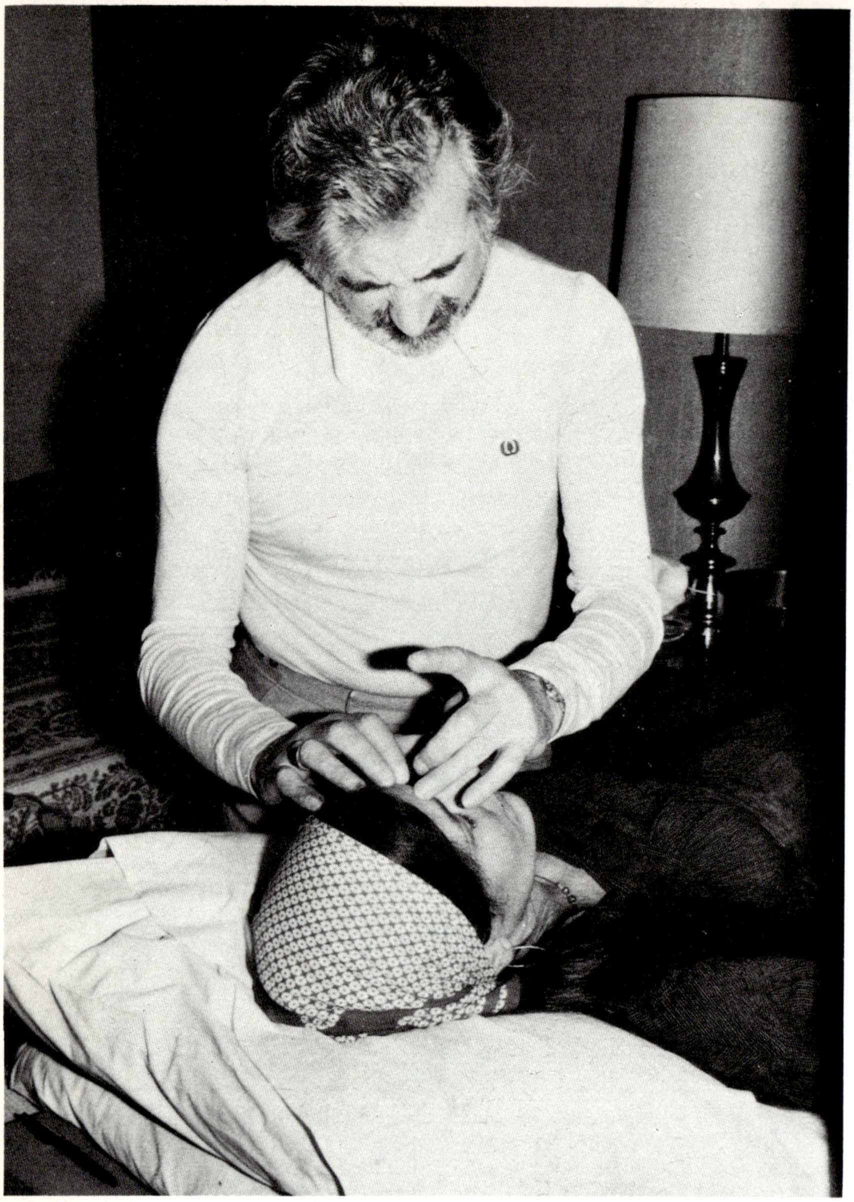

explaining, as he went along, what it was he was doing and why.

In this case there was no miracle cure, but there was some help and a decreased dependence on medication. Dr Lang never promises a cure because there can be no certain outcome with this therapy. From time to time, however, there are outstanding recoveries following Dr Lang's treatment.

In 1974 Joseph Tanguy, a young Paris shop assistant, underwent an operation to investigate a brain tumour. It was found to be malignant and he was expected to have no more than a few months to live. Tanguy's doctor, however, knew of Dr Lang, and advised the young man to consult the healer. Following three treatments over a number of months, the tumour gradually shrank, and subsequent medical tests showed that it had completely disappeared.

One of the more unusual aspects of Dr Lang's work is that it is supported by a number of doctors, particularly in France, some of whom regularly send their more difficult cases to him. Several doctors have vouched for the accuracy of Lang's diagnosis and the effectiveness of his treatment. Dr G. from south-east France, says:

> I have been a doctor since 1970 and I have had the great joy of knowing Dr Lang since 1975. He has my complete trust. Dr Lang's diagnosis does not depend on the questioning of the patient: it is an instantaneous diagnosis. Even before one is able to tell him how one suffers, he is able to say what the problem is. He says it with precision, with a surprising accuracy and with details which would need x-rays and modern laboratory tests for them to be known by any other doctor.

In *Surgeon from another world* by George Chapman in collaboration with Roy Stemman, Dr F. from Marseilles testifies to the cures Dr Lang has brought about:

> Disappearance in one session and, it would appear, looking back over the period of one year, cure of a malignant brain tumour in a young child. In one session, a seven-year-old child who had been completely paralysed from birth started walking on all fours. Disappearance of pain in very severe and advanced arthritis cases, especially coxarthritis (which affects the hip). Disappearance of kidney and gall bladder stones, etc.

George Chapman, controlled by Lang, performs a 'spirit' operation on one of his American patients. Many medical practitioners have testified to the effectiveness of Lang's treatment, and some even refer patients to him

**Further reading**

George Chapman, *Extraordinary encounters*, Lang Publishing 1973
George Chapman, *Surgeon from another world*, W.H. Allen 1978
J. Bernard Hutton, *Healing hands*, W.H. Allen 1978
S.G. Miron, *The return of Dr Lang*, Lang Publishing 1957

## Insight and understanding

There seems little doubt that Chapman has been accepted as a bona fide medium for William Lang by those who loved and knew the man when he was on this earth. Nor is there any reason to doubt the commitment on Chapman's part. He works virtually without ceasing, commuting between England, Europe and the USA, with a team of secretaries to deal with the endless flood of mail and requests for appointments.

Inevitably it has been the healing successes that have caught the imagination of the public. But healing is not the sole aim of the partnership between George Chapman and Dr Lang. Chapman is sure that the purpose lies deeper than alleviating pain and suffering, of great value though that may be. As he said in *Surgeon from another world*: 'The real purpose of his [Dr Lang's] spirit return, I am convinced, is not solely to cure sick people. It is to touch the soul and to give us a new, convincing insight and understanding of the spiritual reality which surrounds us.'

Those who have met and been treated by Dr Lang have their own experience on which to reflect. Others who have not still have the tributes and testimonies of patients, doctors, ex-colleagues and relatives to ponder. Unlike so many chapters in the history of mediumship and survival after death, the evidence for Dr Lang's return stands up to more than a superficial investigation.

# THE Unexplained

# INDEX

# A

# B

# C

# D

# E

# F



# G

# H

# I



# J

# M

# N

# O



# P

# Q



# R

# S

# T

# U

# V



# W

# X



# Y



# Z